WITH BEST WISHES
FROM YOUR CONGRESSMAN

B. F. Sisk

THE YEARBOOK OF AGRICULTURE
1967

90TH CONGRESS, 1ST SESSION, HOUSE DOCUMENT NO. 29

OUTDOORS
USA

The United States Department of Agriculture

THE UNITED STATES GOVERNMENT PRINTING OFFICE

FOR SALE BY THE SUPERINTENDENT OF DOCUMENTS, WASHINGTON, D.C. 20402 - PRICE $2.75

Foreword

ORVILLE L. FREEMAN, *Secretary of Agriculture*

A MOUNTAINTOP SYMBOLIZES MAN'S GOALS, aspirations, and yearnings for the "better life."

A mountaintop symbolizes also the spirit of our 1967 Yearbook and its authors; and the spirit of the Department which I head.

A mountaintop symbolizes conservation.

From the mountaintop, we have a sweeping view of man's total environment— an environment we share with all other living things.

From the valleys below, where our food and clothing are produced, we lift our eyes across tilled fields and green pastures and the timbered slopes that provide shelter for the wild creatures and wood for human creatures to the snowcapped mountain that helps to water the valleys in the heat of summer.

About half of the U.S. Department of Agriculture's staff works in some phase of conservation to preserve the scenic splendor of our mountaintops and our other natural resources, while getting the most use from them. These 50,000 USDA'ers are busy helping to develop our forests and wood sources; helping to develop watersheds and river basins, fish-stocked lakes, and ponds for swimming and boating as well as storing water; helping to develop farms that besides growing crops offer good hunting, fishing, and other recreation.

The scope of these activities is amazingly wide. USDA conservation programs can benefit some 81 percent of the Nation's total land: all the Nation's cropland, grassland, pasture, and range, the vast national forests and national grasslands, and much of the private forest land.

Our conservation responsibilities require us to operate the world's largest outdoor playground—the 186 million acres of the national forests and the national grasslands. This year that "playground" will provide around 153 million visitor days of use for recreation purposes. These forests—*your* forests—have more than 7,000 camp and picnic grounds, able to accommodate half a million people at a time. Nearly 200 winter sports areas, financed privately and operated under paid permits, can simultaneously accommodate 300,000 persons.

In fulfilling another part of our conservation responsibilities in the national forests, we harvest more timber than the biggest lumber company in the world. Last year's harvest was valued at nearly $200 million. This harvest, by private industry, provides not only homes for America, but raw material for newspapers, furniture, and countless other industrial products as well.

We help farmers divert land from unneeded crops to the development of soil, water, woodland, wildlife, and recreational resources. More than 30,000 farmers and ranchers now use parts of their land for income-producing recreation. Some farmers receive small government payments for improving wildlife resources and permitting hunting, fishing, hiking, or trapping on their land.

USDA's researchers and conservationists constantly are seeking solutions to America's water problems. To conserve our water and use it wisely for multiple purposes is a "must."

Last year, three-fourths of the small watershed plans completed with USDA help included among their goals not only flood prevention but recreation, fish and wildlife habitat, and municipal water benefits. About 750 watersheds have been authorized for development since 1960.

Photomaps covering 79 percent of all the land in all the States except Alaska are maintained by USDA. Who uses them? Farmers, of course; but also municipal, county, and State governments, and builders, architects, and engineers.

USDA soil conservationists work with developers to protect and enhance the beauty of subdivisions and shopping centers. They even help pick stable, "no-slide" sites for buildings.

Our rural electrification engineers have found ways to put unsightly telephone wires underground—at lower cost. Our researchers are continually developing new eye-pleasing trees, shrubs, and flowers. Our field agencies help States and local governments acquire croplands for open space, natural beauty, and recreation developments.

These are some of the ways in which we help to create an ever more beautiful America—in the cities and suburbs as well as in the fields and forests and along streams and highways.

Conservation encompasses the full sweep of interrelated natural resources and their management and use. Man is only one element, but he is the dominant element. Emerging now is a special challenge of fitting man's activities and needs harmoniously into his total environment.

We in the U.S. Department of Agriculture are moving forward with bold new actions to restore, conserve, and wisely use our natural heritage and maintain it for future generations.

And the work is vitally important. Let me illustrate.

Each year 3 million more Americans squeeze into our already jampacked cities. Today 140 million people—or 7 in every 10 Americans—are crowded onto just 1 percent of our land. The result is strangled cities, slapdash suburbs, and rush hour nightmares.

But rural America has breathing space—room for people to live, to work, to enjoy recreation, to be part of the land.

Through conservation and the development of our natural resources, the rural areas can be ideal sites for our communities of tomorrow; communities where blight and urban sprawl will be unknown. Rural America can be synonymous with good living.

And you may be able to see that mountaintop from your backyard patio.

Outdoor beauty is crimson clover, a citrus grove . . .

Outdoor conservation is plant, tree, soil . . .

. . . the grandeur of light and shadow on a forest.

The outdoors is variety, color, great solitudes.

Craggy lookout (left) and grazing (above) in Northwest.

Trout fishing in a clear stream, North Carolina.

Squaw grass frames glory of Mount Hood in Oregon.

Mountains and forests are watersheds of the Nation.

Water contrasts: Wilderness lake, Potomac Gorge . . .

Lake Powell. Below, recreation farm pond, Mississippi.

About 2 million farm ponds save water, curb erosion.

Ready to portage around Lower Basswood Falls . . .

. . . in the Boundary Waters Canoe Area, Minnesota.

Raccoon peers from den maple tree, Vermont.

Wildlife, sports
. . . in the forests.

Farmlands, recreation, beauty go hand in hand.

Virginia hunting; New Jersey flowers; Maine riders.

Man can use the outdoors, still conserve wildlife.

Conserving the land: Contours, Nebraska.

*Wild birds thrive
if habitat is right.*

*Game farm pheasant
ready to go free.*

Conserving water: Tree-lined farm pond, Illinois.

Fun at New York farm camp (top), Michigan farm pond.

Kids on pony ride, Green Valley Farm, West Virginia.

Driving range, a farm recreation project in Howard County, Maryland.

Beautification center, U.S.A. The National Arboretum.

*Pyracantha
in Norfolk,
Virginia.*

*Pink camellia
and magnolia
blossoms.*

Outdoor beauty graces home (above), forest (right).

USDA developed poinsettias (left), and Christmas azaleas (right).

Beauty: the Capital and environs. Tulips on the Mall.

Snake Den Lake, Virginia. Below, Jefferson Memorial.

Open space at Reston, Va., and California ranch.

Preface

JACK HAYES, *Editor of the Yearbook of Agriculture*

THIS YEARBOOK OF AGRICULTURE is a handbook of resource conservation, a guide to the American outdoors with its great recreation potential, and a primer of natural beauty. It tells its story largely in terms of people. It covers all the U.S. Department of Agriculture's activities serving farmers and the general public in developing our natural resources so that they can be enhanced while being used productively. These are goals to which all agencies of the Department are dedicated.

Outdoors USA is designed for all Americans—citizens concerned about conservation of our natural resources, hunters and fishermen, family campers, all who are concerned with the quality of the total environment, small fry eager to learn about the outdoors, farmers or rural developers interested in profitmaking recreation enterprises.

Conservation and wise use of our resources pull all this Yearbook of Agriculture's articles together as surely as the book's binding.

As a conservation document, *Outdoors USA* naturally falls into four divisions: The Big Woods (forests and mountains), Water, Beautification, and The Countryside. In all four, the Yearbook outlines new conservation policies of our Government and shows in case history form how USDA agencies are carrying out these policies.

A Yearbook Committee of 17 did the spade work for this book. Since it completed its work Harry A. Steele joined the Water Resources Council, Ralph W. Marquis died, and Edward W. Caveney retired. The list of committee members follows:

HARRY A. STEELE, Economic Research Service, *Chairman*
NORMAN A. BERG, Soil Conservation Service
PHILIP S. BROWN, Farmers Home Administration
EDWARD W. CAVENEY, Rural Community Development Service
RICHARD J. COSTLEY, Forest Service
M. L. DuMARS, Agricultural Stabilization and Conservation Service
FRANK C. EDMINSTER, Soil Conservation Service
T. W. EDMINSTER, Agricultural Research Service
VIRGIL R. HASSLER, Rural Electrification Administration
HOWARD L. HILL, Economic Research Service
THOMAS L. KIMBALL, National Wildlife Federation
RALPH W. MARQUIS, Forest Service
LLOYD E. PARTAIN, Soil Conservation Service
LOUIS E. REID, JR., Department of the Interior
THOMAS S. RONNINGEN, Cooperative State Research Service
LEON R. THOMAS, Forest Service
EDWARD J. WILLIAMSON, Federal Extension Service

Contents

THE BIG WOODS

WATER

BEAUTIFICATION

THE COUNTRYSIDE

The Outdoors
Is for All of Us

JOHN A. BAKER

I LIVE in the city, but I am more at home in the country. I have a very personal relationship with the open land that I simply do not have with congested urban surroundings.

I find rest and comfort in thicket and field—in the quiet rippling of a brook, the thundering solitudes of a waterfall, the silent scampering of a woodland creature, the call of a bird—the sounds and the voices of nature that are apart from the things man builds and destroys.

I need the great outdoors.

So do we all—a fact often ignored as we stack population upon population in our burgeoning cities where millions of every age vie for the limited green space available . . . as we continue to spread our overburdened communities out across the forest and the meadowlands . . . as we seek to satisfy the compelling need for more space to grow in, without providing adequately for the protection and enhancement of the green and flowering landscape that, once overrun, is lost.

Rural America still covers 90 percent of the Nation's land area. Here is the repository of nature's varied gifts which must be protected and wisely managed to serve Americans for all time to come. Here among the forests, the fields, and the waterways are the sites of future homes, factories, schools, highways—the many features of human habitation.

Unless we develop and manage this land in harmony with nature we will live in barren communities.

We have a priceless American heritage in the countryside that belongs to all the people. To assure that this great heritage is preserved, and denied to no one, is a primary responsibility of the U.S. Department of Agriculture—as the rural affairs department at the national level and as one of the major Federal land and water conservation agencies.

Through research, education, and technical and financial support, USDA is working with local people and the State agencies to enhance the beauty as well as the usefulness of the land.

A bountiful and beautiful America is many things. It is the prosperity of its people . . . nature unspoiled and nature improved . . . a well-tended countryside and a well-kept city . . . scenic highways and tree-lined streets . . . the spirit of a people intent upon improving life for themselves and for their children . . . all the accomplishments of individuals, private organizations, and governments.

In our designs for a more satisfying way of living, we have enriched the countryside. We have:

• Planted forests and improved existing woodlands.

• Lined the roadsides and streambanks with grass and other foliage.

• Built dams and reservoirs for flood control, water storage, recreation, and for wildlife conservation.

• Terraced, and contoured, the agri-

☙ ☙ ☙

John A. Baker is *Assistant Secretary* of Agriculture for Rural Development and Conservation.

1

cultural lands to stop erosion and to hold more water on the soil for better crops.

• Secured the soil to the mountains and fields to keep rivers and streams free from silt.

• Shown how to enhance the natural beauty of the countryside while assuring a greater bounty from the fields.

We have accomplished much which is beneficial through our habitation and conversion of the land.

We have managed the vast 186 million acres of national forests and national grasslands under a program of multiple use and sustained yield for many products and uses by all the people. We have maintained around 14 million acres of these national forests as wilderness and primitive areas—a true example of the country of our early pioneers.

But we must do much more to satisfy the needs of a dynamic people!

We constantly are seeking better ways to make the land and the waters serve the Nation—better grasses, shrubs, flowers, and trees for particular growing conditions; better ways to control plant pests and diseases; better ways of making the national forests and grasslands serve you; better ways to make every acre of land count, to make the water we have do triple duty and even more.

We have the means to use the land wisely, profitably, intensely as required by our rapidly growing population and expanding economy—and to assure, at the same time, that the landscape is preserved to a large extent in its natural state. We must plan and decide wisely so that the forest lands and other parts of the rural landscape are not heedlessly diminished. The short-term benefit must not be allowed to cancel out long-term values of our resources.

We have shown many times that man can "invade" the natural environment without destroying nature. But, natural beauty must stand on its own in competition with developments that detract from the beauty of the landscape. Nature's endowments must be considered equally worthy of preservation or enhancement *on balance,* or they may not be considered at all in areas that are under development.

A beautiful landscape must be accepted as contributing to the intrinsic worth of property. Only then will planning and developing for beauty as well as utility be given the attention it deserves.

All too often, nature and man have been at odds in fashioning the American landscape. Our determined invasion of the countryside has brought plunder as well as promise and desecration as well as dedication.

We have to live with the environment we create for ourselves, whether we like it or not. That is why the American people must make a determined effort to create an outdoor environment that meets the high standards of living within most of our homes. The outdoors, too, is our home. We should consider it so and should treat it so.

Every responsible American has his obligations as a conservationist. He is born to the role. Even if he does no more than respect the natural landscape and the labor of those who work to maintain it, he is bound at least not to despoil nature's invaluable gifts.

Spirit Lake at the foot of Mount St. Helens, Gifford Pinchot National Forest, Wash.

Mrs. Lyndon B. Johnson plants a Bradford ornamental pear tree on the grounds of the U.S. Department of Agriculture as a further step toward beautifying the Nation's Capital. The newly developed tree is a result of long search by USDA for a "perfect" shade tree. It produces handsome white blossoms in spring, silvery green leaves in summer, and crimson red foliage during the autumn. With Mrs. Johnson are the Secretary of Agriculture, Orville L. Freeman, and 4–H youths from Maryland and Virginia.

The "active conservationist" advances beyond merely leaving nature alone and being careful not to thoughtlessly disturb it. More and more Americans are becoming active conservationists—in their own yards and neighborhoods and in support of community, State, and National efforts to make man's environment more attractive and esthetically pleasing.

Our reward is a rich one. It is the satisfaction from playing a part in the continuing preservation and wise management of our cherished land. We are proving one vital point: That a great industrial nation with a rapidly rising population *can* abound in great forests and clean streams, rolling meadows, and a carefully tended countryside.

Man needs nature. Research has shown that animals which are forced to live under crowded conditions develop many of the antisocial traits that fill the crime pages of big city newspapers.

And nature needs man.

Properly developed, preserved, and managed, the countryside of our Nation can be improved.

The waters of an unspoiled stream can be put to many tasks and yet the stream's purity and beauty protected.

This is the meaning of conservation and wise use.

It is the key to a healthy, prosperous, happy American people.

It is the objective of the Agriculture Department's programs.

The Big Woods

The Rogue Basin—
Showcase of the West

HILLARD M. LILLIGREN and H. ROBERT MANSFIELD

WITH A ROAR the bright red Forest Service twin-engined plane speeds down the runway, and in a hurry we're airborne. We circle above the town of Grants Pass to gain altitude, the mountains rising high all around us.

While the plane is climbing, let me fill you in on our flight plan. We're going to get a bird's-eye view of over 5,000 square miles of the magnificent Rogue River Basin in Oregon. We will watch the river snake and horseshoe its way through thickly wooded mountains, see scenic wonders like Crater Lake and Hellgate Canyon, fly over white water boatmen foaming down the river on the 4- to 6-day water trip from Grants Pass to the Pacific. With binoculars we may see elk and deer on a lakeshore, or even a bear.

Big Stake for All

Part of my job is to tell you what a great wooded river basin like this means to us and other Americans—the water, power, timber, recreation, natural beauty, and wildlife. Cities, industries, agriculture, and recreation seekers all have a big stake in these beautiful mountains, valleys, and forests. But I'm getting ahead of myself, I can see.

The name is Hillard Lilligren. I'm a Forester assigned to the Rogue River National Forest.

Our flight will take the form of a huge figure 8 lying in an east and west direction. On the eastern loop, we will fly over the Rogue River National Forest and the Bear Creek Valley. During this time I'm the guide and narrator. The western loop will be over the lower Rogue River Valley and the Siskiyou National Forest. I'll be talked out by then, and someone else will take over from me.

The Rogue River Basin was discovered by fur trappers about 1825. For many centuries the basin had been occupied by Indian tribes, later to be called the Rogues because of their warlike attitude toward the settlers. By 1856, all organized resistance by the Indians had ceased.

Today, about 78 percent of the basin is timbered, 9 percent is in cropland and pasture, and the remaining 13 percent is parks, brushlands, and water.

Now we are at 5,000 feet, and you can see the rugged, snow-capped Siskiyou Mountains ahead and to the right. These form the southern boundary of the basin. Below are timbered areas. The clearings you see are where the timber has been cut to feed the wood-using industries down in the valleys.

The land over which we are flying at this moment is in mixed private and Federal ownership. The Bureau of Land Management of the U.S. Department of the Interior manages the Federal portions.

Off the right wing in the distance, the snow-capped peak is Mount Ashland.

Hillard M. Lilligren is a *Forester* on the Rogue River National Forest, Medford, Oreg.

H. Robert Mansfield is a former *Lands and Recreation Staff Officer* on the Siskiyou National Forest, Grants Pass, Oreg. He is now retired.

Over 7,500 feet high, Mount Ashland is known for its ski resort development. The resort is only 2 years old, but it had 85,400 visitors during the winter of 1965–66. Under a special use permit issued by the Forest Service of the U.S. Department of Agriculture, private interests developed this resort on national forest land.

Off to our left is the community of Jacksonville, developed in 1851 and 1852 after the discovery of gold near the site. History tells us that mule drivers made the original discovery in 1851 while they were packing supplies from the north into the California goldfields.

As we approach Mount Ashland, you can see the city of Ashland to the left. This is the home of the internationally famous Oregon Shakespearean Festival, which is now an annual attraction. During 1965, about 53,000 people from many States and countries attended the festival.

Near the center of town is the campus of Southern Oregon College. It had an enrollment of 2,500 students in 1965.

Now we are directly over the Ashland Creek watershed, which is mostly Rogue River National Forest land. The blue water to your left is the Ashland City reservoir. This big watershed covers 22 square miles and provides more than a billion gallons of water annually for the residents of Ashland.

Reservoirs Sighted

As we turn northeasterly, you will see two reservoirs on the right, which were developed for irrigation and recreation use. Water has been impounded behind dams constructed by the Bureau of Reclamation of the U.S. Department of the Interior. To make the maximum use of this water, the Soil Conservation Service of the U.S. Department of Agriculture assists private landowners and the State-chartered soil and water conservation districts with both soil surveys and farm planning. You can clearly see the beautiful green color of the irrigated lands in contrast to the brown of those that are not irrigated.

As the plane turns north, the crest of the Cascade Mountains appears on our right forming the eastern boundary of the basin. For the next 15 minutes you will be flying above the Rogue River National Forest. That spectacular snow-capped peak ahead is Mount McLoughlin. This peak was named for Dr. John McLoughlin, who built Fort Vancouver in 1824 for the Hudson's Bay Company. Its near perfect cone rises a total of 9,495 feet above sea level.

Melting snows from Mount McLoughlin sink deep into the soils at the base, and emerge with a temperature of 43° at Big Butte Springs. In 1966, the springs had a daily capacity of 25 million gallons. This water is piped by gravity 31 miles to Medford, where it also supplies three other valley communities.

'Pastures' for Wildlife

The cleared patches below are areas where timber has been sold and harvested from the Rogue River National Forest. These trees were cut under a carefully planned program which assures that the amount of wood removed does not exceed the amount that is grown.

These openings in the forest also provide "pastures" for wildlife. It is estimated that the Rogue River National Forest supports 18,000 deer, 600 elk, and some 1,600 bear.

These game animals can be hunted during seasons regulated by the Oregon State Game Commission.

The meadows and openings also provide grazing for privately owned cattle that range the mountains in summer and the valleys in winter. In 1965, about 5,000 cattle were grazed on the Rogue River National Forest under permit.

From this point on to Crater Lake National Park we are flying above the Sky Lakes area along the Cascade Crest. Over 100 mountain lakes and 100 miles of trails are available for fishermen and hikers. Because of its rugged beauty, the Sky Lakes area is now being studied for possible inclusion in the national wilderness system.

On the horizon ahead you can see the Crater Lake rim.

Crater Lake was first sighted by John Wesley Hillman, a young prospector, on June 12, 1853. As the result of 17 years

7

Devils Backbone and Rogue River Canyon.

of effort by William G. Steel, Crater Lake National Park was finally established by President Theodore Roosevelt, back in May of 1902.

It was withdrawn from a portion of the Cascade Forest Reserve, which then contained 4½ million acres and ran from the Columbia River to within 22 miles of California.

In 1905, the surrounding reserves were transferred from the Department of the Interior to the Department of Agriculture, and eventually became the national forests of the present day.

Crater Lake has a fascinating geological history. Ancient Mount Mazama, a volcanic peak, was once one of the most commanding in all the Cascade Range. Within the last 7,000 years a great volume of fine pumice was blown into the air, and 5 cubic miles of molten lava was ejected to the southwest. Cracks in the flanks and bottom of the volcano drained another 10 cubic miles of molten material

through the sides and bottom. The top of Mount Mazama then collapsed inward, forming a lake over 1,900 feet deep and more than 21 square miles in area. Subsequent volcanic activity formed Wizard Island as a small cone within the caldera.

Half Million Visitors

As we fly over the lake, note the breathtaking deep blue color. The clear water absorbs most of the sunlight spectrum and reflects the blue rays upward. The water in the lake comes only from rain and snow. There are no inlets, and no outlets except for subterranean seepage.

There were 480,500 visitors at Crater Lake National Park in 1965.

As we wing northwestward, the horizon ahead is the divide between the Rogue and Umpqua Rivers. This forms the north boundary of the basin as far west as the Coast Range. As we leave the northwest corner of the park, we pass over Boundary Springs. These three large springs gush from the forest floor within a few dozen yards of each other. They combine to form the headwaters of the Rogue River, one of the two rivers in Oregon which originate on the west slope of the Cascades and flow westerly through the Coast Range to the Pacific Ocean.

From this point the Rogue River flows 210 miles to the ocean. Following it from its source, we are passing over several Forest Service campgrounds, with fishing readily available alongside the campsites.

Just ahead now is the town of Prospect. The dam and powerplants here are part of Pacific Power & Light Co.'s hydroelectric developments, using water originating in the mountainous national forests to produce electrical power for homes, agriculture, and industry.

Continuing on downriver, we are now over the site of the proposed Lost Creek Dam, with the Elk Creek drainage and the proposed Elk Creek damsite to the right of the plane.

These impoundments of water are planned by the Department of the Army, Corps of Engineers, to serve for flood control, irrigation, power generation, recreation, and for other uses.

In the distance off ahead lies the city of Medford, with its population of 28,000. Orchards in this beautiful valley cover approximately 10,000 acres.

By 1889, Medford had established itself in the fruit industry. The fertile soils, the mild climate, and the exceptionally pure water which flows from the mountains produce an average of 4 million boxes of pears every year.

Start Western Loop

Now we are finishing the eastern loop of our figure 8 flight course, and Grants Pass is again below us. Bob Mansfield, the Recreation and Lands Staff Officer of the Siskiyou National Forest, is now ready to tell you about the interesting country we will see on the western portion of our flight. Bob, it's all yours!

Thank you! We will continue following the Rogue to the ocean. Grants Pass started out as a roadhouse serving travel-weary settlers even before the gold rush days. With the miners of 1849 and the early fifties came blacksmith shops, a livery stable, and stores. Then, when the railroad entered the valley, the town moved "lock, stock, and barrel" about 2

Boaters on Blossom Bar Riffle, Rogue River.

9

miles from the foothills to the tracks. The community, founded by settlers, has always retained its agricultural character. Miners have come and gone, followed by lumbermen who—because of the sustained yield management of the surrounding national forests—are here to stay. Grants Pass, the home of the Oregon Cavemen, has over 11,000 residents, and nearly as many more people live just outside the city limits.

The Cavemen, a unique booster club of Grants Pass businessmen, take their name from the nearby and world famous Oregon Caves. Dressed in animal skins, wearing wigs of coarse tousled hair and mouthpieces exposing great tusks, brandishing heavy war clubs, and giving great shouts, this group looks as if man's prehistoric cave dwelling ancestors are truly in our midst. Each year they delight people at parades and fairs as they carry throughout the Nation the story of the Rogue River Valley.

On the east side of the river you can see the neat geometric patterns of hop fields, while on the west are the deep green squares of mint farms.

Most of the water for these crops originates in the timber-covered mountains which we saw only a few minutes ago on the Rogue River National Forest.

Hellgate Canyon

Coming into view on our right is the famous Hellgate Canyon. Here, for the first time, the Rogue is really constricted and turns upon its side as it winds its tortuous course through the mountains. This is the initial hint of the fantastic beauty which nature has carved into the massive canyon walls ahead.

The broad Rogue River Valley is now behind us, and over 80 miles of canyon and gorge lie ahead. From here to within 9 miles of the Pacific Ocean, the lands are mostly under the management of U.S. Government agencies.

Now we are at the mouth of Grave Creek. Here the road leaves the river and climbs to the mountaintops. The Rogue River Trail begins at Grave Creek. Trail and boat are the only means of travel through the next 20 miles of canyon.

For the experience of a lifetime, you should take the white water boat trip from Grants Pass to the ocean! Boats of special design, with master river guides at the oars and two passengers per boat, take 4 to 6 days to float and fish their way to the ocean.

About 3,000 people make this one-way trip each year. The boats subsequently are hauled back to Grants Pass by trailer.

Folks making this trip enjoy one of the Nation's few remaining stretches of river where the awe-inspiring natural beauty of mountain and gorge has scarcely been marred by man.

Lodges for Boatmen

Now you can see the mouth of Mule Creek, and we are over the lodge and the post office called Marial, in honor of Mrs. Marial Akesson, who built and operates the lodge. A dirt road winds down from the mountaintop to dead end here. Marial Lodge caters to boat travelers, as do Black Bar Lodge and Paradise Bar Lodge. These three resorts provide the only accommodations in 35 miles of wild and beautiful canyon.

Again we leave the roads behind and look down upon 15 miles of river which are accessible only by boat or trail. Here indeed the Creator carved with bold and masterful strokes!

In 5 minutes our plane has traveled the equivalent of 2 days on the river below us and we are now at Illahe, which is the site of one of the last and most savage battles with the Rogue River Indians. This is another portion of the river which can be reached by road.

In an effort to prevent the natural beauty of the Rogue River Canyon being marred by logging and industrial development, the Forest Service is engaged in a massive land exchange project. The program covers privately owned lands along the river from the Illahe area to the forest boundary about 9 miles upstream from the river's mouth. Owners are offered lands or timber of equal value in carefully selected locations in exchange for their Rogue River holdings. By this procedure over 5,400 acres have been acquired since Congress authorized the project in 1958 through extension of the forest boundary to include the lands which lie along the river.

Work is progressing toward the acquisition of over 11,000 acres more before the program is completed.

Under Federal ownership the beauty of the riverbanks and the mountain slopes can be preserved by careful management and the land can be made available for enjoyment by the public.

We have reached Agness. For many years this community of about 80 persons was the most isolated town in Oregon. Forest Service access roads now link it with Gold Beach on the Coast Highway No. 101, and with Powers and Oregon Highway No. 42.

Agness is the upriver terminus of the Rogue River excursion boats. During the summer of 1965, nearly 50,000 people rode the riffles of the Rogue from Gold Beach to Agness and returned, in 50-passenger jet-propelled launches.

Here at Agness the Illinois River joins the Rogue. Both of these rivers, looking so peaceful now, can truly be monsters during floodtime.

On December 23, 1964, these calm waters became raging torrents, wreaking havoc in their path. A great concrete bridge that stood 90 feet above the normal summer water level of the Illinois River was overturned by the violent waters. Numerous homes were washed away, and the receding waters left logs and debris on the roofs of others.

As we fly on down the river, you will notice the many boats containing sportsmen trying their skill at catching steelhead and salmon. Fish up to 30 pounds are not uncommon in the Rogue.

Ahead of you is the mouth of the river and the Pacific Ocean. You have traveled the length of the Rogue. After circling over the busy little city of Gold Beach, we will head back across the Siskiyou National Forest. As we go you will note the many cutting units where timber has been or is being harvested.

The Siskiyou National Forest markets about 192 million board feet of timber each year. This would build a board fence 1 inch thick and 10 feet high from Los Angeles to New York, and then south nearly to Atlanta, Ga.—more than 3,600 miles in length.

The Siskiyou's precipitous hills still see numerous prospectors tirelessly searching for the gold, copper, chromium, nickel, and various other minerals known to be somewhere in its vastness.

As we zoom high above the craggy mountaintops we skirt the edge of the Kalmiopsis Wilderness—a wilderness different from all others—over 76,000 acres of jumbled brown boulders, stunted Jeffrey pines, dense tanoak thickets, and sparkling blue water in rocky canyons. This wilderness was named for what is perhaps the most rare shrub in the world: the Kalmiopsis.

This plant, somewhat resembling a tiny rhododendron, is a living relic from before the Ice Age. The wilderness, and a 3,800-acre botanical area, will preserve for future generations the delicate pink beauty of the Kalmiopsis blossoms.

Smokejumper School

Now we are above the Illinois Valley. Over that way is the town of Cave Junction, and just south of it you can see the mile-long Forest Service Airport where every summer about 40 daring young men are trained to parachute to forest fires—we call them smokejumpers. From here they fly to fight fires all over Oregon and northern California. They may even jump to fires which are as far away as Idaho and Montana.

That impressive range of mountains ahead will force us to climb to 7,000 feet again. And when we reach the other side, we will have completed our figure 8 and come to the end of our trip.

As our plane glides in for a landing at the Grants Pass Airport, let me invite you to dinner. You'll have a choice of salmon or steelhead, caught fighting fresh from the river!

As we walk from the plane to our waiting cars, let's reflect on what we have seen—the broad fields and orchards, timbered slopes, logging operations, mills, playgrounds along the lakes and rivers, and the prosperous cities—all contributing to the economy of the Rogue Basin and the Nation.

11

Traveling the National Forests *Can* Become a Habit

PAUL M. KIHLMIRE

WHAT ARE the oldest living things on the earth?
* Who were the "voyageurs," and what kind of life did they lead?
* Where can you go to enjoy some of the best of "Outdoors USA"?

If your curiosity is already aroused, if you want not just the answers but to see for yourself, then chances are you have the makings of a good traveler—a national forest traveler!

A visit to any one of the 154 national forests may be the beginning of a long and—unlike some habits—rewarding leisuretime career of travel for you, and your family. Let's go visit some national forests and see what's in store for you on these public lands—182 million acres in 39 States and Puerto Rico—managed by the Forest Service of the U.S. Department of Agriculture for your enjoyment and your benefit as well.

We'll assume you have your tent and camping gear, bathing suits and fishing rods, national forest recreation maps, camera, and—perhaps the most important of all—a lively curiosity.

We'll take our time on this first trip since it may be your first visit to a national forest. Let's be off—to the Ancient Bristlecone Pine Forest in the White Mountains of the Inyo National Forest in California. . . .

It's a hot August morning, and we've just filled our canteens at Batchelder Spring near an old tollhouse. We are still 3,000 feet below the realm of the bristlecone pines at 9,000 feet elevation.

The road takes us over a broad flat, past piñon pines—known for their delicious piñon nuts—and through a "fossil area" where there are rocks containing fossils of sea animals that lived about 400 million years ago when the sea covered the area. We stop to look as Mike, who is eager to take his classmates one of the rocks, reads in our Forest Service brochure that it is quite all right to take "a small piece as a souvenir."

We stop again, this time at an overlook a mile above Owens Valley.

From here, we have an excellent view of Palisade Glacier, which is the southernmost glacier in the United States.

But let's move on to Schulman Grove. Here, the forest naturalist tells us, are the oldest known living things on earth—the bristlecone pines.

We find it hard to imagine that some of them were already well started when the ancient Egyptians were building the pyramids 15 centuries before the birth of Christ.

After a tour of the outdoor information center, we take a half-mile self-guiding trail to see the 4,300-year-old Pine Alpha. Less than 10 percent of this old tree—its trunk nearly 4 feet across—is still living.

Each with our own thoughts, we return to Schulman Grove where the sight of our picnic basket brings us with a happy jolt back to the present. After lunch we'll

ψ   ψ   ψ

Paul M. Kihlmire is *Chief*, Branch of Visitor Information Service, Division of Information and Education, Forest Service.

Water fun at Sliding Rock Falls in the Pisgah National Forest, N.C.

continue up to the Patriarch Grove, where the largest bristlecone pines grow. And then, toward the day's end, we'll make our way back down to the Forest Service campground where, after a hearty evening meal, sleep can bring us dreams no stranger than the gnarled and twisted shapes of the ancient bristlecones.

ꙮ   ꙮ   ꙮ

Yes, the national forests contain many natural wonders, and each one could form the nucleus of a national forest vacation. You can visit:

• Hells Canyon, deepest gorge on the North American Continent, where the Snake River flows through the Payette, Nez Perce, and Wallowa-Whitman National Forests of Idaho and Oregon. The canyon at one point is 7,900 feet deep and 10 miles wide from rim to rim.

• The Cranberry Glades of the Monongahela National Forest in West Virginia where wild cranberries and many types of wild orchids grow in arcticlike tundra. You can jump up and down upon the spongy bog and shake a person 150 feet away, believe it or not!

Are you a bird watcher—or perhaps a history buff?

• The largest bird in North America, the condor, is protected in the Sespe Wildlife Area of Los Padres National Forest in California, and some of the rare trumpeter swans live in the Copper River Delta of the Chugach National Forest in Alaska.

• Grasshopper Glacier in the Custer National Forest, Mont., where thousands of grasshoppers were entombed some 200 years ago.

• Pan for gold at German Gulch in the Deerlodge National Forest in Montana, where once a thousand prospectors staked their claims . . . explore dozens of ghost towns within the boundaries of

13

the national forests throughout the West.

• Stop by the Forest Service Voyageur Visitor Center at Ely, Minn., and then explore the water routes of the voyageurs, the hardy French-Canadian fur traders of the 1700's, through the wilderness of the Boundary Waters Canoe Area in the Superior National Forest.

Or would you just plain like to "get away from it all?" Sometimes there's no better tonic than fresh, cool mountain air. One of the highlights of my national forest travels was a jeep trip through the high country around Ouray and Telluride, Colo.—an area known as the "Switzerland of America." Here, on the Uncompahgre National Forest, we slid down snowfields in July and explored the alpine meadows high above timberline. The only trace of man we found were the ramshackle buildings of an old and now deserted mine.

Toward sunset we came across a group of Boy Scouts who had set up camp by one of the three beautiful Alta Lakes and were enjoying a week of "roughing it." Delighted at a chance to show off their cooking skills, the Scouts treated us to a welcome meal of franks and beans. Afterward they paddled us around the lake in canoes and proudly pointed

out the mountain peak where earlier in the week the troop had staked its flag to celebrate a rugged climb which had been successfully completed.

As the darkness approached we pointed our canoes toward shore, where a bonfire waited. But it was getting late; reluctantly, we bade the Scouts goodby and then headed back to civilization.

What does the out of doors mean to you—a place to fish, to hunt, to swim and boat, ski, ride horseback, or hike? Or maybe you prefer a leisurely drive to picnic in a forest setting. There's something for everyone in the national forests.

For fishermen there are 81,000 miles of streams and 3 million acres of lakes and reservoirs.

Millions of big game animals—a major attraction for hunters and tourists alike—live in the national forests.

For the adventurous there are more than 14 million acres of wilderness and primitive areas, to be entered only on foot or on horseback.

Four out of every five well-known ski areas in the West are entirely or partially on national forest land. For hikers and horse riders there are more than 100,000 miles of trails, and for motorists there are almost 194,000 miles of forest devel-

Panning for gold at Resurrection Creek Campground, Chugach National Forest, Alaska.

Campers taking it easy on the lakeshore at Clear Springs Recreation Area, Homochitto National Forest, near Natchez in Mississippi.

opment roads. Campgrounds, hotels, and lodges on national forest land are able to accommodate more than 350,000 overnight visitors at one time.

There is probably a national forest—complete with its natural wonders, points of historic interest, outstanding scenic areas, and opportunities for outdoor recreation of all kinds—within a day's drive from you. If you haven't already, why not begin now to travel the "National Forests—America's Playgrounds"? But be careful—it *can* become a habit!

For information and publications about national forests in your area, write the Regional Forester, U.S. Forest Service, at the appropriate regional address: *Alaska Region,* P.O. Box 1631, Juneau, Alaska 99801; *Pacific Northwest Region,* P.O. Box 3623, Portland, Oreg. 97208; *California Region,* 630 Sansome Street, San Francisco, Calif. 94111; *Northern Region,* Federal Building, Missoula, Mont. 59801; *Intermountain Region,* 324 25th Street, Ogden, Utah 84401; *Rocky Mountain Region,* Federal Center, Building 85, Denver, Colo. 80225; *Southwestern Region,* 517 Gold Avenue SW., Albuquerque, N. Mex. 87101; *Eastern Region,* 633 West Wisconsin Avenue, Milwaukee, Wis. 53203; *Southern Region,* 50 Seventh Street NE., Atlanta, Ga. 30323.

For further reading:

U.S. Department of Agriculture, *Backpacking in the National Forest Wilderness . . . A Family Adventure.* Program Aid 585, U.S. Government Printing Office, Washington, D.C., 1963. 15¢

—— *Camping. The National Forests . . . America's Playgrounds.* Program Aid 502, U.S. Government Printing Office, Washington, D.C. 20402, 1966. 20¢

—— *National Forest Vacations.* U.S. Government Printing Office, Washington, D.C. 20402, 1960. 30¢

—— *Skiing. The National Forests . . . America's Playgrounds.* Program Aid 525, U.S. Government Printing Office, Washington, D.C. 20402, 1966. 20¢

—— *Trees of the Forest, Their Beauty and Use.* Program Aid 613, U.S. Government Printing Office, Washington, D.C. 20402, 1964. 20¢

—— *Wilderness. The National Forests . . . America's Playgrounds.* Program Aid 459, U.S. Government Printing Office, Washington, D.C. 20402, 1963. 20¢

15

A Million Dollar Vacation in a Canoe

ARTHUR W. GREELEY and CLIFFORD D. OWSLEY

IF THERE IS a million dollar vacation anywhere, it surely must be in the Boundary Waters Canoe Area (BWCA) of northern Minnesota.

"What is the Boundary Waters Canoe Area? What do you do there? And just how do you get there?"

These questions were asked by a Washington, D.C., housewife who, with her husband, was looking for a different kind of vacation spot where there would be something to do besides just camp.

Many other vacationing families are in the same boat as the Simpsons, who had picked up some information about the BWCA, but needed to know more about it before planning a vacation.

Mr. Simpson is a professional man, and they have three children—all teen-agers—just about the right age to fully enjoy canoeing, and to be of help in portaging (carrying equipment and canoe over land).

Experienced campers, the Simpsons have their own camper and camping equipment. They know that with a little planning you can find wonderful country for camping, and they were hoping to find a place without motorboats. The Boundary Waters Canoe Area seemed made-to-order for them.

A canoeing vacation in the BWCA offers delights for every family, even the inexperienced. You can get as much help as you need or want; an outfitter will map your route for you, far from motorboats. For $6.50 to $7 a day per person, an outfitter will plan and furnish every-

thing you need. If you wish, he'll also supply an expert guide. But a guide is not essential. With the map that's supplied, even a novice can find his way around in canoe country.

The Boundary Waters Canoe Area is the American half of the famed Quetico-Superior Canoe Area which straddles the border between Canada and Minnesota. In this land of Paul Bunyan legend you will find some truly unique wilderness, some of the finest in North America. In this fascinating country—so well endowed for canoe recreation—there are over 2 million acres of portage-linked lakes and streams, islands, woods and crags which form the tapestry of a region where you will quickly become a modern voyageur as you canoe and portage and camp in the footsteps of the French voyageurs of 200 years ago.

The voyageurs were French-Canadian woodsmen, and they became far-famed as expert canoeists and guides who plied these fur-trading routes before civilization arrived.

On the United States side, this water wonderland lies within the Superior National Forest; and on the Canadian side—within Ontario's Quetico Provincial Park.

It is all one vast region of pine, balsam,

☙ ☙ ☙

Arthur W. Greeley is *Associate Chief* of the Forest Service.

Clifford D. Owsley is *Chief*, Special Reports, Press, and Writing Services Branch, Division of Information and Education, Forest Service.

spruce, and poplar forest which is interlaced with a seemingly infinite variety of lakes and streams.

Here you and your family can embark upon a once-in-a-lifetime adventure, a journey beyond civilization. The slow, natural forces which created this land of lakes and falls and rapids are still at work creating solitude and squalls and cool nights.

Since the canoe is still the most practical means of transport, you'll find yourself drawing on your own resourcefulness which will add further dimensions to your vacation.

How do you get to this wonderful place? It's really quite easy. By way of Ely, Grand Marais, or Duluth, Minn., it is within, at the most, a few days driving time of most of the United States. You can also reach it by American and Canadian rail and airlines.

The first thing to do in planning a trip, if you don't have a local contact, is to write to the chamber of commerce either at Ely or Grand Marais, Minn., or the Minnesota Arrowhead Association in Duluth, and ask for information. They will send you literature and the names of outfitters.

Information on the area may also be obtained from the Forest Supervisor, U.S. Forest Service, Federal Building, Duluth, Minn. 55802.

Study the literature and begin to plan your trip in advance. Good advance planning can insure an enjoyable trip. Write to one or more of the outfitters for prices and reservations. Tell them how long you wish to stay in the area, when you plan to be there, and how many will be in your party. The Simpsons, for example, with three teenagers, probably will need two canoes.

To get an overall introduction to the area, plan to stop by the Forest Service Voyageur Visitor Center, 1 mile east of Ely on Highway 169. The things you can learn there will prove useful.

In planning your canoeing, don't push yourself. It's better to plan a short trip and cover it leisurely, than a longer trip

Campers pause to study the Cliff of the Painted Rocks, Lac LaCroix, which is on the International Boundary with Canada.

Family group at Lower Basswood Falls, Boundary Waters Canoe Area.

which you may find difficult to complete.

Now you have arrived in the area and are ready to begin exploring.

As you approach the jumping-off point, you will find a registration station where each party going into the BWCA must register. Or, if it is more convenient, you can register at any ranger station. Such registration, new this year, will leave a record of where you will be and give the Forest Service information that helps it to manage the area better.

Some folks prefer to use a motor or "kicker" on their canoe. In part of the area, this is permitted; in other parts, no motors are allowed. People who want a really primitive experience head for the "no motor" zones. Any forest ranger or outfitter can provide you with a map that clearly indicates these zones.

Here are some typical canoe routes:

The Kekekabic Loop Route (from the Ely area), 6 days round trip; distance: 49 miles of paddling and 4½ miles of portaging.

The Moose River-Little Indian Sioux Route (north of Echo Trail), 5 days round trip; distance: 38 miles of paddling, 1½ miles of portaging.

The Little Saganaga Route (from the

Gunflint area), 3 days one way; distance: 25 miles of paddling, 4 miles of portaging; river currents are sluggish; route traverses a wild, scenic region.

Travel time which is indicated does not include layovers caused by wind or rain, exploring, fishing, or just plain loafing.

Special features like Indian rock paintings, falls, and other scenic spots are indicated upon your map. You'll want to know how to use a good compass, and how to orient landmarks on the map with it. A little practice is all you need.

The canoe area campsites usually have an open-air toilet and a fireplace.

Timber Harvested

Different from all other areas in the national wilderness system, timber harvesting is permitted on approximately one-third of the area. But you probably won't see any, unless you hike back away from the lakes and portages. Timber operations are carefully controlled to safeguard the lakeshores, and—in about two-thirds of the area—no timber harvesting is permitted whatever.

The entire BWCA is protected by an airspace reservation. You may see the

Forest Service seaplane on fire patrol or other business, but—except in emergency—no private plane is permitted to land or even to fly below 4,000 feet sea level altitude.

As to how long you should plan on staying, probably most families should make the first trip from a few days to a week. The longer you stay, the more food you will have to carry—on your back, a part of the way. You are not limited, however; and some hardy groups have been known to stay out for weeks.

Don't forget to pack a lightweight fishing rod. You can catch wall-eyed and northern pike, lake trout, and, in some places, small-mouth bass. On the American side—in Minnesota—State licenses are required to fish, hunt, and trap—and can be purchased from most resorts, outfitters, and sporting goods stores. In Canada, an Ontario fishing license also will be necessary; but, in Quetico Park, firearms are prohibited.

The fish which rise to a lure in these waters are special fish, as any fisherman knows. The cares and tensions of human society evaporate for the man steering a canoe along the lakes; and no sleep is so refreshing as slumber in a tent or a sleeping bag on the banks of a river.

You'll need a rainproof shelter, warm bed, nourishing food—and a canoe, of course.

The Duluth-type packsack is best for a canoe trip. It has a capacity that seems limitless and wide carrying straps that don't pinch shoulders. Properly packed, it is ideal for carrying gear along portages, and it stores upright in the canoe. It is a

Secretary of Agriculture Orville L. Freeman displays Great Northern pike caught for breakfast during a canoeing trip to the Boundary Waters Canoe Area in Minnesota. Looking on are Mrs. Freeman (left) and President Johnson's daughter Lynda.

simple, large pocket made of duck, closely woven to shed water.

Organize the packs so that one or two contain clothing, sleeping bags, and toilet articles. Tents and cooking items can be stored outside on top. Arrange contents so that the most-needed items are most readily available: For example, pack noon lunches near the top of the food pack.

List of Gear

Including the pack itself, here is a suggested list for each canoeist: Sleeping bag, air mattress, dishes (plastic or aluminum), cutlery; clothing: ankle-covering boots, two changes of wool socks, two long-sleeved cotton shirts, wool shirt or sweater, parka or windbreaker, two pairs of slacks or jeans, underwear, camp shoes and socks, rain gear (poncho or plastic raincoat), brimmed hat, handkerchiefs; also, a flashlight with spare batteries and bulbs, knife, bug dope, suntan lotion, toilet tissue, matches in dampproof container, soap, towel, and safety pins.

Observe commonsense rules of camping, and oldtimers will tip their hats to you. You will be helping to keep the area clean, safe, and natural for those who follow and use it after you.

Small fires or a good bed of coals are best for cooking. If fireplaces are not provided, build your fire on solid rock or sand. Never light one on duff, moss, or against a tree or old log. To extinguish it, use lots of water until ashes are cold to the touch. Be sure there are no hidden sparks. Boil your drinking water or use purifying tablets.

Don't feed bears; they're dangerous. They are attracted by food odors and garbage. Seal food in containers and hang high, beyond the reach of animals—another reason for keeping a clean camp and burning all garbage.

Minnesota laws prohibit the cutting or mutilating of live trees; the dumping of ashes, bottles, cans, trash or garbage into public waters; and fires which are left unattended.

Wildlife and birds are plentiful. You may see deer along marshy shores in the evening or early morning; moose are apt to be out in the water. There are eagles,

osprey, ruffed grouse, and many smaller birds as well.

There is no need to follow a monotonous menu or to use heavy, bulky cans and bottles (which not only add to your pack weight but will create disposal problems as well).

The modern foodpacking industries have made great strides in lightweight, dehydrated, and freeze-dried products. You can cook up a nutritious, satisfying, and balanced meal inexpensively, three times a day. A week of eating for four can go into one packsack.

In this lake-laced canoe country, there are rapids and waterfalls and portages cut out by the Indians and voyageurs so that their journeys could be safely continued. From the water, you can usually see a portage by a break in the tree line or a well-worn surface at water's edge in the recess of a bay. Use the portages; don't take chances with rapids! The voyageurs and Indians used portages, and they were mighty expert paddlers.

Don't leave safety behind on this canoe trip. Always wear a lifejacket when on the water, and you will be prepared for any emergencies.

If the canoe should overturn, stay with it; it will float—and you'll be glad you remembered to wear your lifejacket.

Recipe for Relaxation

When you have paddled these calm waters for a week, when you've been lulled into another world by the panorama of woods, sky, and water, when you've snagged a lake trout and cooked it over a campfire, when you have toted packs and a canoe overland and rested while feasting your eyes on nature's wonderland, when you've slept in a tent with the song of the rain outside—when you've done these things all on your own, you just won't be quite the same person that entered this truly unique area. You'll feel different somehow—and the workaday world won't seem quite so formidable.

And you will certainly agree with the others who have been there before, that—in the Boundary Waters Canoe Area—you found your million dollar vacation, in a 17-foot canoe.

A Forest Ranger's Rounds

ALAN R. DUHNKRACK

THE GRAY-GREEN Forest Service jeep parked in front of the ranger station looked different this spring morning. From inside the jeep peered three young boys, obviously impatient to get started, with big piles of camping gear heaped all around them.

The boys, Dean, Charlie, and Jesse, had been the winners of a Kentucky State Conservation Essay Contest. The prize awarded was a day spent with a forest ranger on his rounds. As district ranger, I was to be their escort.

For an added bonus, we would camp out overnight on the Morehead District of the Daniel Boone National Forest. This forest lies in the eastern portion of Kentucky, and my district is the northernmost of seven.

By now it was 9 a.m., the work crews had been dispatched for the day, office routine had been disposed of, and I stood in the doorway just for a moment, waiting to plunge in.

"Ranger Al! Can't we go now?" That got me started, and the boys and I settled back in the jeep to see what a national forest can say for itself.

Our first stop was to be at the Clear Creek Furnace Recreation Area. The site needed checking after a weekend of intensive use by picnickers.

We swung off the main road, drove through the picnic area, and stopped at the base of the furnace.

The towering stone furnace now standing silent could tell a story of changing times and changing industry. During the late 1800's, the furnace was the center of iron ore production. Great quantities of timber had been cut to provide charcoal for iron ore smelting. But, by the change of the century, this method of iron production had been replaced, and the furnace abandoned.

Growing populations in the area were putting greater demands on the forest's timber, water, and wildlife resources; and by the early 1900's, the forest was in poor condition from overuse.

It was at this stage that the U.S. Forest Service was asked to purchase this land as a national forest. The proper protection and management of the once scarred and barren slopes have restored the land to its fullest potential. Dense hardwood forests, clear streams, and abundant game populations now make this forest a paradise for the outdoor enthusiast.

The boys were attracted by the creek, and so was I, but for a different reason. There, spoiling the clear sparkle of the water, lay refuse from a picnic meal, cans and paper caught along the rocky edges. The four of us gathered up the mess and left it in a trash can, and then kept our eyes open for other litter and signs of vandalism. It is a discouraging thing to see Smokey Bear signs riddled with shotgun pellets, and picnic areas dotted with paper and soft drink containers. The cost of sign repair and cleanup can run into hundreds of dollars for one recreation area alone, enough to open the eyes of any responsible individual.

Alan R. Duhnkrack, a former District Ranger, is now the *Resource Management Staff Officer*, Daniel Boone National Forest, Winchester, Ky.

We piled back in the jeep, our next destination well in mind. The Primitive Weapons Area, about 8,000 acres, had been established by the Forest Service and the State of Kentucky to provide an area for hunters using such primitive weapons as longbows, crossbows, and muzzle loaders, and also to demonstrate wildlife management under the multiple use concept. This is a region crisscrossed with ridges and sandstone cliffs, and in its remote beauty lies much of its appeal.

In these surroundings, Daniel Boone lived with and also fought against the Shawnee Indians. His adventures centered around the Licking River Valley and the Blue Licks salt region to the north. These areas were appropriately named, as it was here that wild buffalo and deer once satisfied their natural craving for salt at the mineral springs "licks."

"What good is all that salt?" came from Charlie, and I went on to tell of its importance to the early settlers for food preservation, and how salt was produced in large iron kettles which were set over wood fires.

Boone's Capture Recalled

Daniel Boone's capture by the Indians came next in my story, and the fact that hunting in this area is limited to the weapons those early pioneers used had the boys drawing imaginary crossbows and sighting muzzle loaders.

There were no real targets in sight except the ever-present squirrels, but hunters bring home deer, grouse, and wild turkey in season. The rugged landscape, with its ridgetops and cliffs, gives the hunters an exciting time, and their response has been most enthusiastic.

Now came the first real business stop of the day—inspection of a timber sale. A big part of my job calls for administration of the sale of mature trees or the thinning of younger trees. The sales are mostly to lumber producers who operate one or more small sawmills.

These sales are a boost for the local economy, through the employment of the men working in the woods, and through the manufacture of wood products like building materials and furniture veneers.

Even the younger generation shares in the profits. But the three boys looked only vaguely enthusiastic when I mentioned that 25 percent of the receipts of the sold timber is turned over to the national forest counties for local school budgets and for county road systems.

The activity of the logging operation seemed a lot more fun. The boys watched wide eyed as bulldozers skidded logs to a central area where they were being loaded onto big logging trucks.

Turkey Family Sighted

Newly constructed logging roads were checked by me for erosion control measures required of the logger. He had done a mighty good job.

Water bars or diversion ditches had been bulldozed across the road at regular intervals to prevent the rain runoff from eroding the steeper portions of the road and washing the soil away. The roads no longer in use had been seeded to cover the turned up earth.

Here Dean was the excited one—not 30 yards from us was a mother turkey with her brood, carefully picking their way, single file, down such a newly seeded roadbed.

Up came Dean's imaginary flintlock and he was the proud possessor of a meal for his pioneer family.

By this time, the boys had absorbed enough of the conservation viewpoint to be dismayed at the looks of a clear cutting of a hardwood stand. Here, all the trees had been cut down. Actually, I explained, this is an approved method of harvesting mature timber designed to encourage the seeds of more desirable species to germinate and grow, forming a new stand. The sunlight now can reach the ground; but prior to harvesting, dense stands of mature trees might have eliminated any such sprouting. Deer also benefit, as the cleared area provides excellent browse for them to feed on.

We had a chance to compare the looks of a younger stand of timber that had been thinned with that of a clear cut area. Thinning accelerates growth of the better trees in a timber stand and insures a good supply of acorns and other tree

22

Hiking trail (lower right) through natural arch, Daniel Boone National Forest.

food (mast) for squirrels as well as other wild animals.

Wildlife was given a helping hand at the site of an old sawmill. The cleared area at the millsite was a natural place for game to seek food. Hence it had been planted with the orchardgrass and white dutch clover which are preferred foods.

The value of wildlife in the Daniel Boone National Forest is most easily seen in the recreation it provides. But the enjoyment of hunting, fishing, and trapping is only part of the picture. Local communities profit from the sportsmen's purchases of gas, hunting equipment, overnight accommodations, items from local craft industries, and farm products like honey and country hams.

Seeing the amount of horseplay in the rear of the jeep, I decided to put the excess energy to work, and we headed for Tater Knob fire tower. The climb up the tower ladder actually slowed them down only slightly—boys being boys— but the long-range view from the top kept the questions flying.

Naming all the landmarks gave me an opportunity to see the area pretty thor-

oughly, but it was the regular towerman who made the most important observation. About half a mile to the north was a patch of pine timber, the tops brown under the sun when they should have been green with new spring growth. This clearly indicated the beginning of an attack by Virginia pine sawflies, and called for insect control work. It would be the start of my schedule of activities for the following week, for sure.

Clearing for Copters

From the tower we could also see a helispot, one of the many clearings developed for helicopter landings in the forest. These clearings are used both for fire control and wildlife management. The forest had been using helicopters for a good many years to fly in men and equipment for firefighting.

The cleared spots, usually on top of the many ridges, serve also as wildlife dining areas, remote from human interference and ideal for browse.

I led the way down the tower stairway, and down a trail maintained by the forest

23

for both hiking and hunting use, and also for access to any fires that occur deep within the forested area.

In the Daniel Boone National Forest is a very intricate system of hiking trails, many leading to scenic overlooks where a family can view the massive cliff line topography along with nature's carvings of natural bridges and arches.

This particular hiker trail, appropriately named Cedar Cliff Ridge, followed the ridge and valley back to Chestnut Cliffs above Leatherwood Creek.

If it hadn't been a working day I would have yielded to the clamoring boys, as the trail is a very inviting one, but instead I promised them a backpacking hike plus a cookout for the following day.

Dogwood at Fullest

We did relax over the lunch that we'd brought along and enjoyed the white dogwood now at its fullest. The dogwood blossoms before the other trees leaf out, making a dramatic opening for the natural beauty of the forest.

The spring rains had encouraged the blooming of the small violets, purple and yellow, the spring beauties. And the mayapples were pushing up through the leaf mold.

After eating, the boys and I continued our rounds following a forest road down Martins Branch, where a stream improvement project crew was hard at work.

This creek helps feed the Morehead Municipal Water Supply, and here in the forest we can help keep the water plentiful and hold down excessive siltation of the reservoir.

The project crew workers were now constructing rock structures along the banks of the streams.

These structures called "gabions" control the flow of the stream and protect the streambanks from eroding. The "gabions" direct the flow of the stream away from the bank, causing the current to carve holes in the bottom of the creek, which make excellent fishing holes. The boys pointed out that the holes would be fine for swimming, too.

Parts of the stream plan needed to be modified, as the streambed was sandier than expected, so I had to spend some time with the work crew.

In any event, it was late in the afternoon when I was ready to go, and later yet when I had rounded up the three explorers. We then headed directly for our campground at Rodburn Hollow.

On the way, we saw what can happen to a forest through human carelessness. Two weeks ago a fire, started by a hiker's discarded cigarette, had raged along a hilltop, burning some 200 acres before it was brought under control.

The boys had never seen such destruction before. The blackened and scarred timber stood awkwardly over the ashy ground strewn with burned brush and fallen branches. The dead trees not totally destroyed would be sold in a salvage sale later on, as a preliminary step of a reclamation job. All wildlife had left the spot, homes and food destroyed for many months. Loss of ground cover made this a weak spot in our control of soil erosion during the spring rains. The forest's beauty was gone. Even three 10-year-olds could get angry at the picture around them, a never to be forgotten experience.

"If I were the ranger, I'd make the guilty people come out here and see what they'd done"—Jesse's comment brought forth murmurs of approval from each of the other boys.

Rodburn Hollow lies just beyond the Triangle fire tower. So after checking in at the tower, we went at once to set up our tent and lay a fire for an evening meal. The boys pitched in, proud to help, but like me, tired from a big day. I could see we would be crawling into sleeping bags good and early.

As the day drew to a close, I realized how much we had seen. I only hoped the importance of the forest and its value were as clear to the three boys as they were to me.

Sheer enjoyment on the part of the vast majority of people ranked high on the list of values. And enjoyment of all of the forest's resources—recreation, water, wildlife, and timber—depends on sound management under a sustained yield plan of multiple use.

A national forest does speak quite well for itself, don't you agree?

Wilderness Adventure

MICHAEL FROME

O F THE TWO of us, the black mare fittingly named Midnight was taking the larger gamble. She seemed to accept it rather bravely, however, heading confidently up the open sagebrush hillside. Meanwhile, I tried to guard the secret from her that she was carrying on her back the rankest of tenderfeet, whose entire preparations for a wilderness adventure in the Rocky Mountains had consisted of two afternoon horseback rides in the pleasant woods of Rock Creek Park back east in the Nation's Capital.

Ahead lay an aspen forest, beckoning like a gateway to the high country, or like a portal connecting the rangeland and roads below, where people dwell and manage their own everyday affairs, with the ancient and totally unmechanized wilderness.

Far behind us, in the distance beyond the Box R Ranch, I could see the silvery threads of Horse Creek and the Green River joining into one. The cottonwood flats surrounding the confluence were the site of the legendary fur trading rendezvous of the 1830's, when trappers and Indians converged after a long winter in these and other western mountains.

Midnight had a sense of such history about her. I felt that her sure-footed, energetic stride, the eagerness for her mission, wherever it might lead, must reflect the bones and blood of her ancestors, who surely had carried the scouts, explorers, the trappers and packers, and trail blazers. And off we rode, sharing our destiny on the rocky pathways of the pioneering mountainmen.

We were part of a group called the Trail Riders of the Wilderness, sponsored by the American Forestry Association. Each summer about 12 such groups, which anyone may join, set forth on pack trips of 8 to 14 days into wilderness areas of the national forests and national parks. The association began these trips over 30 years ago, at a time when the wilderness concept of the Forest Service was young, and when there was need to demonstrate the hardy pleasures derived from exercising the muscles of body, mind, and spirit.

Similar trips now are also conducted by the Wilderness Society in order to continually broaden the Nation's knowledge and appreciation of primeval places and to assure their lasting protection.

The trip on board Midnight, into the mighty Bridger Wilderness, which covers 383,000 acres on the western slope of the Continental Divide in Wyoming, was my first adventure in western wilderness, but by no means the last. This is the kind of experience that calls one back, demanding a return to the natural stillness in the glacial carved valleys and flowering alpine meadows, and to the spectacle of snowy starkness glittering in the bright summer light high above timberline. No resort ever was endowed with better landscaping, nor ever afforded a more refreshing

᯽   ᯽   ᯽

Michael Frome is the author of "Whose Woods These Are—the Story of the National Forests" and "Strangers in High Places—the Story of the Great Smoky Mountains." He is a contributing editor of *Changing Times,* a regular columnist in *American Forests,* and the author of many articles in other magazines. Mr. Frome resides in Alexandria, Va.

25

Midnight and the author, left, above Elbow Lake in the Bridger Wilderness Area.

change of pace from everyday routines.

There were 22 in our group, half of us men and the other half women, of varying degrees of riding ability. There were three doctors finding relief for jangled nerves, a banker, a biologist, schoolteachers, and assorted others sharing equal rank and privilege—which is to say that anyone was welcome to help the cook with dishwashing or to assist on other chores. The 12-day ride started at the Box R Ranch, in a green-meadowed valley at 7,600 feet on the slope of the Wind River Range. The bossman and outfitter, Walt Lozier, furnished food, horses, tents, everything but sleeping bags and fishing gear, and led the way.

We spent 8 of our 12 days in the wilderness on the trail, and 4 in layovers without the need of breaking camp and pitching tents. The daily journey ranged from 9 to 16 miles. But mileage figures actually are deceiving, considering the variety of terrain and trail, uphill, downhill, along rocky crests and precipitous switchbacks, across streams and green meadows. In such an exercise, a horse is man's best friend. "Trust your mount," as Midnight seemed continually to be suggesting, "and we will both make it home."

Pace Is Flexible

The pace of a trail ride, happily, is not geared to moving from one point to another in the shortest possible time, but in providing for activities and interests—fishing, photography, botanizing, birding, and learning many things, one from another—for anyone of any age.

To each his own. For me, on this trail ride and others that I have made since, wilderness has represented the finest possible education in American culture and art, art of the land and of the people.

Fishing and hiking are splendid for physical exercise, of course. But when I followed the trails of Jim Bridger, of Gen. John C. Fremont and Kit Carson, his guide in 1842, and when I came upon the very scenes that were painted by Alfred Jacob Miller in 1837, the Wind River places which he found "as fresh and beautiful as if just from the hands of the Creator," I felt my personal reasons for being in wilderness, and the compelling reason for wilderness to endure.

'No Name Lakes'

Lakes on our route were so numerous that lake namers had run dry of inspiration and simply called one group the "No Name Lakes." They were crystal clear, unpolluted waters, the rare kind you could drink, or swim in when the temperature was warm enough, and fish for trout. At Trapper Lake we encountered company, a handful of canoers and fishermen who had hiked in. They were doing it the hard way, but actually inflicting less damage on the wilderness than were we with our large horse party.

We met a couple who had been in the wilderness for a month; although they were pleased to meet us, they certainly were not suffering from lack of radio or other forms of human chatter.

We were now in the country explored by General Fremont, at the base of the mountain that he climbed and named for himself. With Kit Carson and a full military expedition, he had reached South Pass, below the Wind River Range, and had continued toward the headwaters of the Green River. He was drawn to the higher peaks by their shiny icy caps and was determined to scale the highest.

He was mistaken in his choice, as it developed, although his peak, a jagged truncated mesa of stone, was the most spectacular. He and five companions rode beneath a perpendicular wall of granite working their way to the summit, then dismounted and climbed on foot in thin moccasins made from buffalo skin.

Fremont, ever dramatic, drove a ramrod into the rock and "unfurled the national flag to wave where never the flag waved before."

At the camping ground called Fremont Crossing we were less than 2,000 feet from that point. Around us a concentration of great peaks just under 14,000 feet flanked the Continental Divide: Gannett, the highest in Wyoming, Fremont, Lester, Sacajawea, Warren. From Indian Pass we could see the Dinwoody Glaciers, and the forested trough of Wind River Valley calling from across the divide; the snowy peaks of the three Tetons, far off northwestward, were bright in the haze.

Fremont thought that he was at the highest point in the Rockies, and he was overcome by the "concourse of lakes and rushing waters, mountains of rock, dells, and ravines of the most exquisite beauty, all kept green and fresh by the great moisture in the air and sown with brilliant flowers."

In the decade following, Albert Bierstadt, the artist, was likewise inspired and in 1859 used this setting for his massive painting, "Rocky Mountains," which now hangs in the Metropolitan Museum of Art in New York.

One hundred years after Bierstadt, our trail riders reached the scene. Who among us could fail to be overcome by the power of natural stillness? Or by the artistry of the earth in carving glacial forms and in painting the dark forest or the most delicate wildflower?

Each Day Different

Time in the wilderness never hangs heavy for the traveler. It never blends into monotony. No two days are alike. Given a road, we could probably have driven the same route through the Bridger Wilderness in 3 hours and seen virtually nothing. But the seeming slowness of our method of transportation by horse expands the dimensions of time and allows one to appreciate the fullness of what lies close at hand.

In the Bridger, the life communities changed endlessly from one drainage to another and from one level of elevation to the next. Thus from Fremont Crossing, we rode through a snowbanked pass at

11,000 feet, alongside icebergs floating over the Titcomb Lakes, while dozens of granite boulders, upthrust by glacial action, blocked a stark horizon above us. Then we descended below timberline, a relief from rock and tundra and camped in the Trail Creek Valley surrounded by spruce, alpine fir, and a wall of mountains with an occasional lodgepole pine, brave but weak, growing out of the cliffside. From our later camp at Clear Creek, we climbed White Rock Mountain and came down with fossils of imbedded seashells and crustaceans left by ancient inland seas that predated the Rockies.

Masses of Bluebells

There was no letup either in beauty or discovery, especially for the explorer who came armed with binoculars and with nature guides.

The birder wore out the pages of his guide identifying species which, like the vegetation, changed with elevation, from sage grouse on brushy, arid plains to the chirping rosy finch, horned lark, and ptarmigan above tree line.

In every setting different combinations of flowers grew. Small wintergreen, with white flowers and red berries, claimed the shady dells. Masses of bluebells, buttercups, and tall sunflowers swept across the open meadows.

On the moist meadows and slopes, the small white and golden flowers of the saxifrage rose from slender stalks, and on the hillsides the Indian paintbrush, Wyoming's State flower, almost 2 feet high, with vivid red bloom.

The lupine, as indigenous to the West as the cowboy, was virtually everywhere, with its delicate pea-type flowers of many colors; the prettiest of all, perhaps, being the smallish lupine of alpine elevation, with leaflets not more than a half inch long and with erect stems bearing deep blue flowers.

Trail riders fall into the spirit of a pack trip by pitching in with the chores. First in the morning comes the fire and then comes coffee, and next the roundup of horses after a night's grazing, their cowbells jangling loud enough to waken the last sleepyhead. This signals time to start moving, with towel and soap, for the chilly stream or to borrow a pan's worth of hot water from the cook.

The party's fishermen have contributed their catch, of the early morning or evening before, toward breakfast, which already consists of juice, bacon, eggs, hot cakes, and toast, and consequently defers anew all resolutions aimed at dieting. The only hope of losing weight is to spend energy rolling up the gear, first one's own and then the packer's.

Lunch along the trail always is a sandwich and soft drink stop at a cold mountain stream, a real chance to eat lightly. The pack train rolls ahead with kitchen, bedding, and fishing gear, so that by the time the trail riders make camp in mid-afternoon everything is waiting.

Dinners on the trail are special, and not only in the size of servings. Steaks, fried chicken, and even blueberry pie cooked in a Dutch oven are not unusual. It all depends on the cook. On the Box R trips, Walt Lozier's skillful wife, Nancy, who first came West as a dude herself, is in charge of the cooking.

But what really makes an evening is the campfire, which gets going when darkness finally crowds out the views of distant waterfalls and reduces mountains to silhouettes and shadows. It may begin with singing, accompanied by someone who has thoughtfully brought a mouth organ or guitar, but then we talk about wilderness—reviewing the lives of the Bridgers and Fremonts, the actions of glaciers, and the ways of wildlife.

Age Means Nothing

On each trail ride the American Forestry Association and Wilderness Society assign a doctor and a trip leader. One of the trip leader's jobs is to make the campfire sessions stimulating and worthwhile. On one particular night Walt and Nancy Lozier got the talking going.

"Age means nothing on a trail ride," said Walt. "I'd rather take a 65-year-old who stays conditioned to the outdoors than somebody half his age who doesn't keep in shape. I think it requires at least some sense of humor, too, to really enjoy a trail ride. You just can't expect the convenience and the service of a resort, though we're glad to accommodate those who have diet problems, and even physical disability can be overcome.

"People who come out with inadequate equipment, especially for the changeable weather, run into difficulty. Every outfitter furnishes a list of exactly what to bring, yet there always is someone who shows up minus either a good pair of long johns, a warm jacket, rain gear, or a sturdy sleeping bag. You've just got to ride comfortably, stay dry, and sleep well to get the best out of the trail.

"But the most important equipment is the right attitude. Start as a friend who wants to be helpful. You will make more friends and learn more about horses and camping than you'd ever expect."

The Loziers told us something about their logistical operations. To provide for 22 trail riders required 8 wranglers, plus Walt and Nancy. Riding and pack stock totaled 64 horses and 18 mules. The baggage and food was toted in 40 panniers (pan-yers), canvas- and cowhide-covered boxes strapped to the pack animals.

For a while we discussed whether the size of the party was too large. We had seen some wildlife—a moose across a lake from camp, fleeting glimpses of antelope and deer—but there was no doubt that there were too many horses and people for much more than binocular viewing.

"By the same token," asked someone, "if you have a large number of horses or a series of trail rides covering the same territory in a given year, don't you then run into problems of providing adequate pasturage?"

"What about the problem of litter in the wilderness?" asked another rider. "I looked at the bottom of a beautiful mountain lake today and saw beer cans—even up here in the wilderness!"

A great deal has happened since those questions were asked. The Forest Service has learned, and is learning, improved techniques of management for wilderness recreation. The sponsoring organizations and outfitters are adapting new kinds of pack trips which are designed to protect fragile wilderness values.

Wilderness Patrol

For instance, under William Deschler, supervisor of the Bridger National Forest who accompanied the trail ride which I have described, horses are restricted from some drainages in the Bridger Wilderness, at least temporarily, because of erosion caused by overuse. In addition, a new corps of Wilderness Patrol Rangers,

Square Top Mountain across Green River Lake, Bridger National Forest, Wyo.

headed by Kenneth Symes—another companion on that same trip—is responsible for litter cleanup and for encouraging all back country travelers to respect their wilderness surroundings.

To an increasing extent, the size of parties is being limited to 15 riders. Outfitters are packing their feed in with them; they are helping to provide a truer wilderness experience by refraining from the use of powersaws.

There is, in fact, a trend toward "spot packing," with the outfitter carrying the groups to a single base camp, from which they travel by foot—until the outfitter gets back several days or a week later.

Such improvements serve to expand, rather than to restrict, recreational use of the back country. Guided backpacking trips of the Wilderness Society reduce the costs so that more people can afford the ultimate in outdoors luxury—a bed beneath the stars. And the rides recently established by the American Forestry Association "for families only" enable parents to share the pleasures, as well as the problems, with their growing children.

Trail rides are designed essentially for people who are untrained and hesitant to go on their own, though some experts return year after year. It is also possible for anyone to engage a competent outfitter for any number of days.

The deeper one looks into the wilderness experience, the broader become its horizons, by horse, afoot, and, in some parts of the country, by canoe.

Now that I write no longer as a novice, I know that wilderness is friendly, like that sure-footed, steady horse named Midnight, and far from forbidding. Above all, wilderness adventure breeds enthusiasm, idealism, and love of life. The wilderness adventurer champions enlightened use and appreciation of America's priceless natural domain.

Golden Passports
to National Outdoorlands

LOUIS E. REID, JR.

YOU CAN BECOME a conservation philanthropist for just $7, helping to maintain and preserve the Nation's outdoor recreation heritage.

Thousands of American families did just that this summer. They contributed $7, every penny earmarked to provide more local, State, and Federal outdoor recreation lands and waters.

The selfsame $7 made them Golden Eagle families, holders of annual Golden Passport permits which are valid for admission at the thousands of national forest, park, refuge, and other designated Federal recreation areas.

The Federal Government calls the program for marketing the $7 permits "Operation Golden Eagle."

The money you pay for the entrance permits goes into the Federal Government's land and water conservation fund. This fund receives revenues from sale of Golden Passports and from other sources totaling more than $100 million annually. The larger share of this provides grants which the States, counties, and cities use

✿   ✿   ✿

Louis E. Reid, Jr., is *Chief,* Office of Recreation Information, Bureau of Outdoor Recreation, U.S. Department of the Interior.

to buy and develop badly needed park, forest, and other recreation areas. The rest purchases authorized Federal recreation land and water areas and helps provide for recreation and wildlife at Federal reservoir and other water projects.

You can buy your Golden Passport by mail or at most areas where it is valid for admission. The passport also may be purchased at many State, Federal, and private agency offices across the country.

Where to Write

To encourage you to buy your permit before you start out on your vacation trip, the U.S. Bureau of Outdoor Recreation (it's P.O. Box 7763, Washington, D.C. 20044) will send you a handsome Golden Eagle lapel pin and a Golden Eagle Family Award Certificate, in addition to your Golden Passport, for each $7 order which is received by mail.

If a mail purchase isn't convenient, you can buy your permit in most national parks at the entry booths. Some national forests offer them at entrance booths, but more often at campgrounds or ranger stations. Wildlife refuge offices offer permits for sale. The nearest office of the U.S. Army Corps of Engineers is usually the handiest place to buy them for use at designated recreation areas at reservoirs. The Bureau of Land Management has Golden Passports available at some campgrounds and at field offices which serve various units of the public domain. Several agencies have roving rangers or fieldworkers who will sell you a permit.

The Golden Passport is valid for you and everyone in your car at all the designated Federal recreation areas all year long. But in lieu of the annual passport, some areas have available a 1-day carload fee of $1 or a short-term fee, good only at that particular area and priced at $3 to $5. The price of the latter depends on the nature of the area. At a few areas, you have your choice of all three—the 1-day permit, the short-term permit, or the annual Golden Eagle Passport. There is no charge for children under 16 at any Federal area where Golden Passports are valid for entrance.

The Golden Passport is an entrance permit. It does not take the place of user fees which are charged in some areas for use of duckblinds, bathhouses, and other special services. You should inquire locally for information about those charges. And, of course, the Federal charges don't pay for services you may require from concessionaires, such as cabin rental, food, guides, and the like.

Golden Passports are valid at thousands of the better known and better developed Federal recreation areas at national parks, national forests, reservoir, wildlife, refuge, seashore, public domain, and other Federal land and water facilities. Entrance charges are made only where there has been a substantial Federal investment in recreation facilities. This leaves much national forest land and considerable portions of areas surrounding Federal reservoirs, plus other areas, available without any charge at all.

You can always tell when the Golden Passports, or other permits, are required at a given area by looking to see if a sign is posted which states that permits are required or are valid there. If there is no sign, then there is no fee.

The Golden Passport of a camping family is checked at Monongahela National Forest, in West Virginia.

The Santa Catalina Mountains:
A One-Day Family Trip

CLYDE W. DORAN

A 40-MILE family motor jaunt from Tucson, Ariz., to Mount Lemmon through the Coronado National Forest is similar to traveling 1,500 miles across the United States from Mexico to Canada. Bring your picnic lunch and jump into our family car. Many of the same plants and animals can be seen on the ride from Tucson to the top of the Santa Catalina Mountains that can be found going from the Mexican border all of the way to the Canadian Rockies.

Our first stop is Sabino Canyon, the major drainage on the south slope of the Santa Catalinas. As we enter the national forest boundary, the forest ranger checks our "Golden Passport" and directs us to the Sabino Canyon visitor center.

Sought Cities of Gold

The ranger explains that the Coronado National Forest was named after the Spanish conquistador, Don Francisco Vasquez de Coronado, who marched into what is now southern Arizona from Mexico in 1540 seeking the fabled Seven Golden Cities of Cibola. Today, the gold this brave explorer sought in vain is being discovered in different forms—valuable water, timber, forage, wildlife, and outdoor recreation opportunities as well as minerals of various sorts.

The visitor center at the mouth of Sabino Canyon was opened in 1964—one of the first U.S. Forest Service centers. The attractive young lady naturalist, resembling an airline hostess in her pert

Forest Service uniform, shows us the huge relief map and exhibits, which interpret the human and natural history of the Santa Catalinas. The animals and vegetation that characterize the many life zones of the mountain are vividly displayed at the center.

Live lizards, Gila monsters, and rattlesnakes are part of the displays inside the center, while Gambel quail, cottontail rabbits, and Harris ground squirrels play outside on the very doorsteps. The visitor center's territorial slump-block building harmonizes with its desert setting.

We spend the next hour walking a self-guiding nature trail, where the plant species are named and described on little metal plaques. These acquaint us with the variety of vegetation. The adaptations that plants make to their environment is like studying the characteristics of human behavior—fascinating while a bit overwhelming at the same time.

Other hiking and horseback trails can take us where we may see the grotesque giant saguaro cactus and look for lizards, snakes, ground squirrels, javelinas (wild hogs), and innumerable birds. But since it's a 2-mile hike to Seven Falls, we decide to bypass that today and take the short drive up the Sabino Canyon.

A streamlined road runner crosses the

Clyde W. Doran has been *Forest Supervisor* of the Coronado National Forest for the past 5 years. Son of a forest ranger, he was born on the Alpine Ranger District in Colorado.

Rock towers and natural bridge in the Santa Catalina Mountains, Coronado National Forest.

road near the first of nine picturesque one-way bridges. We drive under towering cliffs along the bubbling boulder-strewn stream.

Family groups are everywhere—wading and swimming in the deeper pools. We catch glimpses of picnickers where white-barked sycamores shade tables and fireplaces. The manmade structures fashioned from concrete and rock blend into the environment like they grew there.

A half million people visit this canyon each year.

Sabino Ortero located his ranch headquarters at the mouth of the canyon in the 1870's. Records indicate that the canyon was named after him.

From the Sabino Canyon we drive back toward Tucson, then take the Hitchcock Highway winding up to Mount Lemmon. Tucson's high-rise metropolitan area and its sprawling suburbs lie beneath in the Santa Cruz Valley as we climb toward the peaks ahead. The bright hot sun reflects thousands of shining dots below, the giant outdoor aircraft storage facilities at Davis-Monthan Air Force Base.

Since the Spanish priest Fray Marcos de Niza visited the site of present day Tucson in 1539, the city has been under four flags—Spain, Mexico, the Southern Confederacy, and the United States. Spain ruled until Mexico gained her independence in 1821. The area was bought by the United States in 1853 through the Gadsden Purchase.

At the outbreak of the Civil War, the U.S. Dragoons were withdrawn, and for a brief period Tucson was claimed by the Confederate South.

After the war in 1871, a U.S. military post was established at Tucson and later at Fort Lowell to protect the settlers from raiding Apaches. Fort Lowell was abandoned in 1891 because the Apache peril steadily decreased following the capture of Geronimo in 1886.

During the 1870's when Tucson had a population of less than 3,000 people, early records show the domestic water supply was obtained from wells only 37 feet deep. The Santa Cruz flood plain was lush with sacaton and other native perennial grasses, inviting cattlemen from Texas and California. Today the ecology of the valley has changed—thorny shrubs

33

predominate, except where the land is irrigated, and the valley's underground water table has dropped between 300 and 400 feet.

The first use on record of the Santa Catalina Mountains for recreation, in the form of relief from the heat, was by the soldiers from Fort Lowell. They hiked to the cool pine-clad slopes by way of Soldier Trail up the Sabino Canyon.

Today we can drive leisurely along the blacktopped Hitchcock Forest Highway, thankful for modern transportation improvements. The highway is named for former Postmaster General Frank H. Hitchcock who was instrumental in promoting its construction by the Bureau of Public Roads and by the Pima County Highway Department.

The county maintains the highway today and keeps it cleared of snow throughout the winter months.

Prior to 1950, the only access to the mountain was via a controlled, one-way and treacherous dirt road built in 1917 on the north or back slope of the Catalinas from Oracle, Ariz.

Now we leave the desert-shrub vegetation type, the level with 11-inch annual rainfall, and climb through semidesert grassland. The saguaro cactus, ocotillo, creosote bush, mesquite, and palo verde (Arizona's State tree) give way to grassland as we ascend.

The soils here look granitic and highly erosive. The Forest Service has to practice good land management to prevent an accelerated erosion. We recall the conservation principles of multiple use and of sustained yield resource management that the forest naturalist had explained to us all at Sabino Canyon.

My daughter Cecilia cries, "Wolf!" as we round the next curve. Would you believe it, a coyote! We all spot the coyote crossing a deep arroyo. Cecilia chatters

Map helps locate points of interest in this sweeping view from Windy Point Vista in the Santa Catalina Mountains, Coronado National Forest, Ariz.

about coyotes, mountain lions, bobcats, and other beasts of prey and sympathizes with the white-tailed deer.

We think about stopping to have our picnic in hopes of seeing the elusive ring-tailed cat in Molino Basin, but decide to drive a little farther. Molino Basin Forest Camp is in the open oak woodland (at 4,500 feet) of the upper Sonoran life zone. In spring, the hillsides are often carpeted with the showy white Mariposa lily. It is here that the beautiful although deadly coral bean grows. Just two of its beans contain enough poison to kill an adult human.

These bright red beans were used by the Indians for jewelry.

800-Foot Fall

At the 5,500-foot level of the Hitch-cock or Catalina Highway we stop to look across Bear Canyon to Seven Cataracts. This is where Willow Canyon enters Bear Canyon with a spectacular 800-foot fall of seven steps.

Farther on the highway enters a pine grove, sheltered in a deep canyon. Bear Canyon picnic ground is in this pocket of trees. Just below the picnic ground is the largest measured Arizona cypress in the world. It is over 70 inches in diameter and a towering 90 feet tall.

Both Chihuahua and ponderosa pines are found here. We examine the difference in their cones and needles while we eat lunch.

A bushy-tailed squirrel is offered a sandwich, but he dashes away in a great and important hurry.

A quarter mile up the canyon from the picnic ground we see the decaying remains of the General Hitchcock Tree. This massive Douglas-fir was rooted in a seep or spring which probably accounted for its large size. When the tree was blown down by high winds in 1952, it was nearly 8 feet in diameter and over 320 years old. A dated cross section of the tree is now on display at the Palisades ranger station.

From Windy Point Vista, a vast panorama unrolls to the south and west. From here we can see Baboquivari Peak, 60 miles to the south on the Papago Indian Reservation, and other mountains straddling the Mexico-United States border. What a spot for the camera enthusiast!

Roadside interpretive displays explain the vegetative life zones.

Nearby Geology Vista has still another interpretive exhibit, dealing with the more common rocks found on the south slope of the Catalinas. Its central location and easy access to the highway make this vista point ideal as a helicopter landing pad during fire season. From here Forest Service men and equipment are ferried in to fight remote fires.

About a mile above Geology Vista we abruptly make our final transition from chaparral to ponderosa pine forest while crossing a low saddle from a south-facing slope to a north-facing one. Rustic routed wood signs remind the traveler of the elevation and vegetation changes.

The next sign points out the way to the recreation developments at Rose Canyon Lake, named for the once abundant wild rose that grew in the canyon. The small lake is used year around for trout fishing—with ice fishing in the winter. Although there are picnic and camp sites to accommodate more than 100 families, most of them are occupied. The Arizona Game and Fish Department must have stocked the lake with trout this week!

Our next stop, San Pedro Vista, gives a distant view of the Galiuro and Graham Mountains. The broad sweep of the San Pedro Valley with the large copper smelter at San Manuel dominates the valley scene. We speculate about the distance to the Galiuro Mountains, and the fun which we could all have during a horseback trip into this roadless Galiuro wilderness area.

The firefighting headquarters for the mountain are at Palisades ranger station. My wife is as fascinated by the Smokey Bear drapes and the rustic furniture as I am by the interpretive exhibits on the trees of the Santa Catalinas. At the ranger station we learn that nearly 300 summer homes, many organization camps for Scouts and church groups, innumerable radio electronic installations, a sawmill, and stellar observatories of the University of Arizona and NASA occupy many sites on the Catalinas.

We are amazed that along the highway so little of this considerable development is visible. One seems completely in the forest wilderness.

Looming over the ranger station is Mount Bigelow. The three tall towers upon its summit transmit a major network's television programs to Tucson and to southern Arizona. The noted tree ring study laboratory of the University of Arizona is also located here. The Bigelow fire lookout tower, dwarfed by the taller television towers, is a key fire lookout in the Forest Service detection system.

Ladybugs Harvested

We climb the lookout and get a breathtaking view of the whole Santa Catalina Range and beyond. We look down into rugged country north and east of Bigelow, where an infrequent mountain lion is reported. In summer the shrubbery is covered with "simmering" masses of ladybugs. No one has yet explained this congregation of beetles. These masses are often harvested—under Forest Service permit—and sold to farmers and to orchardists throughout the country to control insects in their crops.

Summerhaven is a privately owned rustic resort village built on patented mining claims on the headwaters of the middle fork of Sabino Creek. Here food, lodging, and gasoline are available.

Large pegmatite dikes that are found nearby in Marshal Gulch contain many garnets sought after by rock hounds. A trail leads to the "Wilderness of Rocks" in the Santa Catalina natural area where no roads or manmade developments interfere with nature studies.

A small band of desert bighorn sheep range from here to Pusch Ridge. The Arizona Game and Fish Commission permits a limited hunt of mature rams. Hunting for game is permitted on all national forests, and bag limits, seasons, and licensing is controlled by the State. Hundreds of desert mules and white-tailed deer are harvested each year in the Santa Catalina Mountains.

The southernmost ski area in the United States is at about the 8,500-foot level on the Catalinas. The Mount Lemmon Snow Bowl has three ski runs of varying difficulty; and in the ski lodge the visitor can find food and warmth.

The biggest thrill of the trip occurs near the ski lodge when the first wild turkey that any of us has ever seen ambles across the road in front of us.

All of us hope to return during the winter season to ride the Poma Lift, ski, and slide on the whirlybirds, which are fashioned from inner tubes.

The road above the ski lodge leads to the U.S. Air Force Radar Base, on the 9,196-foot summit of Mount Lemmon. Just below the summit, on the north slope of the mountain, there is a stand of subalpine fir, the cone-bearing representative of the Canadian life zone which is found in the Catalinas.

Mount Lemmon was named by John Stratton, who started one of the first cattle ranches on the eastern side of the Catalinas near what is the present site of the U-Circle Cattle Co.

In 1881, a Dr. Lemmon and his bride of a few weeks came to the Stratton's ranch after a tedious trip from Florence. Mrs. Lemmon was the first white woman seen by Mrs. Stratton in the 2 years she had spent at the ranch.

John Stratton guided the Lemmons to the top of the mountain on a botanical trip. Mrs. Lemmon became the first white woman to reach the top, so it was named in her honor in 1882. Few of the mountains in the United States have been named for a woman.

Precipitation at the mountaintop averages 33 inches per year, compared with 11 inches in the city of Tucson, and most of this comes in the winter as snow. The temperature on Mount Lemmon is usually around 20° to 30° cooler than that of Tucson. Last winter the ski lodge operator informed us that the snowfall totaled a whopping 190 inches.

As darkness comes quickly after sunset, we hurry down the mountain to watch the sunset from Windy Point and the lights come on in the valley below. The changing shadow patterns make each turn of the road a new experience.

The Santa Catalinas—this towering "island in the desert"—can satisfy almost any interest you may have in the outdoors.

Forest Patterns

EDWARD P. CLIFF

A WALK THROUGH city blocks that are undergoing urban renewal can be a visual shock because of the shattered buildings and the debris of destruction. But we all know that out of this will rise another complex of structures that will serve human uses better than the one that lies in ruins before us.

In like manner, a walk through a forest area that has been recently harvested can be equally shocking because of the raw stumps and the slash-covered ground. But persons wise in the ways of the woods know that necessity often prompts this "clean sweep." They know that under a forester's plan, a new and thriving crop of trees will rise to replace the one that has just been harvested.

To see and understand the patterns of forest growth, change, and renewal can

One-year-old pine seedling.

open a new perspective on our relationship with nature. Wild old stands have pristine beauty which is instantly felt and appreciated. But a newer forest, man-planned and managed and coming up sturdily where century-old giants formerly stood, also has its brand of beauty—similar in its way to the terraced contours and the orderly vegetative growth upon well-managed farmlands. This perspective, which sees man cooperating with nature for the public good, is one that needs wider recognition among the millions of people who visit the public and private forests of our country each year.

Growth, change, and renewal are evident throughout our Nation's forests. Visitors may come away with the impression that some huge landscaping operation is underway.

Trees are removed in one place, improved for future harvest in another, and planted as seedlings somewhere else.

There is a continuing attack on harmful insects or undesirable growth. Roads and trails run much like garden paths through the choice stretches of natural beauty. Streams and wildlife habitat are spruced up to support more of the forest's fish and wild creatures. And the various watersheds are improved to help supply water required by the towns below, and

꽃   꽃   꽃

Edward P. Cliff has been *Chief* of the Forest Service since 1962. He was formerly Deputy Chief in charge of National Forest Resource Management and served in a variety of other positions during a Forest Service career that began in 1931 on the Wenatchee National Forest in the State of Washington.

"Urban renewal" in the forest—patch cutting of old-growth Douglas-fir. View from French Butte towards Mt. St. Helens, Gifford Pinchot National Forest, Wash.

to provide for recreational opportunities.

Our Nation's forests, except for wilderness and similar areas, come more and more under the influence of man, who makes use of his scientific knowledge of nature to increase the many benefits derived from them. You may observe, for example, some western regions where a logging operation is taking out every Douglas-fir tree within certain selected tracts of the forest. Knowing the reason for this may help you look at these temporarily cleared areas in a different light.

Tree species vary in their ability to tolerate shade. Douglas-fir is an intolerant species; it cannot survive in the cool shade of a heavily carpeted forest floor. In order to germinate and grow, its seeds must have the warmth of direct sunlight and

an exposed seedbed of mineral soil. In the past these conditions, which generated the mature Douglas-fir forests that we see today, were met only in upheavals like fires, storms, or insect epidemics.

To achieve a similar renewal, but without the tremendous waste of nature's methods, foresters often use a system of "patch" cutting. This will produce those "checkerboard" patterns that are visible in some parts of the Pacific Northwest and elsewhere. In a relatively short time, just like an urban renewal project, these forest renewal projects restore the area's beauty and increase its usefulness.

Sugar maple, on the other hand, is a tolerant species. Seeds of this kind can germinate and develop even though little or no direct sunlight reaches the forest

38

floor. Where there is a combination of tolerant and intolerant species, there is usually a wide variety of tree sizes and ages on a single tract. Such forests can be managed effectively under a selective method of cutting. Individual trees are selected for harvesting when they mature.

Or, the poorest individuals might be removed from thick clumps of immature trees to allow the more valuable ones remaining a better chance to develop.

An observant eye is needed to see the various forest patterns and relate them not only to nature, but to society and its needs. In economic terms, these patterns mean a steady flow of saw logs, veneer bolts, pulpwood, fuelwood, and other timber products. And though timber is an important resource, other forest factors dictate that forest management must be compatible with additional resource values, such as water, wildlife, the recreation environment, and esthetic qualities.

The patterns of growth and change, death and regeneration, beauty and use make our forests a continuous source of interest and inspiration to all those who understand them.

For many years, I have had the opportunity to work with and observe forests in every part of the United States. Each forest is different. Each is exciting. Each tells its own dramatic story of life and renewal and of the tangible and intangible wealth that lies within it.

Seeing and understanding the dynamic forest patterns greatly increases our enjoyment and appreciation of nature and the web of life around us. This has been my experience and it can be yours. All it takes is an open mind, a fresh look, a healthy curiosity, and an interest in relationships—in this case, the interrelationship between forests and people.

When you visit any of the 154 national forests, take along a book or two about trees. Ask the district ranger what he is doing, and why. Find out what is going on in the forest. Above all, keep your eyes open. What you see and learn will be most rewarding and stimulating.

Douglas-fir along Quinault Nature Trail, Olympic National Forest, Wash.

A Fishing Trip
to the High Country

JOSEPH W. PENFOLD

THE CABIN was cold that morning when we awakened at daylight, but some wadded newspapers—and kindling split on the evening before—soon had the old wood stove a-roaring and throwing out heat. Meanwhile the boys stumbled from their bunks and looked to the great outdoors.

"Dad," exclaimed the 12-year-old, "it snowed last night!" Sure enough, a 2- or 3-inch fall had covered the ground, and it clung to the willows along the stream. The sage and rabbit brush was all domed with the white stuff—wet and clinging. An early storm, yes, but not unusual along the Continental Divide around the Labor Day period.

"Can we still go to the lakes today?" asked the younger boy. "Can we drive over the pass all right?"

"It probably snowed more up there," I said, "but it's wet snow and should melt pretty fast once the sun gets on the job." And so it proved when, after a quick breakfast and a cleanup, we repacked the car and headed up the long and beautiful climb to the pass.

We had left Denver on the afternoon before and driven up Turkey Creek, across the Kenosha Pass into South Park, called the "Bayou Salade" by the early trappers, and on to the Arkansas River and Twin Lakes. There one leaves the main highway, heads west and up to the 12,000-foot-plus Independence Pass, thence dropping on down along Roaring Fork to Aspen.

Aspen, which was a mining boom-

town in the nineties, is now a world mecca for skiers. As importantly, it is a center from which can be reached some of the best and most varied trout fishing found anywhere in the West, mostly on national forest lands and open to public use. This region was our destination—and we expected to sample at least some of its variety in the course of the several days we would be out.

The Arkansas when we crossed it was low, clear, and looked productive. So we had to try it, we felt, and did for 30 minutes or so, casting our shoehorn-type spoons into a long pool formed by the abutments from an old and long since caved-in bridge. A year or so before, I had snagged a sizable brown right in these waters. One can always hope for a repeat, but we had no luck today beyond a 12-incher caught by the younger boy, much to his brother's chagrin.

We climbed back in the car as the afternoon waned and drove on up beyond Twin Lakes and its tourist developments until we found a cabin for rent with a stove, a couple of beds and mattresses, chairs, a table, and little else. We could have gone on a few miles and pitched our tent on a San Isabel National Forest campground, but the boys figured they would like to fly-fish the stream just above its entrance to upper Twin Lake during the hour of dusk.

❦   ❦   ❦

Joseph W. Penfold is *Conservation Director* for the Izaak Walton League of America, with headquarters in Washington, D.C.

It was slow fishing, but between us we landed enough 8- and 9-inch brookies to make a fine supper. Each to his own taste, but to mine nothing can top a plateful of little brook trout fried to a crisp so you can eat all but the backbone.

As we ate supper we talked over our plans for the next day and decided to hike up to some high little lakes on the back side of mighty Mount Elbert. We had had good luck in them before, and we really go for the above timberline country where they are located.

As expected, the snow melted fast on the road, but persisted elsewhere. We crossed the top of the pass slowly as it's an excellent place to see deer early in the morning. We didn't this time, although the slick of mud on the road and along the right-of-way showed that there had been a good many of them around only an hour or two earlier.

Scary Descent

The first traverse from the top of the pass on down the west side is a dandy. Flatlanders sometimes shut their eyes during the descent. This is not recommended for the driver, however, because it's a longish roll to the bottom. At the very first switchback, a 1,000-foot drop in elevation, there is space for a couple of cars to park without obstructing traffic. Where the little stream enters the culvert under the road, one can find what appears to be a trail heading up the draw through tall bunchgrass. There is also the usual Forest Service sign (we are on the White River National Forest now) pointing to the lakes, the first shown as one-half mile, others at 1½. Don't believe them. At these altitudes distances will seem to stretch out twice as far!

We would be gone but a few hours so we took just our rods, reels, a selection of lures, and some lunch. Except for the rods, all else was stowed in the pockets of our fishing jackets, plus plastic rain jackets with hoods. One can usually expect a shower at some point, and the jacket makes a good break for a sudden cold wind which oddly seems always to come up every time that the sun drops behind a high cloud.

We hiked on up the draw and were soon winded. The boys would want to stop and catch their breath, but I encouraged them on. It takes a bit of time for the body mechanism to adjust to 11,000- and 12,000-foot elevations, especially when your auto transports you from 7,000 feet in too short a time to permit much adjustment en route. Once starting to hike, however, it seems best to continue. Rather than stopping for a breather, you slow your pace by shortening your stride by half. Soon your breath will return almost to normal, though you'll be expanding your lungs to take in more of this thinner air.

Soon we had passed the fork where we could turn left and zigzag up a shoulder on top of which is the first lake. We continued on, however, over the first low ridge—one always expects the lake to be right on the other side, but it isn't, it's over the second low ridge.

By the time we had reached our lake for that day, the sky had become largely overcast, and the temperature was down.

The boys now wished that they had worn their warm shoepacks rather than sneakers. Melting snow is mighty cold, and soaked-through canvas offers little or no protection. While I unlimbered and rigged my rod, they hunted for fuel to build a fire. The only woody material around was dead sagebrush, and that was thoroughly soaked. Consequently, the fire was an ineffectual, smoky, and smelly failure, but the boys forgot all about their cold feet in the lengthy process of achieving it. Meanwhile, the fishing.

High lakes such as this one at about 12,000 feet seldom supported a trout population originally. Many of them are shallow and freeze out in winter. This one, though deep enough at the upper end, had trout, courtesy of a State fish hatchery. The first time I fished it years before, it had a good stock of rainbows in the 12- to 14-inch class. Whether these had been fished out and the lake restocked with brookies, or whether the brookies had been more successful than the rainbows spawning in the few yards of small gravel inlets, I don't know. Whatever the reason, later trips to this lake produced brook trout, lots of them,

41

Trappers Lake, a trout fisherman's paradise in the high country. This lake is in the White River National Forest in Colorado.

but no rainbows. And so it was today, brookies, but not lots of them. Interesting fishing, nonetheless.

Fly rod, 9-foot leader tapered to 4X, and the fly a royal coachman, dry on a No. 12 hook. The sky was heavy with clouds blowing toward the northeast at a fast rate. Since the pocket we were in is sheltered, the surface of the lake was placid, though occasionally whipped with light riffles. Now and again the sun would emerge from the clouds, and for a few seconds slant its bright rays deep down through the clear waters.

If the fly was floating well when the sun broke through, almost every time a trout would move up from the depths to take it. One could follow his trip to the surface and time the strike. After the first couple of these the boys got interested and rigged up their rods using closed-face slip cast reels. To the end of the monofilament they attached clear plastic bubbles and to the bubble a leader of about 6 feet with a dry fly. They tried various patterns, but it didn't seem to make much difference. The trick was to have the fly on the water when the sun broke out of the clouds.

The plastic bubble gives weight for the spinning cast, and with it you can fish a lot of water and reach a long way out in a lake. This day the bubble method pro-

duced about as well as the conventional fly fishing rig. We totaled some 15, all about the same size, 11 inches, but chunky and fat. We would have a trout feast that evening.

Each of us was equipped for either method of fishing. We had found that often, when miles into the back country with only traditional fly rod, reel, and line, we'd come on a situation where a spinning rig offered the best chance of success. So we usually carried the one rod to which either fly or spinning reel can be attached, both reels, and an assortment of flies, small spinning lures, and the useful bubbles. It takes but a moment to switch from one to the other method, and you are equipped for any conditions which you happen to find.

The hike back to the car was downhill and easy, and so the Forest Service distance seemed more accurate. Now the sun was out strongly, so we parked on down the road a few miles—where a weathered and stove-in shack or two marks the onetime village of Independence. This branch of the Roaring Fork up here is small and meanders through fairly flat grassy meadows.

The fish are little and the fishing must be delicate. Approaching the stream on hands and knees for lowest silhouette is acceptable procedure. Tossing your fly across the stream and into the grass, then twitching it back until it drops onto the water, will produce strikes.

The boys, now rigged out for conventional fly fishing, worked over a half mile of the stream while I lay back upon the warm grassy slope and drowsed with a pipe, and let my mind think back lazily to some other trips for trout in the high country. . . .

Snowmass Lake in the wilderness area of the same name, best reached by horseback out of Aspen. And Trappers Lake, a gemlike body of water, on the edge of wilderness and just loaded with fat cutthroats. The string of lakes, many of which now can be reached by car, along the east slope of the Front Range, close to Denver, Boulder, and Fort Collins. . . .

There also are the score and a half or so of lakes in the Rawah Wild Area of the Roosevelt National Forest. One time the dude rancher along the Laramie River packed a group of us up on top where we made base camp beside one of the Rawah lakes. Then we hiked out to the others. A ranger and I fished 11 of them one day, not seriously or for long, but just to test them out. A beautiful hike up one little basin with its lakes, across a saddle to another basin, and then a long circle back to our camp.

Throughout the Rocky Mountains, from Mexico to Canada, are hundreds of these high lakes—in your national forests. All offer superlative scenery. Many have exceptional fishing. And in these days of exploding populations of outdoor minded people, they offer the best chances for a degree of solitude.

Spruce Knob-Seneca Rocks National Recreation Area

THEODORE C. FEARNOW

THE POTOMAC, which flows past the Nation's Capital, carries water collected by faraway Appalachian coves and canyons extending deep into the highlands of Pennsylvania, Maryland, Virginia, and West Virginia. Some of the most beautiful of these remote watersheds are situated in the Spruce Knob-Seneca Rocks Area of West Virginia. Here, at the highest elevations in the Potomac Basin, clear cold mountain streams begin their journey down to the sea.

To the millions of Americans who live in and around the Potomac Basin, this high country is a natural for outdoors fun and exploration. With the creation of the national recreation area here, at the head of America's "National River,"

more and more families from all parts of the country are seeing at firsthand its scenery, wildlife, and its many other natural wonders.

Some of the remote valleys and mountains along the upper Potomac remain practically unchanged from conditions which existed when early settlers arrived on these shores centuries ago. But most of them have had forests cut over and the land placed under cultivation only to revert to the wild as families moved to lands better suited for agriculture. In

ॐ   ॐ   ॐ

Theodore C. Fearnow, a native West Virginian, retired from the U.S. Forest Service in 1965. He now directs land management and conservation work for the Pennsylvania Glass Sand Corp.

43

our century, after 40 years and more of protection by the U.S. Forest Service against soil erosion, insect damage, and forest fires, many of these restored areas are so much like the original cover that modern-day visitors tend to think of them as virgin wilderness.

As its name implies, the Spruce Knob-Seneca Rocks National Recreation Area contains two separate units of land— although the two have been within the protection boundary of the Monongahela National Forest since 1920.

Men like John Kimball, who lives at the upper end of the Smoke Hole in the South Branch of the Potomac, worked with foresters and surveyors during the early days of the national forest when land was being purchased from private owners, then remained as a part of the forest protection organization.

Many other local residents have helped to protect and develop these lands and waters over the years, and their children

and grandchildren now play an important role in maintaining the scenic and natural resources for increased use by outdoor recreation seekers.

The Spruce Knob-Seneca Rocks Area is one of many outdoor recreation units which are part of the 806,000-acre Monongahela National Forest. The name represents a new designation, provided by Congress, for an area within a national forest where the scenic and recreational values will be heavily emphasized. While all its resources will be developed and used under the national forest multiple use principle, the national recreation area will direct its management activities strongly toward the enhancement of outdoor recreation—hiking, fishing, hunting, picnicking, camping, nature study, and related forms of outdoor enjoyment.

Joe Tekel, ranger for the Potomac district of the Monongahela National Forest, who mingles with his many guests at Forest Service campgrounds in the

The family from Philadelphia set up their tent close to the edge of the forest.

woods and along the streams at the head of the Potomac, recently interviewed a visiting family from Philadelphia who camped for a week at the Smoke Hole campground. This group of four (mother, father, and two children, David and Judy) showed by the glow on their faces and the tone of their voices that their

John Kimball, veteran fire warden from the Smoke Hole country, points out some of the flowers which grow on the mountain slopes of the national recreation area.

RIVERS OFF A BARN ROOF

When I was a small boy, my father used to tell me about a barn located at the headwaters of the Potomac River, where a dividing ridge in the Appalachian Highlands separated the Potomac watershed from that of the James.

"The water from one side of the barn roof goes into the Potomac," he said, "while water from the other side drains into the James. Two of America's most historic rivers originate here."

If it still stands, this barn would be near the south end of the Spruce Knob-Seneca Rocks National Recreation Area. This area is often referred to as "the birthplace of rivers." From it streams flow south and east to the James, north and east to the Potomac, and westward to the Greenbrier, Cheat, and Tygart, to become part of the Ohio-Mississippi drainage.

The region is also rich in history and retains much of the pioneer atmosphere created by those who settled it. Perhaps, as future Americans enjoy the beauty of this mountain empire, they can better understand the deep feelings of pride, independence, and self-reliance that are part of the character of the Appalachian mountaineer.

---

visit to the national recreation area was not only health promoting, but highly enjoyable as well.

The peaceful countryside, the rugged mountains, and the music of the Potomac as it flows through the narrow gorge at the upper end of the Smoke Hole provided a striking change from big city living. Visits to Dolly Sods, Germany Valley, and Eagle Rock, and other scenic points provided a new experience for each day of their vacation.

The name Smoke Hole is generally believed to have originated from smokes escaping from caves where the Indians cured their meat over fires. Another explanation is that warm moist air escaping from the caverns meets colder outside air where it creates a smokelike vapor. Still another explanation is that early day "moonshiners" distilled their product in the caves and the escaping smoke curling skyward gave to this remote upper Potomac region the name "Smoke Hole."

All the explanations seem reasonably plausible, and possibly all of them are in some degree true.

Seneca Rocks towers above the North Fork of the South Branch of the Potomac at the point where Seneca Creek empties. This is very popular fishing water. Seneca Creek rises in the high country of the Monongahela National Forest. It is fed by many springs and where it cascades out of the mountains across rock ledges, beautiful waterfalls and deep, cool trout pools have been formed.

The North Branch, after it is joined by Seneca Creek, becomes a fast flowing stream with sufficient water to attract many white water canoeists during the spring freshets.

All hands enjoy fishing in the South Branch of the Potomac near the camping area.

It has been the scene of white water canoe races in the stretch between Mouth of Seneca and Royal Glen. But by vacation time the flow has usually diminished to the point where canoeing gives way to more leisurely wading or floating by fishermen who want to work over carefully each pool and riffle.

Spruce Knob, the highest point in West Virginia, is not a symmetrical dome of the Mount Hood or Mount Rainier type. It is part of a high ridge which gradually slopes upward as one travels south on Spruce Mountain. At its highest elevation it reaches 4,862 feet, and then slopes away to the pass, which the eastern approach road goes through.

Until recently, the summit was accessible only by foot trail with a hike of a mile or so. In 1961, the Forest Service built a scenic automobile road up the west side of the mountain, terminating at a parking area a short walk from the summit. But the summit still remains a

Dad soon provides the main course for dinner by landing a 2-pound rainbow trout.

(left) Entranced with the view from Spruce Knob. (right) After hiking the mountain, the family enjoys a dip in the Potomac's South Branch.

boulder strewn, sparsely vegetated area. The few native red spruce trees branch mainly toward the east—the result of a relentless pressure by the prevailing winds out of the west.

Looking to the north or south the view is limited by other nearby peaks that are only a few feet lower than Spruce Knob. But to the east one looks across the great Allegheny Range to the Blue Ridge in Virginia. When you look to the west the undulating Appalachian Mountains extend as far as your eye can see.

Vegetation of Interest

The present approaches to Spruce Knob are country-type roads that must be traversed with care. Indeed the national recreation area is itself a recent creation. Those who visit it at this stage of development have an unusual opportunity to see the patterns of use which developed as an interested public "discovered" this portion of the Appalachian Highlands.

The high country's vegetation is of special interest to the visitor. Mountain ash, red spruce, and sugar maple, usually found in northern forests, are at home on the higher elevations.

Rhododendron, wild bleeding heart, trillium, and a vast array of colorful blossoms create a natural flower garden.

The history of the high country at the head of the South Branch of the Potomac is directly intertwined with the development of a young nation. First of all, it was known to colonial era adventurers as a vast hunting ground which was accessible only on foot or on horseback.

Logged in 1900

Most of the upper Potomac was logged around 1900, and the more inaccessible timber in the Spruce Knob area was harvested during and immediately following World War I. Brian Van Deventer who lives on Spruce Mountain saw the last trainload of logs leave the mountain in 1925. The steel rails were removed later, and many of the mountaintop roads have been built on grades originally established for the logging railroad. The apple trees which now provide fruit for deer grew from seeds thrown from the log trains by woods workers who ate from lunch pails as they rode the old narrow gage flatcars to and from the loading decks on the mountain.

In this Spruce Knob-Seneca Rocks National Recreation Area the American people have a priceless gem, deeply set in the Appalachian Highlands. The story of its early settlement, use, and restoration is predictive of the measures which may ultimately bring millions of acres of the Appalachian Highlands to renewed attractiveness and productivity. The management principle behind the program has been *conservation through wise use*.

Forests, wildlife, and forage have been managed under sound, long-range plans which treat renewable natural resources

47

as crops which need to be kept up in a thrifty, growing condition.

Under this type of stewardship, millions of acres of Appalachian forests can produce wood, water, wildlife, and forage for public use and enjoyment—while at the same time retaining the necessary environment for a lot of good outdoor fun and sport, providing a recreational outlet for the heavily populated regions which surround these vast wooded areas.

The Monongahela National Forest has been one of the great success stories of West Virginia.

And the national recreation area plan is an extension of the very policies which have made this area such a favorite spot for persons seeking outdoor recreation.

Winter Fun
in a National Forest

THEODORE W. KOSKELLA

THE WORLD is a sparkling, white symphony of new-fallen snow, shimmering with the elegance of millions of diamonds. Evergreens stand etched in crystal beauty, their branches laden with burdens of white against the clear blue sky. The silence of the canyon is broken by the happy chatter of our five children, eagerly looking forward to the day at one of our favorite national forest ski areas. The wind singing through the skis lined atop the car is music to our ears as we travel upward; and so is the quiet chuckle of the stream as it winds along under its coat of blue ice.

New vistas unfold around every turn of the road. Deer tracks meander down to the bank, cross the road, and end at the icy edge of the stream. Now a lordly elk has stopped just above to gaze over his domain, then to trace his solitary tracks on and over the hill.

Rounding a bend in the road, we pass a group of Boy Scouts on an overnight forest encampment, tents pitched on a site of snow. We have a brief glimpse of fires blazing cheerily, happy faces, and waving hands as we go by.

We are approaching higher levels, and now rolling, snow-covered hills glisten in the sun. Cars line the side of the road where it has been widened by the thoughtful snow removal crew. The slope above is dotted with bright-colored hordes of youngsters with toboggans, saucers, sleds and even some inner tubes, all enjoying snow play activities. Our children long to join them, but the ski hill beckons us not very far away.

Another wide place in the road, and here a group of cars with trailers and trucks have unloaded a variety of single track, oversnow vehicles. We count 25 in this group. With packs strapped on behind the riders, they are strung out with the leader disappearing in the trees. What a wonderful way to explore the forest winter wonderland!

Now the canyon narrows and the hills are steeper. We are in the mountains, watersheds of the Nation, bearers of snow for both life and recreation.

As we approach the ski areas, we are

Theodore W. Koskella is *Chief*, Branch of Developed Sites in the Division of Recreation of the Forest Service.

"Snowghosts" loom over skiers on Big Mountain, Flathead National Forest in Montana. The "ghosts" are trees blanketed with snow.

A gondola ski lift in the Lincoln National Forest in New Mexico.

always filled with the same feelings of wonder and of anticipation. Cars, buses, vehicles of all kinds and shapes line the parking area.

Skiers of all sizes and ages wander in and out of the Alpine lodges. Color is the keyword, colors of all shades and hues, stark against the white of the snow. The lifts are more than a part of the color, each chair a different pastel, endlessly climbing the mountain.

After the breathtaking scenery of the drive, it is almost an anticlimax when we are parked and all ready to unload. For a family of seven, unloading the station wagon is no minor chore. Parkas, gloves, and caps must be located; and ski poles matched with owners.

Somehow order comes out of the chaos, and the four girls are ready, all attired in bright colors and snapped into their safety bindings, a "must" on the national forest skiing area.

Our tall, long-legged son helps Dad and Mom supervise the preparation; and soon we are at the ski lift with lift tickets fastened to each parka. We are ready for an exhilarating day on the slopes. A brief stop for Mom to check in with the ski school to arrange for a ski lesson later

in the day. Although she has skied for a number of years, she still has problems with her parallel turns.

Our youngest daughter joins a school friend on the rope tow and the bunny hill. She is an ardent beginner, and a "terror" in the snowplow. She will spend the morning on the rope tow, then after lunch bravely reach new heights on the T-bar which moves her higher upon the ridge, more challenge to her little self and friends. Our second daughter joins a group of friends on the T-bar hill where she will work on her stem-christie, and later during the day take a group lesson.

Another couple of weekends and she will be riding the double-chair lift to the top of the mountain.

The older members of the family are all skiers of the national forest ski areas from way back, the children having commenced skiing before they started to school. We have been fortunate to have lived within the shadow of a national forest and within a short drive of a ski area. It's no wonder we love the slopes, the camaraderie, the excitement.

So now on this glorious, sun-drenched day, with fresh snow upon the slopes, it doesn't take us very long to head for the "powder." This is the next best thing to heaven! Long, lazy glides, deep lifts, the spray of snow as your skis glide through the untracked expanse of white, weaving in and out among the scattered trees on the slope—too soon you are at the bottom of the hill, ready for the lift again.

Most ski areas have ski runs that will satisfy skiers from the novice to the expert. Through the years our skiing family has progressed from one run to the next, always taking pride in our accomplishments. For all but the two youngest members of the family, we have mastered all of the runs, advancing from the snowplow to stem-christie to parallel skiing. Now the area is ours to enjoy—the ski-packed runs, the broad expansive bowl areas, and the runs through the trees, which beckon young and old alike. Mounds of snow formed by the carving action of many skis on the slope and referred to by skiers as "moguls" are always a challenge to the youngsters, to jump or not to jump! The swift descent

Above Timberline Lodge in Mount Hood National Forest, Oreg.

down a well-packed run offers fulfillment to any skier. A brief respite as you ride back up the lift once more.

Back on top, we—like the lordly elk—can now survey our domain: The wind-swept ridges, the timbered peaks, white mountain valleys with roads winding on and away into the distance.

Away from the main ski trails are the touring trails. In the distance we see a family on snowshoes, with packs on their backs, enjoying a day's carefree outing in the forest. Another group skiing into the parking lot has just returned from a cross-country ski touring trip. The non-skiing tourists wander around the area, some taking round trip rides on the lifts, enjoying the activities on the slopes and the magnificent scenery. All of these activities, by young and old alike, provide a peaceful therapy for the human race.

The hours pass so quickly, there is barely time for lunch. One begrudges the time away from the slope. The rustic lodge is inviting, a fire blazing cheerfully on the hearth, smiling service from the snackbar, exchanges with other skiers while eating; and then, back to the slopes.

Too soon, the sun starts to cast long blue-purple shadows on the snow, and there's a chill in the air; and you realize that the day is almost over. When the last ray of sun has sent its last fling of color across the snow, it's time to depart, time to leave all the wonder and excitement.

And so we undo the safety straps, snap out of boots, wearily pack all the skis onto the rack, ever so wearily pile into the car, and once more we are on our way back. We are more silent, wearily happy, reliving the day's glory; but we are also happily content. We have gained new strength from the hills, new purpose in life, new incentive for the days ahead; and we have truly lived this day. We have been privileged to spend a wonderful, purposeful day at one of the 200 national forest ski areas.

Snow Rangers

GEORGE W. TOURTILLOTT and GERALD F. HORTON

IT TAKES two things to make a ski area, a mountain and some snow; and thousands of new enthusiasts are taking up the "challenge of the boards" with every new year. Most of the major snow-covered mountain ranges in the West are in the national forests.

The very same two things—snow and mountains—which are required for a ski area, are, unfortunately, the two ingredients that create dangerous avalanches—commonly called "White Death."

It was the threat of the avalanche and its record as a killer of man in the western mountains that created the snow ranger. He first started on avalanche control work in the winter of 1937–38 at Alta, Utah, in the Wasatch National Forest.

This mountain valley, once the site of a lusty mining camp, was becoming well known to skiers. It was a valley of danger where more than 120 persons had lost their lives as a result of avalanches before it became a major ski area.

Thus, development of Alta and other major ski resorts in the West was dependent upon controlling the avalanche. The Forest Service set out to do it, and did, with its dedicated corps of snow rangers.

What is a Forest Service snow ranger and what are his responsibilities? It takes many things to make a snow ranger. The snow ranger must be in excellent physical condition, be a good skier, and be an accomplished mountaineer. He must like to work with people and do things for them. He should have at least a high school education, and the more college courses in geology, physics, and related fields he has, the better.

He studies snow, terrain, wind, and weather. He learns the conditions that spawn avalanches. He learns to forecast avalanches—and to bring them roaring on down the mountainside to reduce their Herculean punch. The snow ranger learns to do this by using artillery, blasting with TNT, and by the ticklish art of actually skiing avalanches down.

The snow ranger, dressed in a green parka which has a bright yellow shoulder patch, means safety for you on national forest ski slopes, as he pulls the trigger on a 75 mm. recoilless rifle, skis waist deep in powder testing snow stability, or talks with the ski area's operator as he goes about his daily routines to protect the public from the hazards of deep snow on steep mountain slopes.

The safety he represents is not limited to his knowledge and his control of the avalanche hazard. There are ski lifts and tows to be inspected for safe operating conditions, the work to be done with the National Ski Patrol to provide safe ski slopes, special-use permit requirements for public service to be administered. There is cooperation with area operators, ski schools, State road crews, and safety education for the skiing public involved—all a part of the snow ranger's job.

Let's take a closer look at his work and follow him around the clock—and

George W. Tourtillott is *Forest Supervisor,* Wasatch National Forest, with headquarters at Salt Lake City, Utah.

Gerald F. Horton is *Staff Assistant* in charge of Recreation and Lands, Wasatch National Forest.

around the mountain—for a whole day.

The alarm rings at 6 a.m., and Ray, as we shall call him, is out of bed into a dark, cold morning to take weather observations. It is 3° below zero, and crystal clear under the starlit sky. It's a little lonely on the way out to the weather station and that boot full of snow takes a little while to melt. But it doesn't really matter because Ray's fingers are so cold he doesn't notice it anyway.

The weather and snow conditions are recorded, the pencil back in the pocket, and the mitten back on the cold hand. Decisions must be made. There was some wind last night and a foot of new snow. Better shoot with the recoilless rifle this morning to test for avalanche conditions and to bring down any slides that might prove to be dangerous!

It is a long walk through the deep snow to the kitchen of the ranger station where hot coffee and a warm stove are very welcome sights indeed.

Ray's radio call to the valley gets the weather report on its way. It also gets the latest information on skiing conditions to the eager skiers who will be starting for the mountains in 2 or 3 hours.

Seven o'clock breakfast is ready, and Ray bangs upon the floor to awaken his fellow ranger, Neil. For safety reasons, Ray can't handle artillery or explosives just by himself.

A call to the area operator's bunkhouse alerts the ski patrolmen that their help will also be needed so as to accomplish the morning's work. Neil's wife, Joyce, and the kids are also on the alert list. It is 15 miles to school in the Salt Lake Valley.

Breakfast over, Ray and Neil pack the explosives, fuses, and other equipment into rucksacks. They meet two ski patrolmen and discuss the morning's program.

A few shots from the 75 mm. rifle bring down two medium-sized avalanches. The situation isn't so bad, but it means more control work and testing must be done.

Incidentally, the noise from the shots echoes throughout the valley and wakens the guests inside the lodge. "Ray's alarm clock," is what they call it.

Ray's 3 years of experience at the area, and the information yielded by the early shooting, tell him which runs are safe for the public this morning. These runs are marked "open" on the ski run control sign. The runs which are doubtful and should be tested are "closed." This is a responsibility that cannot be taken lightly.

At the top of the lift the snow rangers pair up with the ski patrolmen, and the

Firing 75-mm. recoilless rifle to test snow stability, Wasatch National Forest, Utah.

two teams start on their morning's work. Here is a favorite ski slope that must be tested for snow stability. A 2-pound block of TNT is thrown out from a safe position on the ridge. The explosion does not set off a slide, and the run is opened.

The next charge, on another ski run, starts a medium avalanche. And so it goes through the morning: Test ski the small areas and use explosives on the big ones.

Ray leaves Neil with a ski patrolman to continue this work in areas adjacent to the main ski runs and then goes back to the ranger station—where he checks in with both the district forest ranger and the forest engineer.

The annual chair lift inspection and one of the frequent rope tow inspections are scheduled for the morning. The uphill facilities must meet requirements set by the American Standards Association for Aerial Tramways in assuring safe uphill rides for the general public.

Winter sports area, the Mt. Hood National Forest in Oregon.

Rope tows are a simpler matter, and this is mostly Ray's job. He must check the safety gates, check rope twist, track conditions, the warning and information signs, and all other safety factors. If there are any deficiencies, the tow stops until these have been corrected.

Then, on to the ski lodge that is also on national forest land under special-use permit. As such, it has to meet certain standards of public service and of safety. Does it meet all these? Better inspect and write up the findings.

There is one more meeting scheduled for the day with the district ranger again and a discussion of plans for a new ski lift. What is the avalanche hazard at the proposed area? Acceptable? How about parking? Where is the best location for the lift line, the first aid room? Will they interfere with the new campground?

Where will the new ski runs be? How much timber should be removed in clearing for ski runs? What will be the impact upon soil erosion and esthetics? What special measures must be taken to safeguard all the national forest resources?

It will take several trips to determine the potentials as a ski area and to coordinate the multiple uses this particular parcel of national forest land can produce.

Ray's day has been long, but it is not over. There are inspection reports to be filled out. And the State highway foreman wants to talk about additional snow removal on the road. There is a movie and talk on avalanche control for the guests at the lodge at night, a program which Neil will take over.

New snow tomorrow may bring additional jobs: Perhaps an avalanche rescue for a victim or a suspected victim, a lost skier to organize a search for, a training session with the National Ski Patrol, or a test pit to be dug in the 10-foot snowpack to analyze its structure and stability.

What has happened at the plots where chemicals were sprayed to increase the bonding of snow layers in hopes of improving the stability of the snowpack?

Skiing is a rapidly growing sport in which the national forests will continue to play a very important role. The snow ranger has an interesting job with never a dull moment.

The Appalachian Trail—
2,000 Miles for Hiking

EDWARD B. GARVEY

THIS is the story of the Appalachian Trail, stretching a long and scenic 2,000 miles from Maine to Georgia. This also is the story of the outdoor trail clubs which make use of this great trail.

The clubs that use the trail are many. Big clubs like the Appalachian Mountain Club of Boston with some 10,000 members. Middle-sized clubs like the Potomac Appalachian Trail Club of Washington, D.C., with 1,200 members. Small ones like the Georgia Appalachian Trail Club of Atlanta with perhaps 150 members. But the trail is open to all. No admission fees . . . no turnstiles . . . just the endless trail . . . all 2,000 miles waiting for individuals or groups to hike it.

But let's go back a bit. What *is* the Appalachian Trail? Who owns it? And how long has it existed?

Go way back to the year 1900. Climb Stratton Mountain in Vermont with our friend Benton MacKaye, then just a young man in his twenties. MacKaye, still a young man although now in his eighties, recalls that long-past time clearly. He studied the sharp peaks north and south until they faded out in the distant haze.

Could a footpath be built someday to connect those peaks? Even the ones far, far south that were beyond his vision?

It was not until 1921 that MacKaye put his thoughts down upon paper— writing in the *Journal of the American Institute of Architects* an article with the title of "The Appalachian Trail, A Project in Regional Planning." From that point on until 1938, many individuals and groups planned and worked until the trail was completed. Ownership of the trail is divided up as follows:

	Miles	Percent
Private	866	43.3
State	452	22.6
Federal	682	34.1
Total	2,000	100.0

The surging population plus the big demand for mountain homes, and the development of ski resort areas and other uses, has caused severe inroads on the trail, especially in the private sector. A number of bills were introduced during the 89th and 90th Congresses to give the trail Federal recognition and protection.

So now you have a little background on the trail. A quick study of the rough map shown elsewhere in this article will give you a very rough idea of the location of the trail in each one of the 14 States through which it passes.

But you may desire more precise information on the exact location of the trail.

The road maps issued by all major oil companies show fairly accurately where the trail intersects each primary highway. Furthermore, the highway departments of all the States involved erect highway crossing signs identifying intersections of highways and the trail. These range in

❦   ❦   ❦

Edward B. Garvey is *Secretary* of the Appalachian Trail Conference. A former employee of the Soil Conservation Service, he now serves as the Finance Officer for the National Science Foundation.

Watauga Lake in Tennessee, one of many scenic attractions along the Appalachian Trail.

sizes from the modest 24-inch oval in Connecticut to the huge 24- by 72-inch sign erected in New Hampshire.

So now, if you wish merely to locate the trail, you have a very good chance of doing so by using the highway map and keeping a sharp eye open for the highway crossing sign. With no more investment than this, you can locate the trail, park your car, and hike up the trail a mile or two to find out what it is like.

Once on the trail you may find directional signs informing you of the mileage to points of interest along the trail—such as distance to the next overnight shelter.

Many individuals, however, prefer to acquaint themselves thoroughly with the trail maps, guidebooks, and articles before they hike the first step. There are a number of ways you can acquire such information. You might telephone your local newspaper, ask for the sports department, and ask one of the editors for information on hiking clubs in your area.

Or you might inquire from your local library if it has available one of the guidebooks issued by the Appalachian Trail Conference. Yet another possibility is to contact one of the eight national forests or the two national parks through which the trail passes. But the surest way is to write to the organization that coordinates the activities of the clubs and individuals that maintain the 2,000-mile trail. This organization is the Appalachian Trail Conference, 1718 N Street NW., Washington, D.C. 20036. Ask to be furnished with the free information packet. Ask also to be furnished with the names of hiking clubs in your area.

The Appalachian Trail Conference consists of some 25 to 30 hiking clubs that share responsibility for maintaining the trail. Most of these clubs schedule weekend or Sunday hiking trips on almost a year-round basis. If one of these clubs is located near you, you may contact a club member and be informed as to date, locale, and other particulars for forthcoming hikes. In this way you can arrange to hike with a group of people, and the more experienced hikers will be glad to answer your questions regarding maps and equipment, overnight shelter accommodations, and so on.

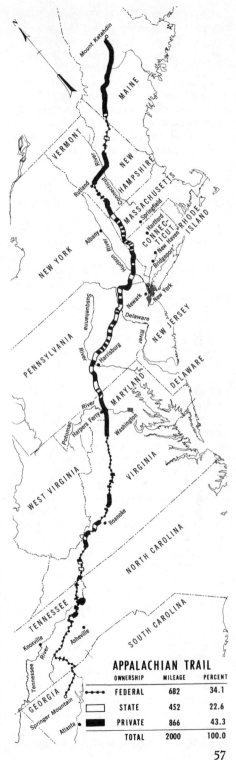

APPALACHIAN TRAIL

OWNERSHIP	MILEAGE	PERCENT
FEDERAL	682	34.1
STATE	452	22.6
PRIVATE	866	43.3
TOTAL	2000	100.0

235-917 O - 67 - 7

But you may live in a location where there are no hiking clubs. Or you may be one of those who prefers to hike alone, or with your family, or with a few close friends. And you have questions as to trail locations, locations of drinking water, shelters, and perhaps equipment.

If you have already written to the trail conference, you will have received with their information packet a list of the publications that are available.

10 Guidebooks

One of the publications so listed is ATC Publication No. 15, *Suggestions for Appalachian Trail Users*. Also on the publications list are some 10 guidebooks.

Each of the guides is a 5- by 6-inch book not quite an inch thick, and this has durable plastic covers. The guidebook contains detailed trail data on some 200 to 300 miles of the trail, and frequently it will describe interesting side trails.

Every book is divided into a number of chapters, with each containing detailed information on a length of the trail that extends for anywhere from 5 to 20 miles. At the beginning of the chapter is listed the names of any maps that pertain to the section of trail being described. Each section of the trail is described twice in the book—once from north to south—and again from south to north. Following are excerpts from one such guidebook (*Guide to the Appalachian Trail in Central and Southwestern Virginia*):

"For maps, see U.S. Geological Survey Natural Bridge and Peaks of Otter Quadrangles, U.S. Forest Service Glenwood District of Jefferson National Forest; and Glenwood District, Jefferson National Forest; James River to U.S. Route 11 (P.A.T.C. Map No. 13)."

And here's another excerpt from this same chapter—

"Cross overgrown wood road at 5.2 m. In hemlocks, at 5.3 m., cross small brook.

"Beside large hemlock, cross another branch of Cornelius Creek in ravine at 5.58 m. Ascend steadily, slabbing ridge crest encircling headwaters of Cornelius Creek. Beyond, Trail is walled in by rhododendron.

"On crest, at 6.23 m., in rhododendron,

pass worn crosstrail. (To left leads 100 ft. to Black Rock, affording extraordinary view west. To right leads 0.3 m. to Blue Ridge Parkway at a point 16.3 m. south of U.S. Route 501.) Route here leads thru sparse mature timber.

"Cross branch of Cornelius Creek at 6.53 m. Here side trail leads 500 ft. to the Cornelius Creek Lean-To. (Built by U.S. Forest Service in 1960; accommodates 8.)"

Wouldn't you like to hike in the above area? Say about the first part of June when those rhododendron bushes are covered with fist-sized deep pink flowers? And though the guidebook doesn't say so, the lean-to itself is surrounded by those very same rhododendron bushes—and you walk through them to get to the swift flowing spring which offers excellent drinking water.

I would advise any hiker to buy the guidebook. Half the fun of a trip is to study the book before the trip begins and then to go through it afterward and make annotations in the margins about things personal to you—the date that you hiked a particular trail, the place where you saw a hen turkey with her young or saw a fox or a bear.

Tips on Equipment

Since most hiking is done within a hundred mile radius of the hiker's home, it follows that a single guidebook will serve the average hiker for years. Certain trails will carry an especial fascination for a particular hiker, and they will be revisited from time to time.

Now just a few words about equipment, and then you will be off all on your own. There are overnight shelters about every 7 to 8 miles along most parts of the trail. These are used by the hardy minority. The majority prefer to day hike only—going back home at night, or perhaps using a nearby motel.

If you are in the majority group, you need not purchase a sleeping bag, an air mattress, or ground cloth. A light day pack in which you carry rain gear, food for 1 day, map, guidebook, compass, and a few other incidentals will suffice.

Those who wish to pursue the matter

of hiking and camping equipment more carefully would do well to purchase the publication *Hiking, Camping, and Mountaineering Equipment* that is issued by the Potomac Appalachian Trail Club of Washington, D.C. This bulletin priced at $1 is a 60-page compendium of tested equipment and food with the sources of supply and the prices shown. Used extensively throughout the United States, it is revised approximately every 2 years.

You now know something about the Appalachian Trail, the longest continuous marked footpath in the world.

Perhaps you now have the guidebook, an oil company road map, and a more detailed map—such as a U.S. Geological Survey or a U.S. Forest Service map. Make arrangements with a friend, member of your family, or office acquaintance and explore a section of this famous footpath. Good hiking!

The Ski Patrol and Safety in the Snow

NORMAN A. BERG

AMERICA'S ski slopes are safer than ever today thanks to the ski patrol.

More than 9,000 unpaid volunteers in about 600 separate patrols help keep skiing safe for both skilled skiers and "dopes on the slopes." Over a thousand ski patrollers are women. There are also junior patrolmen, 12 to 17 years old.

The ski patrol does its job in dozens of ways—by first aid and rescue operations; making "sweeps" of ski runs each night to be sure no one is left lying in the snow with a broken leg; helping with bindings, messages, and directions; and constantly fostering greater skiing safety.

Some patrolmen are hired by ski facility operators in order to provide protection for their patrons.

The work of the ski patrol has become increasingly important due to the fast increasing popularity of skiing. More people, of all ages, get into the action each year. Since 1950, participation has grown annually by some 10 to 15 percent. Now there are nearly 5 million skiers.

Modern snowmaking equipment is extending the skiing season. And it also makes skiing possible in places where the sport had previously not existed.

The ski patrol was born of need. Back in 1938, a New York insurance broker, Charles Minot Dole, fractured an ankle on one of New England's ski slopes. For an hour he lay in the snow and cold, while a friend, Frank Edson, went for help. Several hours later, Dole reached a doctor after a ride down the hill on a piece of corrugated tin. He did not have the benefit of a splint on his broken ankle. Later, still encased in a cast, he received word that Edson had died in a similar accident. Finally up and around again, Dole was determined to find some way to prevent skiing accidents. When they did occur, he wanted the skier to receive the care needed.

"Minnie" Dole carried his campaign to other skiers in each section of the land.

❦   ❦   ❦

Norman A. Berg is *Deputy Administrator* for Field Services, Soil Conservation Service. He helped expand the snow survey network in Idaho after World War II, and for several years was an active snow surveyor.

Gradually he gained support that in working for safety on skis, skiers would be protecting both themselves and their favorite sport. And slowly the National Ski Patrol System—a cooperative effort which was organized by skiers—took form.

In 1939–40, the National Red Cross created the initial "Winter Manual" as a guide for training patrols in the care of winter accident victims.

Following World War II, growth of the patrol system kept pace with the public's booming interest in skiing.

Ski patrollers cooperate with national forest and park services, safety councils, and the National Ski Association.

SKI SLOPE DOPE

Ski slopes are lands of many uses. They produce trees, serve as watersheds, and may provide grazing for livestock and big game. Recreational skiing is harmonious with multiple land use. The snow cover yields moisture for next season's crops. Access roads serve both skiers and those who harvest the timber. And the ski lifts carry the summer visitor as well as winter vacationer to the "top of the world" for panoramic views.

A typical skiing area includes land for slopes, housing, and parking facilities. Ski areas need 100 acres or more of 10 to 60 percent slopes with north to northeast exposures. Northwest exposure can be used under excellent climate conditions. Other favorable soil properties for skiing areas are: Adequate soil depth to grow grass to prevent slippage and erosion, medium texture, and good drainage. Water areas and water impoundment sites are needed for artificial snowmaking.

Several acres of relatively level land adjacent to the slopes are also needed for the ski lodge and parking facilities.

The ski patrol is fundamentally a rescue organization. It warns of dangerous conditions. And at the same time, it tries to eliminate hazards if possible.

Those who wear the patrol badge and parka must be certified for competence.

The ski patrol leader and at least two members of each patrol have to meet the National Ski Patrol System standard requirements for first aid training and for skiing ability before the patrol can be accepted for national registration.

"National Patrolman" is an honorary appointive position. All U.S. Forest Service snow rangers are automatically eligible for the badge of a National Patrolman, and many of the Soil Conservation Service's snow surveyors also qualify.

Traffic on the ski slopes is often similar today to the jams on highways. Skiing is fun and can be perfectly safe, but only if ski safety is learned and observed by everyone from novice to expert. The ski patrol has some basic rules to help you enjoy skiing. They are:

• Make sure all your equipment is in good condition and adequate for you. Use your safety straps.

• Find out the proper way to carry your equipment.

• Never ski a hill you aren't ready to handle. Proper instructions will help you to enjoy it.

• Learn how to use tows and lifts properly. Loose clothing or long hair, unless properly worn, can entangle you with the tow or lift. Keep ski tips up when getting on or off chair lift. Make certain that nothing will catch when you get off a tow.

• Learn how to fall properly.

• If you fall, get up immediately and go to the side of the slope to make any necessary adjustments.

• If you make a "sitzmark" (hole in the snow), fill it up so the next skier won't trip on it.

• Don't swing poles above your waist.

• Yield to the skiers downslope. A "track left" or a "track right" warning doesn't give you the right of way.

• Don't ski when you are tired. Never ski off alone.

• Ski in control and enjoy yourself.

The National Ski Patrol faces a new problem with the use of one-man and two-man snow machines for recreation purposes in the mountains. In 1965, some 500 people on 250 snow machines made a trip the same day into Yellowstone Park in deep snow during March. This new type of recreation creates an obligation

Snow ranger and a ski patrolman demonstrate first aid for a ski accident victim. Winter Park Ski Area, Arapaho National Forest, Colo.

on both private and public lands to see that safe routes are provided and minimum training standards met before the recreationist ventures into the mountains in the middle of winter.

Ranch and farm operators, living close to good snow machine hills, can tap the income-producing potential of this new sport by providing sleeping space, servicing of equipment, safe traveling areas, and possibly eating facilities. Oversnow machine clubs are growing with fantastic speed. They may even match the power-boat devotees in numbers in the next few years. Yet hazards are far greater on the snow than in boating because of the remote terrain, the cold, high-speed winter storms, and lack of training.

An entire new technique of mounted one-man oversnow machine patrols is becoming necessary. These ski patrolmen will need to be highly trained in skiing, survival, avalanche, mountain climbing, and the operation of oversnow machines. They also have to know the terrain

extremely well and must map and mark avalanche paths on all routes.

A great deal of this work will be in the national forests; however, many private lands will be used for oversnow recreation activities.

These private lands may be developed first because the oversnow machines are not compatible to ski areas. They leave tracks in the snow that trip skiers and thus are barred from operating in and around ski resorts, except for maintenance and for emergency purposes.

❧   ❧   ❧

The next time snow floats gently from the sky, observe carefully. The crystals are hexagonal.

If you ski, observe carefully; the National Ski Patrol badge is also hexagonal. The National Ski Patrol System's rust colored parka is the symbol—coast to coast—of active ski patrolmen. Its wearer could be your own neighbor, a "Good Samaritan of the Snow."

61

Hunting—An American Heritage

D. IRVIN RASMUSSEN

TAKE a boy hunting, and you will relive an experience long forgotten. You will see the woods, streams, forest animals, trees, and all outdoors in a new light. No, not exactly in a new light, but it will be new to you because you have forgotten something that you once thought you would never forget.

Take a boy hunting and you will see, smell, and wonder as you did long ago as a boy when you first became acquainted with the world of the great outdoors.

Through your young companion's eyes you will once again thrill to the clean air, the jump of the heart as a ruffed grouse explodes from its hiding place in brightly colored leaves, the ghostlike appearance of deer in single file as they make their soundless way through the forest. Your jaded senses will come alive as you once again wonder at the quiet and the beauty of a forest covered with new-fallen snow.

Where will you hunt? Well, the U.S. Department of Agriculture has a vast hunting preserve that is managed just for you. For you and for all of the 197 million citizens of this great land.

There are 154 national forests and 19 national grasslands located in 41 States that make up the national forest system. It includes a total of 186 million acres. This is an area of a little less than 1 acre for every man, woman, and child in the United States. These lands, with their wildlife resources, comprise the finest, most widespread, and accessible aggregate of public hunting grounds that are available anywhere. These are yours to use and enjoy along with all other citizens.

In 1965, hunters spent an estimated 14 million visitor-days on these publicly owned hunting grounds. Around two-thirds of these users were primarily interested in big game hunting. And the remaining group hunted a wide variety of small game that includes waterfowl and upland game birds and mammals.

Many of these hunters combined their hunting trips on the national forests with camping, travel in wilderness, horseback riding, sightseeing, or with other outdoor recreational activities.

Hunting and fishing on all the national forests are regulated by the fish and game or conservation departments of the respective States. This involves the issuance of licenses that permit hunting and fishing and the enforcement of State game and fish laws and regulations.

Habitat for Wildlife

The role of the Forest Service in wildlife management is to provide and manage the habitat or home on which the animals are dependent. This includes land and water areas for both game and nongame animals. The objective is to produce the optimum food and cover that the different wildlife species require.

Trained biologists are employed to provide the skills which are needed for professional wildlife habitat management as an integral part of the overall forest multiple use program. Roads, trails, and campgrounds are built and maintained to help

D. Irvin Rasmussen is *Director,* Division of Wildlife Management, Forest Service.

distribute the hunters throughout the vast hunting areas.

The legal harvest of big game in the national forest system in 1965 was approximately 604,000 animals. About 85 percent of all these animals were mule, whitetail, and blacktail deer. Another 10 percent were elk or wapiti. The remainder of the harvest included moose, pronghorn antelope, bighorn and Dall sheep, mountain goat, bison, black bear, Alaska brown bear, grizzly bear, peccary, and the European wild boar.

In addition, a total of some 14,000 wild turkeys were taken by hunters in 22 States during 1965. This take of wild turkeys was the highest for any of the years for which records exist.

30 Percent of Big Game

Your national forests accounted for about 30 percent of the Nation's annual total big game harvest. More specifically, these lands produced over 80 percent of the elk, bighorn sheep, and mountain goats, nearly 60 percent of the mule deer, and more than 35 percent of the bears, peccaries, and blacktail deer for the Nation's hunters. They also yielded 13 percent of the pronghorn antelope and 11 percent of the whitetail deer harvest.

We are often asked, "Which national forest has the best deer hunting?" or "Where are my chances best to get a deer?" There is no single answer beyond this—deer and other game are where you find them. You can find and legally hunt either mule or whitetail or blacktail deer on each and every national forest. On 30 of these forests, there are both mule and whitetails. Mule deer can be hunted on over 90 national forests in 14 of the Western States and whitetails on more than 50 forests in 38 States.

No other big game animal is as abundant or as widespread in distribution as deer, although the black bear is hunted on at least 120 national forests.

Elk provides hunting on almost all of the national forests in the Western States —with the exception of California and Nevada. Moose hunting is limited to Alaska and to certain forests in Montana, Wyoming, Idaho, and Utah.

If you wished to go to a national forest to hunt Dall sheep, it would be on the alpine mountain peaks of the Chugach in Alaska; for Alaska brown bear, the Tongass or the Chugach; the Coronado and Tonto in Arizona have a near monopoly on the peccary.

The Rocky Mountain bighorn sheep, although they are not truly abundant anywhere, present a very rugged challenge to hunters on some 24 national forests in Wyoming, Montana, Idaho, and Colorado, where a limited number of permits are issued every year.

Small game which is found on national forest system lands consists of a wide variety of both mammals and birds. Millions of these game animals are taken each year. They include practically all the native forest, grassland, and desert game species in the United States.

In addition, waterfowl are present both year long and during the hunting season in numerous areas. In the North Central States and Mississippi Valley—as on the Shawnee in Illinois, the Chippewa in Minnesota, and the Mississippi National Forests—water impoundments have been developed, and other management practices and improvements have been installed to provide resting, feeding, and nesting for both ducks and geese.

Packing out an elk above a fog-shrouded canyon in Flathead National Forest, Mont.

Bow hunting, where odds favor the quarry, is gaining in popularity. This hunter is in Dixie National Forest, Utah.

Introduced exotic game birds have also become well established in certain locations to the point that they are providing a large amount of hunting each year.

Examples are the chukar partridge in several of the Intermountain and Pacific Coast States, and the Hungarian or gray partridge in the grassland areas of the Dakotas, Montana, and Wyoming. The Chinese pheasant, a bird primarily of the cultivated fields, is hunted on 10 of the 19 national grasslands.

However, the native forest and grassland species provide the primary attractions for some 4 million visits by small game hunters. These include eight species of grouse, six species of quail, three kinds of doves, four kinds of tree squirrels, and several kinds of rabbits, as well as raccoons, foxes, and opossum. Of all these game birds and mammals, only the mourning dove and cottontail rabbit are found throughout the 48 contiguous States. Yet, each section of the country

has one or more small game species that are hunted with enthusiasm by visitors to the forests and the open ranges.

In our Southern States, the bobwhite quail, the mourning dove, gray and fox squirrels, raccoon, and red fox all have their enthusiastic and devoted followers. A recent nationwide survey indicates that more shotgun shells are used in hunting bobwhites than in hunting any other of our game species.

In certain wooded areas of the South, Midwest, Northeast, and especially in the rural Appalachian region, the gray and fox squirrels continue to be the preferred small game, unchanged since the pioneer days. The challenge presented in hunting ruffed grouse amid the colorful fall foliage of the Northeastern and Lake States ranks this as "tops" in outdoor recreation for hundreds of thousands of hunters each succeeding year.

The valley quail rates "tops" in popularity in California. In Arizona, this honor goes to the Gambel's quail. On national forests in Montana, you can make your choice of the blue, spruce, ruffed, sage, or sharptailed grouse. In the State of Alaska, it is the ptarmigan.

Rabbits, with the cottontail as the most popular species, attract more hunters by far than any other small game animal. Cottontails make their home primarily in fields, fence rows, and brushy areas; the jackrabbits prefer the open rangelands; and it is the snowshoe hare that resides in the woods and provides most hunting on the national forests. Hunting of snowshoes with energetic and noisy beagles is a regular midwinter activity, often at temperatures close to zero, in the north woods of Michigan and Wisconsin and New England.

A major hope for continuing all the pioneering elements of our American tradition of hunting will depend on the future management of the millions of acres of publicly owned forest and rangelands. Here, with scientific wildlife management, these lands can yield annual crops of big and small game for millions of the Nation's hunters as part of a balanced land use program.

Adventures in Family Camping

DOROTHY BOYLE HUYCK

A SENSE OF adventure is the first essential to a pleasurable camping experience for a family.

Whether you are going camping with the simplest tent or the costliest trailer, a hearty feeling for adventure comes in handy. It gets you through those rainy tent raisings or the times when leveling a trailer is complicated. It's also the adventuresome attitude that sends you down a backwoods trail to a meadow which is full of wild strawberries.

Encouraged in youngsters, a sense of adventure grows from early sand castles built by a lake to the later delights of canoeing in the wilderness.

Various types of adventuring attract people to camping. Some families want to "get away from it all"—and they find the national forests provide opportunities for enjoying many different natural settings. A campground in Monongahela National Forest is situated in a dense patch of flowering mountain laurel; one in Superior National Forest is enhanced by the solitude of the Boundary Waters Canoe Area; campsites in Green Mountain National Forest lie in rolling New England hills. In these and many other locations, getting away from it all permits campers the pleasures of an easygoing pace while enjoying a handsome natural landscape.

Other camping families are actively sociable. Their adventures wouldn't be complete without chatty visits around a campfire over king-sized cups of steaming coffee. Sometimes they're fleeing from inhospitable apartment houses or unneighborly neighborhoods to seek new friends while vacationing in a campsite that's preferably not too far back in the woods or too remote from other campers. A privately owned campground, developed in a rural area by a farmer who has turned part of his land to recreational usage, often appeals to this group of campers. The fact that private operators will often accept advance reservations also has wide appeal in this day when campgrounds are crowded.

Still other families have found camping an economical means of traveling to the Nation's great scenic and historic landmarks. These are the transient campers who schedule "one night stands" en route to major destinations. Their itineraries are likely to include overnight stops at campgrounds operated by private owners and by municipal, State, and Federal agencies as well.

It's only the availability of inexpensive camping facilities that makes travel possible for the many tourists whose curiosity outreaches the coins in their pockets.

A wide variety of gear to fit all these types of camping experiences is available. But it's strongly recommended that new campers beg, borrow, or rent camping equipment before making a final purchase—in order to decide on the type of gear which is most appropriate to their individual tastes.

ॐ　　ॐ　　ॐ

A freelance writer of many articles on recreation, conservation, and travel, Dorothy Boyle Huyck has tented with her family for 18 years. She is *Camping Consultant* for the American Automobile Association, publishers of the "AAA Camping and Trailering" Directory.

Girls prepare their plastic tent for a night in the outdoors, on the Angeles National Forest, Calif. Rope is strung from tree at rear, lashed to poles, and tightened around rock on ground. Other rocks hold corners of tent fast. Sleeping bags are inside tent.

Campers heading for remote locations often find that a tent, air mattresses, and sleeping bags are most suitable.

Tent trailers, travel trailers, pickup campers (that fit into pickup trucks), and camper buses are typical of the recreational vehicles which have attained new popularity in recent years. With this category of equipment, "roughing it" is vastly modified, and many of the conveniences of home take to the road.

The advantages—and disadvantages as well—of each of these types of equipment need to be considered before making a family purchase.

Decisions on equipment should take into account not only the kinds of camping experiences anticipated, but also the size of the family, financial outlay (which can vary from a hundred to thousands of dollars), available storage space, and convenience factors.

Advance planning should also include looking through some reputable camping directory for overall information about campgrounds and obtaining more detailed maps or brochures about specific areas that will be visited. With the use of a camping directory, it's possible to plot an itinerary before leaving home— one which provides alternate choices in campgrounds (valuable planning when that "Campground Full" sign has been hung out) or permits making advance reservations with private owners. This "homework" can also include sending for individual maps of the national forests plus brochures from national or State parks as well as private owners. Advance planning has its own anticipatory pleasures and pays off handsomely during the actual camping trip.

The family that attempted to put up a newly acquired tent in the not very natural environment of a third floor apartment—complete with a parquet floor— later appreciated all the expert assistance available during a series of family camping classes. Courses in camping techniques are increasingly available for the newcomers to the camping fraternity.

Classes may be sponsored by local recreation departments, school systems, family camping clubs, YMCA's, or similar service organizations. These provide a substantial boost to your outdoor cooking know-how, proficiency in handling gear, and understanding of the natural environment. Exposure to a family camping course can be one of the best investments which a beginner can make.

The "trial run" that escapes parquet floor problems and takes new campers to the woods or seashore for a taste of the real thing is certainly advisable in advance of any major expedition. Wrinkles in working with the equipment can be ironed out, individual responsibilities can be assigned to each member of the family, and, in many cases, it is discovered that some of the gear is simply excess baggage—to be left at home during a more extensive trip.

Safety precautions while camping include care in the use of fire, watchfulness when parking the car or the trailer, and a regular check upon the whereabouts of the children. Campground operators have some grim tales to tell about parents who would let others assume the responsibility for their youngsters and teenagers alike. Camping at its best is a relaxing family adventure, but it's not a time for letting the small fry roam at will—straight to a rushing stream. Nor can the campground operators be expected to supervise teen-age activities without the assistance of responsible and concerned parents.

Considering the increasing use of the Nation's campgrounds, it's become more important than ever for campers themselves to be interested in the maintenance of campsites. A campground quickly becomes a slum when trees are stripped of limbs, tables are festooned with carved initials, or the toilet facilities are littered.

Courtesy and consideration for other campers is as vital outdoors as it is at home—almost more so, since four walls can contain noise to some extent.

Happily, most campers are thoughtful, considerate types who have a wide reputation for being the friendliest people on earth. They love to swap tales of their adventures over well-brewed tea or hearty coffee. Advice and assistance from the seasoned veterans can aid the beginner in getting out of all sorts of strange situations. And the veterans are not above laughing at their own mistakes, both past and present, like leaving the tent stakes at home for the first time in 15 years. It's a congenial business, camping—in a congenial outdoors. But do go armed with a healthy taste for adventure.

On the Lewis and Clark Trail Across the Bitterroots

ED PARKER

ATOP a ridge of the Bitterroot Mountains in Idaho you walk a narrow trail.

There's an excitement in you which builds with each step, for this centuries-old trail, in places worn almost knee deep in the earth, is a significant part of our country's early history.

Indians, explorers, prospectors, trappers, settlers, Army troops, and nameless others—all passed this way countless times in countless numbers. And among those who found this trail in the wilderness and followed it on across the forbidding mountains were Lewis and Clark.

Now the earth drops steeply from each side of the trail, and the view is from horizon to horizon. You are surrounded by rugged, mountainous country, remote from civilization, and looking much as it did when Lewis and Clark first saw it in 1805. Yet just a few hours ago you breakfasted at a hotel coffee shop back in Missoula, Mont.

The Lewis and Clark Expedition was one of history's greatest overland explorations. Altogether the expedition traveled some 7,500 miles through the wilderness from St. Louis to the Pacific Ocean and back. The trip lasted 2 years 4 months 9 days, and by far the most difficult times

෴ ෴ ෴

Ed Parker, formerly with the Forest Service, is now in the Bureau of Land Management, Department of the Interior.

of the journeys west and east were those spent in crossing the Bitterroots.

The expedition west nearly failed as it struggled for 9 days around and across the rugged mountains and through dense forests. The Indian trail that the party followed was narrow and twisting, difficult to stay on, and often blocked by wind-felled trees. The first snows had fallen, and game had left the high country. The men were reduced to a diet of horsemeat and soup before they breached the mountains and arrived sick and exhausted at an Indian camp on the Weippe Prairie.

Their return trip in June 1806, under the expert guidance of three Nez Perce Indians, was less difficult, but still arduous and exhausting. By forced marches over snow which was packed so hard it supported their horses, they made the trip from Weippe Prairie to Lolo in 7 days.

Lewis and Clark did not find the easy water passage to the West which they had sought, but the expedition is considered by many historians as the single most important event in the development of the Western United States. Politically it secured the recent American purchase of the Louisiana Territory and extended American claims to the Pacific. Economically it provided the first knowledge of the resources which eventually led to the opening of our western lands for development and for settlement.

It took the determined and brave men of the Lewis and Clark Expedition—the Corps of Discovery—9 days to cross the Bitterroot Range. You, today's automobile traveler, can drive through the mountains in an easy 4 hours along U.S. 12, the Lewis and Clark Highway, which was completed during 1961.

I followed the trail of the expedition across the Bitterroots with keen anticipation—I had never been in these mountains—and with a purpose. The Forest Service was beginning planning for the interpretation of historical sites and the development of other visitor services along the highway and on the primitive Lolo Trail Road higher in the mountains.

Al Swift and I had come from Washington to work on this planning with Ken Keeney, Chief of Information and Education for the Forest Service's Northern Region, and others of his staff.

It was a clear-sky day when we left Missoula for our on-the-ground look at

The old and the new in outdoor travel, Bitterroot National Forest.

the historic Bitterroots. We took U.S. 93 south and west for 11 miles to the community of Lolo. Here we turned westward on U.S. Highway 12.

On September 9, 1805, Lewis and Clark had reached this same point after traveling north from Lost Trail Pass through the beautiful Bitterroot Valley. By a creek they called Travelers Rest (Lolo Creek), they had camped for 2 days, their hunters shooting game for food and the horses grazing the surrounding meadows. And here they, too, turned westward toward the imposing Bitterroots, taking a trail used by the Nez Perce who lived west of the mountains. Every year the Nez Perce, including the women and children, crossed the mountains over this trail to hunt buffalo on the plains farther east.

Ahead of us then, as we left Lolo, were the mountains which had nearly turned back the expedition. For about the next 160 miles we would follow Lewis and Clark's route across the Bitterroots, more than 100 miles of it through the Lolo and the Clearwater National Forests.

U.S. 12 winds through the mountains along the water grades of the Lochsa and Clearwater Rivers, and roughly follows the expedition's route and the old Nez Perce trail for some 50 miles to a point just beyond the Powell ranger station. There the expedition left the valley of the Lochsa, which had become increasingly narrow and choked with brush, and climbed to the ridges above.

The rest of the way across the 6,000-foot mountains the Nez Perce trail stayed along the ridgetops, avoiding the steep-walled canyons that the Indians had long ago found impassable for men and horses. Since about 1860 this trail has been called the Lolo Trail, a name which now is also applied to a Forest Service road that is often on and always very near the historic Nez Perce trail. In a great many places along the road the old Indian trail is still visible even today.

So it is that the traveler today has his choice of taking the modern highway through the canyons of the Lochsa and the Clearwater Rivers or else the primitive, and ridge-hugging, Lolo Trail Road. Take both, and you will have a memorable journey, I can assure you.

Plan at least 2 days for your exploration of the Bitterroot country; or more if possible, for there's much to see and do. This historic land is also rich with unusual natural beauty—dense forests, deep canyons, high alpine meadows, mountain lakes, and white water rivers. Fishing is excellent. So don't make yours a fast rush on down the highway when you travel out this way.

We made ours a 2-day trip, traveling the length of the Lolo Trail west for the first day and staying overnight at Orofino. Here on the banks of the Clearwater River the sick and hungry men of the expedition camped while they hewed and burned out the "holler" of the five canoes that would carry them on to the Pacific. We returned to Missoula over the highway, disappointed only that rain kept us from crossing over one of the suspension bridges that span the Lochsa and hiking for a ways into the Selway-Bitterroot Wilderness.

Tips for Campers

If you are camping, you'll certainly want to stay longer than 2 days. Along the highway are a number of the Forest Service campgrounds from which you can explore the country and enjoy its pioneer atmosphere. If you are not camping, a circle trip like ours—beginning on either side of the mountains—is an excellent way to see this country. Take rain gear in case it's needed and make the wilderness walk which I missed.

The interpretation of the historical sites and the development of the other visitor services along these roads are not yet complete, but they are well underway. Watch for Forest Service signs along the highway and the Lolo Trail Road. They give mileage distances, locate off-highway trails and roads, and interpret points of interest and historic significance like the campsites of Lewis and Clark and other places associated with the expedition.

U.S. 12 is a modern, 2-lane, all-weather highway, but to travel it your car should be in good condition and have a full gas tank. A breakdown could delay you for several hours, and please note that there are no service stations for nearly 100 miles between Lolo Hot Springs, Mont., and Lowell, Idaho.

The Lolo Trail Road is unpaved, narrow, and crooked, but the experienced and careful driver can travel it safely in the summer months. Before driving this road, however, take the precaution of checking its condition with a forest supervisor or ranger at Missoula and Lolo in Montana; at Orofino, Kamiah, and Kooskia in Idaho; or at the Powell and Lochsa ranger stations which are on the highway inside the forest. These Forest Service offices also can supply you with a forest map showing roads, trails, and other points of interest, among them:

Fort Fizzle—Nez Perce Indians revolted in 1877 against living on a reservation, and in July they fled the Idaho Territory by way of the Lolo Trail. Led by Chief Joseph, 250 braves, 450 women and children, and 2,000 horses crossed the mountains with Gen. O. O. Howard leading Army troops in pursuit. An attempt to block the Indians near Lolo failed when Chief Joseph kept his people high upon the ridges and simply slipped past the fortifications in the night.

Lolo Pass—Highest point (5,233 feet) on the Lewis and Clark Highway. On the crest of the Bitterroot Range, it marks the Montana-Idaho border.

Packer Meadows—Lewis and Clark fed their horses and camped in this large alpine meadow near Lolo Pass. It was a favorite stopping place for Indians.

Bernard De Voto Memorial Grove— A stately grove of towering cedars on the Lochsa River, dedicated to the famous historian·and conservationist.

Powell Ranger Station—The expedition camped here on the way west, and from here left the valley to travel the ridgetops. The Lolo Trail Road begins near the station.

Colgate Warm Springs—Named for the cook of a hunting party that went into the Lochsa Valley in the winter of 1893. Heavy snows threatened to trap the party, and when Colgate became ill he was abandoned. His grave is nearby.

Jerry Johnson Hot Springs—Named for an early-day trapper, miner, and outdoorsman. The saline waters of these warm springs attract elk and deer.

Indian Post Office—Two mounds of stones on the Lolo Trail, built before the time of Lewis and Clark. The old trail turned off the divide at this point, and these mounds evidently marked the turn. Historians doubt the more romantic story that Indians passed messages by piling up the stones in various arrangements.

Indian Grave—In 1893, an Indian family picking huckleberries, hunting, and fishing along the Lolo Trail became ill. A 14-year-old boy, Albert Parsons Mallickan, died and was buried here.

Indian Crossing—Near Indian Grave the Nez Perce trail fords a creek. Here the trail cuts deeply into the streambanks, one reminder of the centuries that man has walked along this trail.

Lots of Big Game

Wildlife—Mountain goats, deer, elk, and moose may be seen any time of year. Deer and elk gather on the south-facing slopes during winter, and as many as 100 of them may be seen along the highway on a February or a March afternoon. Bear, coyote, and bobcat also are present. Fish include rainbow and cutthroat trout as well as the steelhead, an ocean-going trout that returns like the salmon to its headwaters birthplace to spawn.

Selway-Bitterroot Wilderness—Largest in the United States, its 1.2 million acres are parts of four national forests: Clearwater, Nez Perce, Lolo, Bitterroot. Suspension bridges across the Lochsa River connect with trails leading into this land of primitive beauty which lies south of U.S. 12. You can travel by foot or horseback. Horses are available from licensed local outfitters and guides.

These are only some of the things that you can see and do in the Bitterroots. You can also camp, fish, picnic, hike, climb mountains, hunt, or just enjoy it all.

You can enjoy, also, one experience unusual for automobile travel. As you drive the Lewis and Clark Highway and the Lolo Trail for some 100 miles through the forests, you will not see a commercial building of any kind, nor even a single billboard. Here is an unspoiled part of our great American outdoors.

And it's all yours to enjoy.

The Rancher and Our National Forests and Grasslands

ROBERT S. RUMMELL

CARL, time you get the horses, break-fast will be ready." That command from his father was the start of a day momentous to 15-year-old Carl Franklin. For this was June 1, the day the Franklins' cattle were to be put on the national forest for a summer of grazing.

Carl and his father had started their herd up the trail from the home ranch 3 days before, and today would complete the trail drive. The district forest ranger was due to be at the Shake Creek Gap at 8 o'clock to count the cattle in. The Franklins would push their herd up Meadow Creek and out onto the broad bunchgrass slopes of the Flat Ridge cattle allotment where the cows and their young calves would rest up and then begin their summer foraging.

Carl remembers well the brown saddle blanket that almost kept off the chill as he stared up from his bough bed at the dawning east. "Well, let's go. Those old cows sure know where we're a headin'. They'll be at that gate all by themselves afore long, I reckon."

As Carl and his father rode behind the red and black and brown cattle, now bawling as they sensed the closeness of their summer home, Carl thought with pleasure of what lay ahead. This was to be his first season to stay alone with the herd. He would put up at the cow camp. There would be wood to cut, his own meals to cook, and horses to wrangle. He would pack blocks of salt where the cows would find and lick them into rounded mountains and valleys, and then into blobs of nothingness. He would ride fence and ax free the winter-fallen lodge-poles, and splice and stretch and staple the sharply barbed wire.

There would be other tasks. So many he would have but little time to search out the den of coyote pups yammering away at the moon. Or see if Old Crip, the three-legged bear, was still around.

But it takes a man to punch cows. Carl was 15. And a man. So there was a job to do. That's the way it is.

ʊʒ   ʊʒ   ʊʒ

Years passed and now the herd was Carl's. It was another summer, and Carl took the cattle to the forest for grazing.

"Well, Mr. Franklin, all the 115 head counted in. Your permitted number right down to the last set of horns." District Ranger John Simmons reminded Carl of that other ranger who had met him and his father at the Shake Creek Gap that other June 1. The summer Carl first spent alone with the Franklin herd. "Your cows wintered real good! They'll stay sleek-coated this summer. Your range sure has improved under that new management plan we worked out."

John Simmons had come to the Flat Ridge District two summers ago. In this short time, he had become acquainted with the 200,000 acres of forest and range-land in his district and its problems. He

ʊʒ   ʊʒ   ʊʒ

Robert S. Rummell is *Staff Assistant* in the Division of Range Management, Forest Service.

had traveled from the dry foothills, up through the easy-laying pine forest, on through the higher timbered slopes, and up into the subalpine grassland. He knew all the permittees and their home ranch locations and grazing practices. He had discussed range management with Carl, and he had ridden the range with him.

"Putting that fence across Battle Flat has turned the trick. That and the new watering pond have stopped overuse of the grass. Your cows don't concentrate on the meadows anymore."

That fence and the watering pond were a part of the plan for managing livestock on the Flat Ridge allotment under multiple use. For Carl Franklin and District Ranger Simmons had spent many hours discussing how to develop and manage the range resource on Flat Ridge. They wanted enough forage for Carl's cattle.

At the same time, they tried to consider all of the needs and requirements of the land and its users. They wanted to maintain a good grass cover for watershed protection. Carl and John knew that the elk which foraged on the higher reaches of the allotment would require grass and sedges, so they reserved some of the allotment's grazing capacity for big game.

Their plan for restoring the grass cover on Battle Flat, where the good forage plants had been replaced by sagebrush, was to spray-kill only part of the sage; and the rest was to be left for sagegrouse cover and food. Because increasing numbers of picnickers used the aspens at Shady Grove, the plan was adjusted so the cows grazed there only after Labor Day. This left the grove and its picnic area free of cattle during most of the picnicking season.

Sport fishing and livestock grazing go together in the Umatilla National Forest, Oreg.

"I believe we've got her coming our way, John. The grass is strong and getting better. I'll be back to push 'em through the gate again next year."

So it had gone each opening day of the grazing season for the Franklins and for the thousands of other cattle ranchers over the years. And for the sheepmen, too, with their bands of ewes and lambs moving into national forest system lands.

Since 1905, livestock have grazed the national forests under permit. Ranchers owning livestock and land apply for the privilege of grazing their livestock. If they qualify and the grazing is available, they are then issued a permit. And there is a charge made for this grazing.

Graze in 39 States

Although the first permits were issued in the Western States, grazing now is permitted on the national forest system lands in 39 States. Only in 9 Eastern Seaboard States and Kentucky and Hawaii is there no livestock grazing under permit.

It is a big spread—this national forest system, with over 100 million acres divided into 11,600 grazing allotments and grazed by 7 million cattle, sheep, and horses. It has more than 50,000 miles of fence and 38,000 livestock watering developments. Included are 4 million acres of the national grasslands, largely in the Great Plains States, and another 4 million acres of the intermingled or adjacent private land for which administration of grazing is waived to the Forest Service.

To the Carl Franklins and to the 20,000 other Franklins and Joneses and Rodriguezes who graze their cattle and sheep on the national forests, the forage from these public lands is an important part of their total ranching operation.

Take Carl Franklin. Over the years he has built up the productivity of his home ranch—through seeding grasses on the native range, using his range properly, and by practicing good irrigation on his meadowland. But even with this effort, Carl still finds that summer is a critical forage supply period. And this is where his national forest grazing permit helps. The grass in the mountains is green and nourishing in the summer, and his cows give rich milk for their sucking calves. While his brood cows summer on the forest, he grows hay on his home ranch meadows for winter feeding. His operation is in balance.

Carl's grazing fees are set to return fair market value to the Federal Government for his use of the public lands. A portion of these fees is returned to his county for aid in financing schools and roads. In enabling Mr. Franklin and other ranchers to realize the full production value of their privately owned lands, the national forest system promotes community stability. These ranches are taxpaying, income-producing businesses which are the foundations of many communities.

Two contrasting localities show how the national forests fit into local livestock ranching economies. The first example could be Carl Franklin's community.

In northeastern California, 147 ranchers graze 19,000 head of cattle on the Modoc National Forest. This is around 25 percent of the cattle in Modoc County. The ranchers want to graze more cattle, but the ranges presently are fully stocked. As additional grazing becomes available through range improvements and development, the ranchers will have a chance to use it. Average permit in this area is for 130 cattle with the average operator grazing about 30 percent of his livestock on the forest range.

The second locality is in the mountains of northern New Mexico. Here live many small stockmen, largely of Spanish-American origin, whose families have grazed livestock on the national forest for many years. In this dry but beautiful country, 425 permittees graze 10,000 cattle on the Santa Fe National Forest. Ownership of cattle averages 35 head per rancher with the average cattle permit 24 head.

As on the Modoc, demand is high for the grazing from the Santa Fe National Forest. The stockmen depend very greatly upon this grazing, too. Of the 425 Santa Fe permittees, 198 own only an acre of land each; another 172 own from 2 to 40 acres; only 38 own more than 40 acres with 17 owning no land. And instead of a 3- to 4-month grazing season, these ranchers graze their livestock on the forest an average of 6 months a year.

73

In these two widely contrasting ranching localities, national forest system lands play important roles. In both, ranchers need and depend upon the national forests for livestock grazing. This grazing helps sustain the agricultural way of life and its economy for the communities where these ranchers live. Just like in Carl Franklin's community.

✿ ✿ ✿

Yes, Carl Franklin knew that, God willing, he would be back next year to graze his cattle on the national forest. Just as he had come back each June for 35 years. Even though productivity of his home ranch has increased through good range management and he has a much more efficient operation, Carl still needs the summer grazing from the Flat Ridge allotment. Carl's ranch today supports more cattle than it did 35 years ago, and they are better and bigger cattle at that. On his mountain grazing allotment, the productivity, too, is greater. Instead of the one hewn-log trough at Punch Spring that watered cows from a square mile of range, Carl now has a pipeline that feeds three different troughs. Where the Flat Ridge once was one big pasture, it now is fenced into four units. Sure, rotation of the cattle between pasture units on the Flat Ridge takes more time than just turning them in at Shake Creek and picking them up as they drift back there by themselves in the fall. But this lets Carl keep an eye on his quality cattle. They do very well under rotation; and the Flat Ridge range is in good condition.

And all this is the measure of District Ranger John Simmons' and Rancher Carl Franklin's success as a cooperating team of public land administrator and private user. Cattle will keep on grazing the Flat Ridge allotment, as an important use of these national forest lands. This piece of the national forests sure is contributing its bit to the public good.

Tips on Hiking

HENRY F. NICHOL

HALFWAY up Old Rag we stopped for a few moments to catch our breath and to enjoy the magnificent view. "I never dreamed you had trails like this in the East," exclaimed one member of our group who had recently moved from the west coast.

Many people do not know about the many fine hiking trails that can be found in every part of the country. The Ridge Trail up Old Rag Mountain, located within 100 miles of Metropolitan Washington, is one of the most interesting and scenic trails to be found anywhere. Yet we saw less than a dozen people on this trip, even with ideal weather.

Another outstanding trail which also is known by only a few people is the Blue Billy Goat Trail within just a half hour's easy drive from the center of Washington. This amazingly beautiful trail along the rocky gorge of the Potomac River near Great Falls should be enjoyed by many more people than the mere handful usually encountered on a weekend.

✿ ✿ ✿

Henry F. Nichol is *Assistant* to the Associate Administrator, Soil Conservation Service. He serves as USDA Representative on the Staff of the President's Council on Recreation and Natural Beauty and as Chairman of USDA's Working Party on Outdoor Recreation.

The first tip on hiking then is to find out where the trails are in your area and to make good use of them.

Various hiking and outdoor clubs are ready sources of information in almost every community. State and Federal forest and park officials are likewise gold mines of information about trails.

Hiking is not only one of the best forms of physical exercise, but one of the best forms of mental diversion too. It is both relaxing and stimulating. It is good for all ages and especially valuable as a family and group activity.

Since hiking varies so widely in the distance covered and the types of trails and terrains, it is not feasible to prescribe any general rules or guidelines. Short and frequent hikes, requiring no preparation or special equipment, should be encouraged for most people.

The longer hikes, usually requiring advance planning and preparation, may be somewhat more challenging.

Helpful Hints

Hints I have found helpful include:

• Keep in condition by walking at a fast pace for at least 15 minutes every day. Climbing stairs instead of using an elevator, and running short distances are also excellent ways of keeping in shape.

• Wear only comfortable clothing, and when you are hiking in the mountains or in areas subject to sudden changes in the weather, take a windbreaker, a sweater, or other protection against cold and rain. Two pairs of socks, one thin and one thick, are advisable on long hikes.

• On any hike nothing is more essential than good, comfortable shoes.

• The equipment you take might include matches in a waterproof container, a knife, compass, map, adhesive bandages or other first aid items, insect repellent, and a flashlight.

• Food can vary from a box of raisins or a candy bar on a short hike to dehydrated meals cooked over a small stove during a long hike.

• Items such as binoculars or cameras may be taken along, but be careful not to overload yourself with too much gear.

• On longer hikes keep a comfortable,

Members of the Wanderbirds Hiking Club of Washington, D.C., enjoy a winter hike through the mountains.

steady pace and take frequent rest stops.

• Drink only safe water. If in doubt, boil the water or use purification tablets.

• Avoid the busy highways. When you have to use a highway, keep as far over on the left as possible.

• Leave word at home or some other place where you are going and when you expect to be back.

• On almost any hike, a map is a good idea. If going into unfamiliar country, a detailed map showing contours and landmarks is most helpful.

• Take along a field guide on wildflowers, birds, rocks, or other subjects depending upon your particular interests. This can add greatly to the enjoyment and educational value of your hike.

Some of the best hiking can be found on the longer trails.

The Appalachian Trail, extending a long 2,000 miles from Georgia to Maine, provides a unique opportunity for exploring the Eastern United States. And in the

West, the Pacific Crest Trail, which will eventually stretch all the way from Mexico to Canada, goes through 19 national forests and offers the hiker a fine variety of incomparable scenery.

Much of the most beautiful scenery in the national parks and the national forests lies hidden away from the highways. How much more fun it is to get out of your car and enjoy the stimulation of an invigorating hike in the outdoors!

Trail System Studied

Increasing opportunities for hiking would be made possible under the nationwide system of scenic trails which has now been under consideration for several years. This trail system is designed to provide hikers with vast opportunities to view the wealth and splendor of America's outdoor world for a few hours at a time, on 1-day jaunts, overnight treks, or expeditions lasting for a week or more.

The proposed system would include not only the long national trails, but the shorter trails in the State parks and other recreation areas and trails in and near our metropolitan areas.

Hiking provides everyone with a unique opportunity for enjoying and appreciating the great outdoors.

A final tip for hikers:

Help others enjoy their trip as much as you by keeping in mind as you hike, "take nothing but pictures; and leave nothing but footprints." Throwing all your litter along a trail or leaving a dirty campsite is unpardonable. Good manners in the outdoors includes always carrying out any unburnable trash and keeping the trails and the countryside free of cans, glass, plastic, and tinfoil.

My friend from the west coast who was hiking Old Rag Mountain for the first time has added another dimension to this principle of keeping our country beautiful. Whenever he came across a bit of litter on the trails, he picked it up and stuffed it into a pocket of his knapsack.

We need a lot more hikers with this kind of an attitude.

Ranger Don L. Gerred and members of his Boy Scout troop cooking lunch on a hike in the Talladega National Forest, Ala.

Forests—Where the Waterflow Starts

MARVIN D. HOOVER

I ALWAYS stop a moment at Berthoud Pass when driving west from Denver. The mountain peaks and the valleys form an ever-changing panorama, with trees making a tapestry of every shade of green on the slopes up to timberline at 11,500 feet. A few patches and strips of wind-battered and shrubby trees creep a little higher, but above them to the crest grow only the grasses and herbs of the alpine tundra. Mountain lands just like these are the source of the Rio Grande, the Arkansas, the South Platte and the North Platte, and the Colorado Rivers.

Nearly all of the water for these rivers comes from the small proportion of their drainage basins higher than 8,000 feet. The water-yielding zone is covered with forests of Engelmann spruce, subalpine fir, aspen, and lodgepole pine, except for the fraction too high and cold for tree growth. The climatic factors that favor the trees also provide enough water for the streams to flow down into the lower, drier countryside.

The high country gets less rain and snow than you might suppose. The year's total at Berthoud Pass is only 35 inches. Some parts of the mountains receive a little more, but most of the water source area has an annual total of 25 to 30 inches. If you live east of the Mississippi, your hometown probably gets more moisture than these mountains. But a lucky chain of circumstances helps convert the rather scanty input of precipitation into streamflow and soil moisture for tree growth. The key factors are: The cold climate,

a short growing season, the uneven distribution of the snowpack, and snowmelt timed to release water when it is most useful. Mountaineers claim there are two seasons—winter and the Fourth of July.

The long, cold winter keeps snow from melting from November until April.

Snowfall gradually accumulates in a continually deepening blanket which we call the snowpack. All the winter snow crop is held in cold storage. None is released until the warm weather. Mountain streams are trickles under the snow.

Melt begins slowly in April. It speeds up by early May, and the streams begin then to rise rapidly and eventually reach a peak in June. About 80 percent of the annual total flows off during May, June, and July. The release of snowpack water coincides with the beginning of the heavy water use downstream for croplands and cities. The concentration of high flow into a short period holds down the losses and efficiently fills up storage reservoirs.

Mountain trees and plants use moisture for only a few months. No season is completely free of frosts. Vegetation must be hardy and adapted to a growing season only 50 to 75 days long. Snowmelt water is available when the days are longest so that the plants can make optimum use of sunshine. They really hustle to get out flowers and mature seed before the winter

Marvin D. Hoover is *Principal Hydrologist* and a *Project Leader* for watershed management research at the Rocky Mountain Forest and Range Experiment Station, Fort Collins, Colo.

returns. This grand period of growth and flowering is the time when most people visit the mountains. It is a beautiful and serene time. Only rarely is there violent weather. Even the winds are still, as if husbanding their strength.

I wish more people could see the winter conditions. They are important to understand. It is a tremendous experience to see the wind sweep the ridges—it helps explain the variable depth of the snowpack from place to place, which at first appears so haphazard. It only takes a few hours of wind to do lots of snow moving. Most winter days, winds are light, the sky is deep blue, and the snow peacefully glitters in the sunshine. These are the days skiers remember and boast about to make skiing in Colorado famous.

Snow Plumes

But these tranquil periods are broken by cloudy weather and new snow. Typically, the snow falls at night, riding down on gentle winds to pile up on tree crowns and whiten the peaks. It doesn't stay long at its first landing points, though. Just about daylight, the wind begins to roar among the ridges and to spill in gusts and eddies down into the valleys. Windward slopes are swept clean, their snow load carried out in plumes far beyond the crest to powder down miles away. Trees shake and sway, spilling the load of snow from their upper branches. The swirling eddies reach into the trees, seize snow, and carry it high in smoky plumes.

Wind currents reshape the snow surface, building deep drifts in protected places like the lee side of ridges, in the forest edge beside large clearings, and in sheltered openings within the forest. Fresh-fallen snow sifted through the tree canopy to the ground beneath stays there, but that held on the foliage is carried away. Thus the shallowest snowpack in the forest is immediately under trees, and the deepest is in the best sheltered openings. This unequal distribution of snow is beneficial to water yield. Snow accumulates where it is least exposed to evaporation. When it begins to melt, a smaller proportion is used to saturate soil, and more water reaches stream channels.

At Berthoud Pass, a sign beside the road says this is the Continental Divide, separating the Atlantic from the Pacific watershed. This was a fact one time, but now water is too important to the bustling cities, nestled along the eastern edge of the mountains on the plains more than a mile lower than the divide. Some water still flows west in the Colorado River, but not as much as when the early fur trappers traversed this pass.

Now there is a widespreading network of canals, ditches, and pipelines leading the water around and through the mountain crest. The spring water crop is harvested just as are the timber, forage, and the wildlife and fish crops.

Water users are asking land managers to favor more water production. At the same time, more people from the cities are flocking to the slopes of their own watersheds for recreation. These people want the mountains to be unspoiled, but they expect them at the same time to: (1) Furnish the water to raise their food and keep their lawn green, (2) supply forage to livestock and big game, (3) produce wood for their houses and newspapers, and (4) provide campsites with most of the comforts of home. No wonder that the forest ranger managing these lands to meet all the demands has little time to appreciate their scenic splendor!

So far as water is concerned, we can manage the mountain forests to produce more. The range of conditions within the forest zone is wide. Near timberline the growing season is extremely short, and the trees can use but little water themselves. Their snowtrapping function is important. Anything to improve snow retention here would be beneficial. Planting of trees where nature has been unable to reforest the large patches burned over by old fires would be all to the good.

At the lower margin of the forest zone, trees growing along streams and in moist areas use more than their share of water. There is very little doubt that streamside aspens escorting mountain streams down to the plains are living on water taken from the stream. That water could be used for other purposes, but which purpose is most deserving? Water for your garden is more important than water for

78

the aspens, but a choice like this also involves brook trout to satisfy a fisherman and golden-hued trees to delight an artist or a photographer.

Most of the mountain forests lie between these extremes of either totally benefiting or being totally parasitic upon streamflow. For each portion of this intermediate zone there is an ideal pattern of forest and opening that most efficiently traps snow and reduces the quantity of water used in tree growth. We don't absolutely know the best arrangement for each spot, but we are learning fast. We are confident we want a forest with open-ings rather than a large clearing with strips of trees. The openings can be as large as 10 or 20 tree heights wide on slopes naturally protected from wind, but should be smaller on exposed ridges.

The potential benefit to water yield is demonstrated just west of Berthoud Pass, 50 air miles from Denver, on the Fraser Experimental Forest.

We increased streamflow 25 percent from a 700-acre watershed by cutting half the area in a checkerboard pattern of clear-cut strips alternating with uncut forest. The cleared strips range in width from one to six tree heights.

Taking the Edge Off "Roughing It"

DOROTHY MARTIN MASON

HEAVENS GATE! What a wonderful name for this bit of the high country, Terry Atkins thought as she sat eating lunch with the family. From here they looked off into the heart of the Seven Devils Peaks, craggy and formidable, and down into the depths of Hells Canyon, deepest on the continent.

Jim was telling the children that way down there some 6,000 feet a band of Nez Perce Indians led by Chief Joseph swam the Snake River in 1877 to escape the white men. The family did not want to visit the spot because the summer's temperature in the river valley hovered somewhere around 115°.

Up on the rocky promontory, however, the breezes blew cool, and the morning hike had been really comfortable. They had left the little Forest Service campground early before the sun was high and had come up the trail. If all the days of this next week were as much fun at this had been, she believed that this would be the greatest vacation ever.

Of course, the family said this after each camping trip. They had taken the edges off roughing it during the past few years. Now back country camping had become pure enjoyment.

These off-the-track campgrounds with only 3 to 10 units were usually delightful—nestling in a bowl of mountains or commanding a lake view or overlooking a babbling stream. Away from the crowds the family developed its self-sufficiency, pursued hobbies more freely, and learned more about nature. They looked forward all year round to camping.

During the winter the family sat down around the kitchen table and planned their trip. She and Jim decided what

۞ ۞ ۞

Dorothy Martin Mason, formerly Public Information Officer with the Forest Service, is an experienced backpacker, camper, and hiker.

part of the country they wanted to see. Then with the children they studied one of the many camping guides on the market and picked out a small campground to use as a base of operations. The guide tells how many family units there are and who runs the campgrounds. They had found that the Forest Service in the U.S. Department of Agriculture administered more of these small back country camping spots than any other single agency. However, there were some run by agencies in the U.S. Department of the Interior, by the States, and by a number of private individuals.

Then they sent for and read descriptive pamphlets on the area, even a history from the library, and studied maps to decide what they would like to do.

Each selected one thing. Timmy, the oldest, wanted a hike on this trip. One day they would all go rock hounding because this was Susie's hobby of the moment. Jack, their youngest, wanted to backpack. The forest ranger at Riggins suggested that for this they go to Horse

Campers leisurely finish lunch on a bluff overlooking the South Fork of the Flathead River, Flathead National Forest, Mont.

Heaven, following the old Boise Trail which had been used to drive livestock from the high ranges down into town on the way to the market.

They had stopped at the Forest Service office to check on campfire permits because in some places they are required. They had asked a few questions about the road and got some good ideas about places to go for their activities.

Campfire Tradition

Jim, as usual, wanted a day of fishing. Terry had selected a day in camp when everyone could do as little or as much as he wanted. They might draw, swim, read, or look for birds. This should probably be a day when there were other campers around. So it would give the youngsters someone else to do things with and cut down on the possibilities of bickering. Perhaps that night they might share their campfire. The family campfire each night was an important tradition. Some nights they sang; some they told stories or read local tales. Sometimes they got educational and played word games to sharpen their vocabularies.

A big factor in the success of the Atkins family trips is that activities are planned but not scheduled, and ground rules are established in advance. Each member of the family knows that one day they will do what he or she wants, but he doesn't know what day this will be. Terry and Jim choose the day, depending on the weather and how the children feel. One of the rules of the trips is that everyone must participate in all of the activities.

Using this system they combine individual hobbies with the family activities. The hikes go to points of interest; rock hounding ends with a dip in a mountain lake away from camp; identification of edible plants is combined with backpacking, and they bird watch and study flowers anytime, all the time.

Also, the youngsters have definite responsibilities in addition to jobs around camp. With a little help, they choose and pack items needed for comfort and entertainment in the car. Terry takes care of surprise games and snacks in the car. They often stop to explore a little stream, read a historic marker, pick wild berries, or perhaps visit a craft shop.

The children also select the clothes that they will take—and are responsible for keeping them clean on the trip. Laundromats are a great help when the family is on main roads, but in the back-country camp the children have to be nudged.

Drip dry fabrics and cold water soap powder for woolens make clothes care relatively painless.

Camping with a family is easy if you plan carefully. Most parents are concerned about two other items besides the children—cooking and cleanup.

Food manufacturers have simplified the former. Back in the roaring twenties when automobile camping had a great boom, canned spaghetti and codfish balls were standard fare. Canned beans with hotdogs bought in the last town the car went through were a treat. Families got milk in bottles which could be kept cool in the springs or streams and eggs for breakfast. Sometimes they got fresh vegetables from a farmer to have with the hamburger or the ham.

Must Stock Up

The present-day automobile campers, frequently on the move or staying near the main highways, can, with a portable icebox, carry more fresh foods. The back-country camper, however, must stock up on foods that will not spoil. He can find a large assortment of prepared foods at almost any grocery store.

There are dry soups, for taking the chill out of the bones on cold or damp days, and instant desserts. There is rice with mushrooms and noodles with almonds to serve with canned meat. Some groceries carry freeze-dried turkey tetrazinni, shrimp supreme, chicken a la king—all lightweight and tasty.

Browsing through the sporting goods catalogs or stores, the camper can find dried, freeze-dried, and puff-dried vegetables—even salads. These lists grow longer with each passing year.

Breakfast choices range from regular cooked cereals and dry milk to freeze-dried combination packages of scrambled eggs and ham with hash browned potatoes. When hiking, many families lunch on cheese, hard salami, nuts, chocolate or hard candy, raw carrots, and dried fruit. Instant fruit-flavored powders you mix with clear cool water make a good drink.

The dishwashing monster looks large and black to the inexperienced camper. The housewife sees pots and pans blackened with the smoke of the open fire. The best way to slay this dragon is to use a gasoline stove. Some burn fuel oil or gas without lead. Others use canned gas. If you do supplement the stove with the open fire, rub soap on the bottom of the pan. When it is put into water, both soap and soot come off. Just to be on the safe side, carry pans in a cloth bag so that the black can't get into the rest of the family duffle.

To take more of the edge off roughing it, pack some little bits of creature comforts in the gear. Terry Atkins collects small jars to carry just enough hand cream, face cream, and suntan lotion for the 1-week camping trip. Some folks take moistened pads in aluminum foil packets to wash face and hands at lunch and at the end of a hot and dusty hike. A little solution for eyes is refreshing after a day in the sun. Many like lightweight swimsuits for baths in lakes or streams.

Those who normally use a pillow at night should take an inflatable one for the car and camp. Many prefer to change into sleepwear at night and not get into the sleeping bags in camp clothes. Most campers who hike take lightweight shoes to wear around camp. Any who enjoy a bit of gracious living indulge in hot tea, cocoa, coffee, bouillon, or cold fruit-flavored drinks with hors d'oeuvres every night before dinner. A family doesn't need all of these refinements of civilization. One or two make all the difference between comfort and discomfort when "roughing it" in the back country.

Equipped with guides and maps and with some imagination in applying the experience of others in handling your four C's—children, cooking, cleanup, and creature comforts—you, too, are ready to pack up and take off on a back-country camping trip. Have fun!

War on Forest Fires

MERLE S. LOWDEN

A SMALL WISP of smoke slowly drifted up over Butte Creek Rim. Jo saw it first. Was it a fire? As dependable Forest Service lookouts, Jo and Jim Worthey must be sure before they reported it to the fire dispatcher. Once reported as a "fire," this smoke would become the focal point of the firefighting efforts of the more than 250 employees of the Lassen National Forest. And if it should grow bigger, there was always the backup help from hundreds more U.S. Forest Service firefighters in California as well as other States.

This time both Jo and Jim were sure. They immediately directed their firefinder on the smoke and started to fill out their report—degrees of azimuth, distance, type of topography, size of fire, and the type of smoke. Then they transmitted it to the dispatcher at the headquarters for the ranger district. Little did Jo and Jim realize when they started this report the many exciting events and grim tragedy that would take place the next few days, almost at their doorstep, in the mountains of northern California.

Before the Cabin fire was stopped, some 4,000 acres of beautiful pine forests would be burned and leave a graveyard of trees for many years to come.

Their actions started a "battle" that engaged more than 600 men, 16 tractors, 3 helicopters, and 9 airplanes. Before it was stopped, this fire cost $200,000 to put out and destroyed a million dollars worth of timber, recreation, watershed, and other resources. Although a detailed investigation was made, the Forest Service still is not sure who caused all this

trouble, except that someone was careless with just a small "warming" fire.

This was but one of the 100,000 forest fires which are started by man's carelessness in the forests of the United States each year. However, there were double this number before the Smokey Bear program was launched 25 years ago by the Forest Service, the State forestry departments, and the Advertising Council. Every year the Forest Service spends nearly $50 million preparing for these fires and in fighting them.

To meet the threat of forest fires, it has become necessary to organize, train, and to have ready the largest fire department in the world. It can call up thousands of men who have had fire "battle" training at some time in their career.

There are available 400 smokejumpers, 800 ground tankers, 200 helicopters, 100 air tankers, and other airplanes forming an armada of more than 1,200 aircraft.

I first heard of the Cabin fire at Reno where we were completing a fire-training movie. It wasn't long before I was on my way to the scene of action. I don't "chase" fires, but I do like to know what goes on. By checking the firefighting, I get an excellent indication whether the months of training and preparation have accomplished their purpose.

It was only 9:16 a.m. on a Saturday morning when the Wortheys made their discovery. They had been up since 6 o'clock scanning their territory closely. Jo

Merle S. Lowden is *Director*, Division of Fire Control for the Forest Service.

and Jim were 2 of the more than 2,000 lookouts that serve as sentinels to report any smoke they see on the 154 national forests in the United States. It had been a quiet year, and they were beginning to think they were to get by without any bad fires on the Lassen. Don Renton, the district ranger, Earl Nichols, the forest fire staffman, and Irv Bosworth, the forest supervisor, had all been thinking—and hoping—the same thing. Our record had been good all over the West, and the Forest Service fire leaders were hoping that their luck would hold.

Smoke Increases

The smoke began to increase even as Jim gave his report to the dispatcher at the ranger station. There was increasing tempo and excitement in his voice as he reported: Bearing, 153°20′; distance, 7 miles; area, flat; type, pine; size, about three campfires, and the smoke going straight up, light blue in color.

The Lassen uses a system of automatic dispatch which means that all fire forces within a given area converge on a fire as soon as it is reported. In less than 5 minutes, three "ground" tankers were speeding for the fire. Within 45 minutes, four men with pulaski tools and shovels were trying to put a fireline around the fire which had increased to one-fourth acre. The "pulaski" men were cutting brush and tree limbs with the ax side of their tools and digging a trench with the hoe side.

For a while it was a race between time and fire with the men feverishly building a fireline. They threw dirt on the flames where the fingers seemed to reach out. Then they tried desperately to clear the grass and needles to dig a trench. It was soon apparent it was going to be a nip-and-tuck affair if they "got" the fire. About 10 a.m., a "strong, erratic" wind came up and that decided the issue. Ed Cunningham, district fire control officer (and the fire boss at that time), saw several of the fellows "lose" their portions of the line. The fire spread across their trench in spite of all they could do.

By 10:30 Ed knew they needed more help so he radioed for more ground tankers and crews. It was clear to the men back at headquarters that there was much trouble ahead. It was time to call for air support and heavy equipment. Air tankers were ordered from the zone dispatcher in Redding, and tractors were requested from the local loggers.

Within a half hour the wind reached about 25 miles per hour, and the fire was spreading rapidly to the northeast. It was certain that the firefighters had a "project" fire on their hands. Preparations were proceeding rapidly back at forest headquarters in Susanville and at the Redding zone office to get the men and machinery to "handle" it. This meant getting firefighting overhead from other parts of the Lassen Forest and from other national forests. Word was spreading all through the region that a big fire was in the making on the Lassen.

The lead plane pilot, Ernie Gentry, was over the fire by 11:30 a.m. It was Ernie's job to direct the air tankers following him where to drop their loads of water and chemical mix. They must

Fighting the Cabin forest fire.

go just where the fire boss wants them. By now Earl Nichols had taken over as fire boss and was in a helicopter above the fire. He was directing the action on all fronts. The first job assigned the air tankers was to cut off the head of the blaze at the northeast corner and hopefully to keep it from getting as far as the Butte Creek Rim.

Once the fire had "hit" the rim, it was pretty sure to go over the top and to spread on across the plateau. That would mean practically having two fires—one above and one below the rim. Three drops were made upon the head, and momentarily it looked as if they might stop it sufficiently for the ground forces to rush in and hold it. This hope was short lived because two large "spot" fires showed up ahead of the cutoff point. Burning embers had blown ahead and were starting more fires. More air tankers were not immediately available, so the planned stand had to be given up.

Shifts Strategy

By noon the fire was burning hard on all fronts. The pickup in wind made the fire spread much faster. Fire Boss Nichols had to change his strategy. As he saw it, there was no use to hit the "head" of the fire directly. He decided to concentrate on the flanks and try to squeeze in the head. The next few airdrops were helpful, but the fire outflanked the men. It was now a case of dropping back, redirecting the crews, and being sure to hold each flank.

It wasn't an easy thing to rustle up crews on this Saturday afternoon in the middle of the hunting season. Loggers were caught working in their gardens, painting their garages, doing the family shopping and dozens of other weekend chores. A number out hunting were not aware of the fire until they came home at night. Many crews came from State conservation camps. These are prison inmates placed in the camps to rehabilitate themselves and forest areas.

Camp for 500

Loggers had to find truckdrivers to haul in tractors. Drivers had to be found for these "dozers" and taken to the fire.

All this required time, and time was precious. Carefully arranged plans made months in advance paid off.

A camp must be set up and back-of-the-line forces made ready to support the men on the fireline. Perishables were added to the food caches, assembled tools were placed onto trucks and dispatched to the fire. A camp was set up at an old cabin in a clearing on the west side of the fire. This was out of the timber where the camp could be protected from the fire if it got away on that side. The camp boss got preparations underway to feed and sleep 500 men. He must be ready before the crews came in from the line at dark. Even the timekeepers were on their way to camp to start setting up time slips and checking men in and out. Many men were doing dozens of jobs in many locations to support firefighters both on the ground and in the air.

Back at the fire things weren't going

(left) The night's firefighting strategy is mapped out by the Plans Chief. (right) Helicopter scouts the fire and transports firefighters.

so well. On the north and east sides it was burning hot, and smoke was blowing low. The west side was easiest to get to, and some progress was being made there. However, the fire had crossed the main road and spotted to the top of the rim, three-fourths of a mile ahead.

Airdrops were successful on the west side in the sagebrush flats, and this tended to "push" in that side.

However, once the fire was on top of the rim it spread very rapidly and soon burned across a powerline. This cut off the power in Susanville and much of the surrounding country at 3:39 p.m. Now local people who hadn't heard about the fire knew something was wrong. The important Black Mountain Experimental Forest was less than a mile to the northeast and real fear arose that the fire would get into it. This could mean loss of valuable study plots. A fire could destroy research findings in the making for years. Fire must be kept out of this experimental forest at all costs.

Air Tanker Aid

From 3 until 7 p.m., it was a hectic struggle on the northeast side. It would seem the crews were going to hold their line. Then a gust of wind would come and drive them back. Air tankers were making drops to knock down hotspots and help the ground crews. Bulldozers were busy widening lines, and crews were firing material inside the line to get the ground cover "burned out"—before a "run" got started farther inside. Everyone gave it all they had in this struggle. By night it seemed the crews might win.

The plans chief was making plans to complete the line and to strengthen it during the night. Crews and machines must be made ready for the wind that could be expected the next day. Orders went out to get a line as close to the fire as possible, around the perimeter, making sure all material was "burned out" inside the line. This would require more railroad flares and firing torches to do the burning during the night.

Some new crews came in about dark.

A flareup on the east side of the Cabin fire.

They were fresh, and after a good meal were ready for the night shift. Other crews had to continue through the night despite the fact they had started work during the afternoon. It was not possible to man all the line and do the other jobs that must be done that night with fresh men. This sometimes happens on the first day on fires when men have to work extra long hours until enough help arrives. By 2 a.m., the 15-mile perimeter had been circled with a fireline and the fire was at least "contained."

Shortly after daybreak I made a helicopter reconnaissance with Nichols, to see how the "battle" had gone during the night. Reports from men coming off the line were good.

As we flew above the treetops, we inspected conditions on the ground through intermittent smoke. Wherever we could see there was a good "line" and men were hard at work.

They had a "black" line and had done a good job in using fire to fight fire.

This was most encouraging. The night crews had done the gigantic job assigned to them. How well it was done would be proven by whether or not the fire held through the day. Men were astir all along the line. Things must be well set to meet the predicted high wind at noon.

By 8 a.m. Sunday morning there were more than 600 men on the fire, 16 bulldozers, and 20 ground tankers. A temporary lookout was posted on a hill to the north to watch for sleeper spots from any brands that might have been blown ahead on Saturday and were yet to flare up. In fact, several fast-spreading spots were found on Saturday and some on Sunday. Crews were assigned especially to this spot fire search job. Smoke blowing close to the ground made the job a particularly difficult one.

It was a tough, hard job all day for the crews strung out along the line. Roads were built to get tankers and their precious water close for the mopup work. One flareup occurred on the east side. Three air tanker drops held it in check. A new 250-man camp was established near the northernmost point of the fire. The Weather Bureau meteorologist had set up his portable office-camper at the experimental forest and gave hourly reports over the air on local wind direction and speed, temperature, and humidity.

Part of the 4,000 acres of California pine forest destroyed in a single fire that was caused by some unknown person's carelessness.

He studied the general area forecast carefully and gave Nichols detailed information on what wind, humidity, and temperature conditions we could expect around the fire for the balance of the day and for the following day.

The strongest effort Sunday was put on the east side since the forecast was for another west wind. On the third day when the wind shifted and came from the east, firefighters were shifted and concentrated on the west side.

The mopup work continued for several days. Crews were gradually reduced as the work became more routine and hours of work became shorter. It was the time then for me to move on and perhaps get in on another fire battle someplace else.

The only live fire was now far inside the perimeter. Because of the heavy timber in the fire area, there was often deep fire in trees or logs. It was not until October 10 that the mopup was completed. Even then, occasional patrols continued for a whole month longer.

When the fire was all "over" it was hard to believe that one man failing to put out his "little" warming fire could be the cause of all of this trouble. Blood, sweat, and grief put out by 600 men had done the job, but it all seemed such a waste. The 4,000 acres of beautiful pine forest wouldn't be replaced for a hundred years. Part of nature's wonderland and its beauty was gone. Must man always be so careless?

How Not To Get Lost

CHARLES ELLIOTT

WHEN we found him, he was a sorry sight. His clothes were in tatters, his hands bleeding. Before we reached him, we saw him fall. He lay a moment, pulled himself to his feet, staggered a few yards through the woods and fell again. When we lifted him off the ground, he tried to break away and run, like an animal from the wilds.

Somewhere he had thrown down his rifle, so after we got him out, we went back to find the gun. His tracks showed that for 2 days he had circled in the forest, within 200 or 300 yards of the road. His senses were so dulled by fear and exhaustion that he did not hear the cars going by or see the lights at night. We found him just in time.

This man, like countless others before him, had simply panicked when he realized he was lost. What had been a near disaster might have turned out as only a pleasant adventure, had he taken a few precautions before he stepped out of the highway or off a known trail.

The better the woodsman, the more likely he is to make plans NOT to get lost, especially if he is going into country new to him. There are certain basic steps that he will take to bring him safely out of the woods or bush, even before he makes his first boot track there.

The best source I know for boning up on any region in advance of a trip is a map. Few areas on our continent have not been mapped with a reasonable accuracy. Topographic or aerial survey sheets may be obtained from the U.S. Coast and Geodetic Survey or from the State or province in which one plans to

ψ   ψ   ψ

Charles Elliott is the *Southern Field Editor* for *Outdoor Life* magazine. He lives on Flat Rock Trail in Covington, Ga.

go hunting, hiking, fishing, or exploring.

The features that I study longest on my map are the manmade boundaries. Every place upon earth has boundaries of one kind or another. These may consist of the roads, railroads, fences, trails, and pipe or power line rights-of-way in the backyard of civilization—or of the lakes and streams, the mountain ridges or ranges, and the swamps in the far wilderness. I will have the features firmly fixed in my mind before I go into the woods and will know where and how they are located with relation to both my starting point and where I plan to hunt, hike, or fish.

Let's see how it works. I am hunting north of camp and west of a river that flows by the camp. No matter how many turns and twists and circles I make on the trail of a deer or elk, if I am hunting, or in trying to find a certain scene, if I am on a photography mission, I am still on the same side of the river and north of camp. No matter how turned around I may get, when I am ready to go back to my quarters, it involves the simple matter of going generally east to the river and following it south to camp.

The same principle works with a logging road, trail, lakeshore, or ridgetop.

Regardless of the weather, forecast or anticipated, I always carry a compass in the woods. And if the country is vast and wild and new to me, you'll find a spare compass in my packsack or my pocket. I use a compass frequently, too, when the sky is overcast or worse.

Whatever sense of direction that a man may claim, it's still largely a question of observation. Both consciously and subconsciously, a woodsman keeps an eye on his surroundings. So he remembers the peculiar formation of a mountain, the direction water flows through a swamp, and many little features about every trail he travels—how a tree leans across it, an uprooted stump, a rockslide. He remembers the way the ridges run, the general direction of the streams. With these in mind, he may be turned around many times, but he is seldom lost.

There are exceptions, of course, and upon occasion a man does get involved with the elements or in some unusual situation that puts him into the "lost" column. A rainstorm or sudden blizzard may catch him without a compass in his pocket. Darkness may find him in rugged terrain, where travel is uncertain or hazardous without a light.

When this happens, the normal first reaction is the dread of embarrassment as a result of his poor woodsmanship or concern for the worries or the inconvenience that he will cause his companions when he doesn't show up. If he is inexperienced, this false pride may lead him to keep on the move in a misguided effort to locate the camp against all odds, and with the possibility that he will walk in circles or in the wrong direction and eventually beat himself out physically and mentally.

If he is an old hand at the business of woodsmanship and his companions are experienced, he eliminated a part of this worry before he left camp. He either told his campmates where he would be or showed them on the map and explained approximately what route he would take into and out of the area. On the other hand, if he is not in by night, they won't try to track or find him in the darkness.

The next day they will give him a reasonable number of hours to show up and then know about where to look.

I have spent many such nights in the woods, when I considered it unwise to find my way home in the darkness or in a storm. Some of the nights were in unfamiliar territory, and I didn't have the slightest idea exactly where I was— only my general location—so that at the moment I was as "lost" as the friend we had found stumbling through the woods.

Under these conditions, I always stop before that time of evening the mountainmen call "big dark." There is light enough to gather wood, and I stack up about four times as much as I think I'll need. A night fire is far hungrier than you think, and those snags and limbs are easier to find in the daylight. I rake back all leaves, needles, and debris in a big circle to save the possibility of a forest fire. If a storm is brewing, I cut boughs and build myself a crude shelter.

The sight, sound, and feel of a fire lifts a man's spirits and helps to give his misadventure an aura of stimulation. He feels on top of the situation.

At daylight the next morning, two courses of action are open to me. If I am reasonably sure of my location and direction and that I can get back to camp or to my starting point, I put out my fire—down to the last wisp of smoke. Then I move, blazing a trail which even a city slicker could follow. Occasionally I may leave a note, stuck in a split stick or on a limb about head high, where it can be seen for a long way through the woods. Anyone looking for me in that country cannot fail to find my trail.

If I am not certain of my location or directions, you couldn't budge me with a team of mules. I keep my fire going and, from time to time, put on green boughs or some damp leaves to send up a column of smoke. If I stay in one place, I will be much easier to locate.

The Idaho Department of Game and Fish has recently issued a pamphlet on getting lost. Included in the recommendations on "What To Do Before You Start Out" are the following suggestions:

* Have plenty of dry matches, waxed or in a waterproof box.
* Be sure you have a compass, one that is reliable and that you can trust.
* Carry a map of your locality, even if it is only a sketch map.
* Discuss your plans with other members of your party. Do not change these plans when you are alone.
* Learn how to start a fire. A piece of candle inside your pack is always dry and makes an excellent fire starter.
* Watch where you are going. Do not hunt or wander aimlessly. Have a plan —and stick to it. Be doubly careful in stormy weather.
* Any hunter who is inexperienced should never be out alone.
* Be careful when crossing ridges. The slope on the other side may be in an entirely different watershed.
* Always try to get back to camp well before it gets dark.

But If You Do Get Lost

KENNETH M. COLE, JR.

IF YOU GET LOST, with just a little knowledge you can turn what some people call a hardship into an enjoyable stay away from the woes of modern society. Many a high-pressured business-man would willingly get himself lost in the outdoors for several days if he only knew how enjoyable it can be with a minimum of know-how.

When you get lost all you need to do is to "Lean On Survival Training," and in this chapter I will attempt to give you some of that training.

I will deal with five major subjects, all of them beginning with the letter "S".

The first is SAFETY.

Yes, safety. But this is not safety from wild animals or from the enemy if you are in the military. The No. 1 danger in the woods when you are lost is YOU.

Probably 3 out of every 10 people who have enjoyed the outdoors have been lost for at least a few minutes.

When you think you are lost, sit down on a log or a rock or lean against a tree and recite something that you have memo-

❦ ❦ ❦

Kenneth M. Cole, Jr., is *Director* of Schiff Volunteer Training at the National Professional Training Center, Boy Scouts of America, in Mendham, N.J.

REFLECTOR-TYPE FIRE

Uprooted tree

Ledge overhang is better

and you may even spot a highway or a railroad from this vantage point.

Nowadays, the first way someone will look for you is by air. In a swamp or in dense growth you are very hard to spot.

The second S stands for SIGNALS.

Any time that you go into the woods, somebody should know where you are going, and when you expect to return. Then, when someone comes looking, you should be able to signal to them.

The best way that you can signal in the daytime nowadays is with a good smoky fire. In most of our country either a fire tower or airplane will quickly spot the smoke. A fire warden will come to your rescue. At night, a bright fire will bring help if someone knows you are lost.

ONE-TREE LEAN-TO

Small conifer.

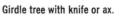

Girdle tree with knife or ax.

rized so as to bring your mind to a point where you have it under control.

Don't run wildly helter-skelter! If you must move, don't follow streams unless you know the stream, and in that case you are not lost. Streams normally flow through swampland before they reach a lake or a river. Though there are more edible plants per square inch in a swamp, there may also be quicksand, poisonous snakes, and other hazards.

If you must walk, walk uphill. At the top of most hills and mountains are trails leading back to civilization. If there are no trails, you are much easier to find above the timberline or on top of a hill,

Grab lower branches and pull over. Cut some of the lower branches and throw them on top.

DOUBLE TRENCH FIRE

In the old days whenever you got lost, you could fire your weapon three times. Today lots of hunters fire a half dozen shots without hitting game. However, if you save your shots until after dark and fire one shot, then wait for a half hour or so and fire another, in less time than it takes to get your third shot off a game warden or the ranger should be there to show you the way out of the woods.

90

The third S will stand for SHELTER:

In summer or winter when you are lost the elements are your worst enemy. The human body cannot stand long periods of heat or cold and it never can take a great deal of moisture.

So to protect yourself against the elements requires different things in different areas during different times of the year.

You have to protect yourself from the heat of the sun on the plains or the desert. And you must slow down the rate that the sun is evaporating your body moisture. Keep your clothes on and keep your head covered. Try to find shade or try to make shade. Make sure that you have prepared a way of signaling, then stay out of the sun and lie still to conserve your energy and water content. If you must travel, do it during the early morning and in the late afternoon.

In other places or at night, you must protect yourself against the cold. Then a fire becomes one of the simplest forms of shelter. And once you have a fire going you have company. It's much more reassuring to sit with a fire in the woods, especially at night, than it is to stay all alone in the dark. A fire can also serve for a signal, as I have mentioned before.

If you use the fire with a reflector such as a cliff, large rock, or the root cluster of an uprooted tree, you must sit between the fire and the reflector. An overhanging rock is even better. If there are no objects which can be used for a reflector, you need two fires and then you sit or lie between them. Even after the fires go out, the coals will warm you.

In the fall during dry weather you can kick a large pile of leaves together and burrow in to spend the night. Always remember that you need more protection under you than over you.

The fourth S is SUBSISTENCE, or food obtained from the wilds.

You should know the edible plants in your region.

Information about these can be obtained from your local 4–H representative, your State university, or your State department of agriculture.

The fifth S is SOCKS, dry socks.

This is one few people ever guess. If your feet get wet and it is cold weather, you are done for if you don't dry them quickly. In the summer, wet feet may result in chills and fever or worse.

Minnesotans Plant Trees

CLARENCE PROUT

SERVICE clubs, churches, and other organizations in northern Minnesota know that money does grow on trees. They have found that the green of forest planting furnishes the green to assist in financing their organization projects.

This work was done under contracts made with Minnesota's State Division of Forestry, which has responsibility for 54 State forests with close to 3 million acres of State land within their boundaries.

The planting of trees with the primary objective to restore barren areas to green forests has many important side benefits besides the growing of forest products.

The reforestation program has helped to reestablish game habitat, to stop threat-

Clarence Prout retired in 1965 after 40 years of forestry work in his native Minnesota. He was Commissioner of Conservation in 1961 and Director of Forestry in 1948 and 1963.

ened soil erosion, and also to beautify the countryside. Up to 275,000 trees were planted during one weekend.

Noncontract tree planting is carried on by many other organizations in Minnesota, serving without pay. They include Girl Scouts, Boy Scouts, service clubs, the Camp Fire Girls, 4–H Clubs, Future Farmers of America groups, and a number of sportsmen's clubs.

The Minneapolis Women's Chapter of the Izaak Walton League has sponsored a tree-planting program on the Sand Dunes State Forest, which is just north of the Twin Cities.

The Sand Dunes State Forest before those plantings was a vast sea of shifting sand with large blowouts scattered across the area. (These "blowouts" are holes or depressions on the sand dunes caused by the wind blowing the sand away in a whirlwind fashion.) This forest is now stabilized as a result of pine plantings by volunteers and is a prime area for campers, swimmers, and bird watchers.

The Scout groups generally make their planting projects a camping trip on a weekend. Excellent camping facilities are available on the Sand Dunes State Forest.

Each year as these participating groups return for the annual planting program they see the results of their past efforts. Trees are growing everywhere; the sand dunes have been stabilized; deer, grouse, and other animals have returned.

The pride of the tree planter is hard to describe when he returns with his group each year and surveys the results of past years of growth. He assumes a proprietary interest in the forest, pointing out to newcomers and the neighbors what he and his friends have helped to accomplish in the field of fruitful conservation.

The success of all of these organized efforts is the result of careful planning and the educational program of the forestry fieldman. This entails meeting with all the leaders and members of the various groups being invited to help. It takes field trips, demonstrations, and patient efforts to start up the program.

The program can become a flop if the job is not planned to the smallest detail. The area to be planted must be ready to receive trees. The planter's training must be thorough and clear. Timing must be carefully arranged so that the trees and the planters are at the right place on time.

In the contract tree planting, churches were the first organizations contacted.

The churches of Tower, Soudan, and Ely, Minn., were asked to help in reforestation of the Burntside State Forest, which is located midway between and north of the towns. This forest was being cut over to harvest the old growth pulp species of jack pines, aspen, and black spruce. Topography of the area is rough, rocky, and semi-isolated.

The problem was presented to officers from the churches of each community.

After discussions with authorities in the Minnesota Department of Administration, a contract form was developed and given an OK by the State attorney general.

The contract provides that the contractor hire, transport, supervise, and pay the labor. In the case of church groups, all moneys are given to the church as the contractor. Contracting groups agree to accept all responsibility for care of the trees after they are delivered, inspect all planting sites before signing the agreement, and plant all the plantable area as defined by the forest officer in charge.

Results were excellent. The churches all lived up to their contracts. Planting survival was above average, and cost of reforestation was well within the average. The church groups planted 215,000 trees on the Burntside State Forest in 1965 and 229,000 in 1966.

All site preparation was done by the State—land clearing, burning debris, and marking the sites. Tree distribution was the responsibility of the forest officer.

All of these reforestation programs, whether by private enterprise or by an agency of the State or the Federal Governments, have added to the beautification of Minnesota. This is particularly true of the restoration of old burns to green forests and the planting of lands cleared for agricultural purposes—lands which should not have been denuded of natural vegetation because the soil was not suited to growing domestic crops.

Hundreds of miles of highways and trails have again become tree lined and pleasing to the eyes of the traveler.

White Water Float Trip

JOHN M. HERBERT

SPRAYED by clear, cool water you wonder if the bow of the rubber raft will rise enough to clear the churning rapids still ahead. It does, though the raft buckles sharply when it hits the bottom of a trough. The boatman skillfully guides it into a black water chute to miss protruding boulders. This is one of the thrills of floating the Middle Fork of the Salmon River in central Idaho.

The Middle Fork—some 110 miles in length—is a famous white water stream. During the first 40 miles, it drops 60 feet to the mile—and the rest of the way 16 feet per mile. It flows through one of the deeper canyons in the West within the Idaho Primitive Area situated in the Boise, Challis, Payette, and Salmon National Forests. There are 11 major rapids plus many other stretches of white water which present no special problems. There are no roads along the banks, and no signs of civilization—with the exception of a few landing strips, isolated homesteads, and an occasional pack stock trail bridge or a fireguard station.

A majority of persons who float the Middle Fork (motorboats are banned) arrange for an outfitter to provide everything except sleeping bags and clothing. You can run the entire river by putting the rubber boat in at Bear Valley, accessible through a gravel road from Stanley,

❦ ❦ ❦

John M. Herbert is *Assistant Regional Forester* in charge of recreation and lands activities for the Intermountain Region of the Forest Service with headquarters in Ogden, Utah.

Bow sweep comes clear out of water as you rock your way down the Middle Fork.

YMCA boys from San Rafael, Calif., "running" Salmon Falls on a float trip by rubber raft down the Salmon River in the Payette National Forest, Idaho.

or start out from one of the landing strips lower down. In the latter case, the outfitter will fly you, the collapsible boats, food, and gear over the 9,000-foot ridges to one of the landing strips 5,000 feet below. Such a flight is a thrill in itself as the narrowness of the canyon gives one the feeling of being able to reach out and touch the sheer walls. A third means of reaching the river is by horse, thus combining a pack and float trip.

Your rubber boat will normally be the four-man size capable of hauling three passengers plus the oarsman and gear. Some are equipped with "sweeps"—large oars mounted on the bow and the stern which, when propelled by skillful and strong arms, serve to keep you off of the rocks and upright through the falls. Others are guided by oars in the conventional position. A 30-inch canvas shield on the forward half helps to keep you and all of the equipment dry.

With just the exception of Dagger Falls near the headwaters, all the others can be negotiated without unloading. The sheer drop—25 feet in 50 yards—over two ledges requires use of a long rope to

get the rubber boats over Dagger Falls.

Each of the rapids presents a special navigation problem, and the strategy followed varies with the depth of water. In July, normally the best month to run the river, many ledges and boulders are covered which in August are exposed or just under the surface. A difference of a few inches of water creates new hazards. That is why your boatman will tie up at the head of major rapids and walk along the shore to study the depth, currents, and position of underwater boulders.

During maximum high water—usually in June—the river rises 6 or 7 feet, and it can be dangerous. The torrent which pours through the narrows and the rapids throws up rollbacks which can flip or swamp a boat. Several lives have been lost during this high water, and prudent people avoid the Middle Fork then.

The river falls 8 to 10 feet in a distance of 50 yards in a typical rapids. Usually there are sharp rocks or ledges to be avoided. The oarsman will guide your boat into the slick at just the right place, and you will feel the acceleration before the bow hits the bottom of the trough.

There is a thrilling moment when the impact jolts you and makes you wonder if the nose will come up. For an instant there is daylight under both ends as the boat slithers over the rollback. Again it crashes to the bottom of the trough, sending water spraying in all directions.

For periods of an hour or more, you float along on placid water about as fast as a person walks. This is when you can enjoy the beauty of the canyon walls, the vegetation, fishing, and bird and animal life. Mountain sheep as well as deer are seen by most river travelers. Fishing for cutthroat and rainbow trout in the many deep holes is a major attraction.

You will make camp on a sandbar in the shade of a ponderosa pine or patch of aspen and have time to swim and hike or explore one of several caves inhabited by the Sheepeater Indians years ago.

A trip on the Middle Fork is a once-in-a-lifetime experience.

You can obtain a brochure telling about the Middle Fork and how to arrange for a float trip by writing the Regional Forester, U.S. Forest Service, Federal Office Building, Ogden, Utah 84401.

Wood for the Campfire and the Fireplace

WALTON R. SMITH

THERE'S not a better feeling in the outdoors than to have camp made and be sitting in front of your fire, ready to cook an evening meal while the red sky in the West gives way to a myriad of windows from heaven.

And indoors there's no feeling of well-being like a brisk blaze in your fireplace at home during the first chill evenings of fall. I even enjoy a good fire on summer evenings in my cabin in the Smokies.

Wood is our universal fuel for fireplaces, stoves, and campfires. It is readily available in most parts of the world, it is clean and easy to handle, and it is relatively inexpensive. A little knowledge about the best kinds of wood to use, how to lay and start a fire, how to make the fire last for a long time, and how to handle it safely will help you enjoy your outing or get the most out of your fireplace back home.

The conifers—pines, cedar, spruce, fir, hemlock, and other trees with needlelike leaves—contain a pitch or resins. These trees have wood which burns vigorously when dry, but the resins or pitch give off a dense smoke. They are good for starting fires and some give off much heat, but they will black up cooking pans, soot chimneys, and clog stovepipes. Nevertheless, these are widely used and are just about the only type which is available in some parts of the country.

The broadleaf trees commonly called hardwoods—the oaks, the maple, birch, beech, hickory, gum, poplar, cottonwood, and many others—do not contain resin and do not give off as much smoke. However, they include very light woods like cottonwood and buckeye and very heavy woods like oak and hickory, and there is a great difference in the way that they

Walton R. Smith is *Assistant Director* of the Southeastern Forest Experiment Station, U.S. Forest Service, Asheville, N.C.

burn, the heat they give off, and the amount of ash that they leave. They have other characteristics, too, which make them desirable or undesirable, such as quick burning, a tendency to throw sparks, or difficulty in igniting them.

Generally speaking, a ton of coal gives you around as much heat as 1 cord of heavy wood, 1½ cords of mediumweight wood, or 2 cords of lightweight wood.

Let's attempt to give you a little table (opposite page) that may help in selecting your firewood from the more common species. My ratings may differ from yours because I don't care too much for fires that pop sparks or blacken pans.

Starting a Fire

Now that we have a picture of many different woods available to us, let's look at the task of laying and starting the fire, whether it be indoors or outdoors. A good fire builder recognizes that he must have tinder, kindling, and fuel, and then fire building becomes easy.

Tinder can be paper if you're home, but in the outdoors one looks for the dry, dead twigs on the lower part of the trees, dry cedar bark, birchbark even when it's damp, or if none of these are available, shavings from the inside of a dry split log. Dead pine needles, leaves, and dry grass can be used for tinder if it hasn't rained recently. Rule 1—be sure and have a good hatful of tinder.

Kindling is pencil-sized dead twigs broken from standing trees (usually you will find lower limbs are dead or have dead twigs), dry bark from logs on the ground, pine cones, and the other woody material that breaks rather than bends. The Boy Scout rule is "if you can't snap it, scrap it." Rule 2—you should have a good sized hatful of kindling.

Fuelwood will range in size from as big as your finger to a log 8 to 10 inches in diameter. Seldom will you use logs larger than this except in a very large fireplace or where you have set up camp for several days and want to keep a fire continuously. Be sure your fuelwood includes plenty of small pieces and plenty of dry material or you may find the fire

The hunter's fire is a camper's favorite.

is hard to maintain for cooking or for warmth. Rule 3—if you think you need three armfuls of wood for the night, get six or prepare to stumble around in the dark looking for some more.

When your material is assembled, lay your fire by piling your tinder in a close pile about the size of your hat. Then crisscross your smallest and driest kindling over the tinder. Then, with your back to the wind, light the tinder, and the wind will quickly spread the flames throughout the pile. If there is no wind, fan the fire with your hat. Add the rest of the kindling, and when the fire is roaring, add fuelwood to it as needed.

If you plan to use the fire for cooking, there are a number of styles that you can copy from the woodsman. I like the trapper's fire in which two fairly large logs about 4 feet long are laid on each side of the fire, 8 to 12 inches apart toward the wind and 4 to 6 inches apart at the throat. It helps if you will flatten the top of the logs with your ax. Then your pans and pots can rest on the logs,

---

DON'T BEND THE ANDIRONS

One word of caution about the fireplace. Many beautiful andirons have been burned up because red hot coals have accumulated up and around the andirons. This permits them to get hot as in a blacksmith's furnace, and the weight of the firewood then bends them out of shape.

Always keep enough coals cleared out under the andirons so that a continuous flow of air feeds the fire and keeps the heat going up the chimney.

---

and you have a long narrow controlled fire that is easy to fuel and easy to cook on.

Some like the lazyman or star fire where longer logs come into the fire like spokes from a wheel. The logs are pushed in as they burn. This means less ax work, but a larger clearing for safety.

Some prefer the picturesque hunter's fire with forked sticks supporting a cross pole over the fire from which pothooks can hold the utensils any desired height above the fire. A single stick stuck into

RATINGS FOR FIREWOOD

Name of trees	Relative amount of heat	Easy to burn	Easy to split	Does it have heavy smoke?	Does it pop or throw sparks?	General rating and remarks
BROADLEAF TREES						
Ash, red oak, white oak, beech, birch, hickory, hard maple, pecan, dogwood.	High	Yes	Yes	No	No	Excellent.
Soft maple, cherry, walnut	Medium	Yes	Yes	No	No	Good.
Elm, sycamore, gum	Medium	Medium	No	Medium	No	Fair—contains too much water when green.
Aspen, basswood, cottonwood	Low	Yes	Yes	Medium	No	Fair—but good for kindling.
Chestnut, yellow-poplar	Low	Yes	Yes	Medium	Yes	Poor.
NEEDLELEAF TREES						
Southern yellow pine, Douglas-fir	High	Yes	Yes	Yes	No	Good but smoky.
Cypress, redwood	Medium	Medium	Yes	Medium	No	Fair.
White-cedar, western redcedar, eastern redcedar.	Medium	Yes	Yes	Medium	Yes	Good—excellent for kindling.
Eastern white pine, western white pine, sugar pine, ponderosa pine, true firs.	Low	Medium	Yes	Medium	No	Fair—good kindling.
Tamarack, larch	Medium	Yes	Yes	Medium	Yes	Fair.
Spruce	Low	Yes	Yes	Medium	Yes	Poor.

the ground at an angle to hold one pot over the fire is called a dingle stick.

There are many other choices including pit or trench fires to save fuel, rock fireplaces, platform fireplaces, or the reflector fires that you build in front of a tent.

If you are using your fire to cook with, remember the old woodsman's adage that flames are best for boiling, but coals are best for broiling. You can get flames by adding a pine knot, split kindling, or dry twigs. To get coals you must wait for the wood to burn down to coals, or you might add charred brands or charcoal from an old fire if available. Allow yourself a full hour from the time you start the fire until you start cooking.

If you want the fire to last a long time in a campfire or in the home fireplace, you can accomplish this by packing round logs rather tightly over the fire and covering partly with ashes from the fire.

Don't burn your house down or mar your vacation with carelessness. Fire is a wonderful ally, but a dangerous enemy. Your campfire should not be built until you have cleared a 10-foot circle down to mineral soil or rock. Your roaring blaze in the home fireplace should not be left alone without a good strong fire screen to prevent sparks or brands from popping or rolling into the room.

If you desire a little novelty in your fire, at home or in the woods, you can get it by using certain chemicals to give a variety of colors. Make up water solutions and soak pine cones, split sticks, or blocks of wood in the solutions, then let them dry out for a day or so. Throw one or two on the fire when you want a color display. You can get red by using strontium nitrate, purple by using lithium chloride, blue by using copper sulfate or cobalt, orange by using salt or calcium, green by using barium, and you can color it yellow by using sodium.

Blue Mountains Water
Is Liquid Gold

LeGRAND OLSON

IF YOU LIKE to get out and travel this great land of ours, the chances are that you may visit Blanding in southeastern Utah someday. I think you will like it.

Improved roads are bringing more and more vacationists every year to recreation sites on the nearby Manti-La Sal National Forest which embraces the Blue Mountains. Canyonlands National Park, Glen Canyon Dam, and Lake Powell are also in the southeast corner of Utah, and they draw visitors from all over America.

Blanding is only a way station compared with these great scenic attractions, but if you ever drive through it you will

want to feast your eyes on this small town nestled like a jewel in a setting of red sandstone and piñon pine. You may even want to stay awhile and ponder how water can be the wellspring of new life for a turn-of-the-century pioneer town.

For Blanding has just about everything that you'd want to find in a small town: Green lawns and flowers, a well-kept city park, spacious school grounds, a public

❧　❧　❧

LeGrand Olson is the *District Ranger* for the Ephraim Ranger District, Manti-La Sal National Forest, with headquarters in Ephraim, Utah.

library, and—something very important in the Southwest or anywhere else—a good supply of clear water. People here are planning for a good future.

But the picture was different a decade ago. Then you would have found water rationing, dried up lawns, and murky water—the results of a sick watershed. And people were discouraged.

They had just invested 26 years of disappointments, frustrations, and about $440,000 in a water system. They had tunneled through a mountain to divert the water from Indian Creek to Johnson Creek. Even after this, water was still scarce and highly contaminated.

However, you might understand their predicament better if we go back to 1905 when Blanding was settled.

In this part of the arid West, settlers looked to the mountains for their water supply. Here it was the Blue Mountains, about 20 miles from Blanding, within the Manti-La Sal National Forest. An upthrust in the geologic past raised these mountains to a height of 11,300 feet above sea level. Like a green oasis they supply water through several permanent streams.

One of these streams, Johnson Creek, provided the water for Blanding.

Ten miles of canal and storage ponds were needed to get the water to the town. The need was great—the canals were dug and ponds were constructed. The water thus supplied would become warm and stale, but the hardy pioneers accepted this. The water system was later improved by the installation of a pipeline which replaced the canals. The pipeline supplied needs for a few, but as the community grew it became inadequate.

The need for more water had long been recognized. Dave Black and Walter Lyman had conceived a plan of tunneling through a mountain to divert water from Indian Creek to Johnson Creek.

There were enough people in favor of the project to start the tunneling in 1922. They hoped that gold would be found, as some gold had been mined nearby. Progress on the project was slow, and work would periodically halt due to lack of funds and public support.

There were disappointments, frustrations, and final triumph when the "gold"

was found 26 years later as the tunnel was completed. The "gold" was liquid—the water of Indian Creek. And the final thrust was made possible through a loan from a State agency—the Utah Water and Power Board.

The amount of the water available was not the only problem that faced the people of Blanding. Floods in the high mountain watershed filled up the canal and pipeline with dirt and with other debris.

The source of this trouble was easy to determine. A number of the steep slopes of the Blue Mountains, in common with many of the western public ranges, had inadequate plant cover as a result of past excessive grazing. Lacking this protective mantle of vegetation the watershed could not receive and dispose of the water, but reacted just like a "tin roof." The water deposited on the ground rapidly ran off—eroding the exposed soil and carrying it off, some of it as far as the kitchen sink.

A need for further action was evident—even though Blanding already had invested in this household water system an average of about $1,500 for each of the 300 families in the community.

Work With Ranger

The initial step, taken in 1948, was to form a watershed committee. This committee's members were the mayor, city councilmen, two of the livestock users of the region, and the school superintendent. Working very closely with Forest Ranger Julian Thomas, they explored every angle.

The committee recognized the desirability of removing the livestock, but to reduce a means by which some of their people made a living was a serious matter. In the end, however, the committee requested that the Forest Service eliminate grazing use from the watershed above the pipeline intake for household water, control public camping on those areas, and rehabilitate the damaged watershed. Agreement on the program was reached in 1956, and restoration work started.

Mechanical treatment of land on steep mountainous terrain is costly. Terraces or contour trenches were designed to hold and to absorb a high intensity storm of 2 inches of moisture in 2 hours. These trenches and barren areas were reseeded to grass to hold and protect the soil. When finished, nearly $50 per acre was invested in areas treated by trenching and seeding.

But the results were impressive. Dirty water in the pipeline is now a rare occurrence. Bacteria count is way down, and streamflow holds up much longer during the dry summer months. What was formerly a sick and eroded area is developing into attractive scenic land.

Blanding community, looking forward to growth and development in the future, has supplemented its water supply with a well, a water treatment plant, and two storage reservoirs.

Today this community has delightful public park areas, spacious school grounds, and well-kept lawns and flowers. Colorful Indians are seen on the streets, and remnants of their ancient culture are being preserved. There is adequate space, and more important, water to expand and benefit from a new resource—tourism.

Remember if you do visit Blanding that what you see is the result of people working together with the Forest Service to restore their watersheds. Their work has made better living today and will benefit the generations to come.

And lovely—and vigorous—towns like Blanding are the result.

How To Select
a Christmas Tree

LESTER E. BELL

SOON IT WILL BE TIME to pick out a Christmas tree again! You are one of a vast army of people who will be selecting Christmas trees for their homes, dooryards, and businesses. Figures for recent years show that about 1⅓ million families will select metal or plastic ornaments, while 33 million or more families will have natural grown trees.

What kind of tree will it be? Of course, in most cases it will be an evergreen. What species you get will depend to a large extent on where you live. Some 25 different species are used for Christmas tree purposes. In some of our larger cities, you may be able to select from as many as seven or eight species. But if your home is a ranch in the west of Wyoming and you have to select your tree locally, you may wind up settling for a lodgepole pine. Or if you are down in the back country of the southern Appalachians, a

redcedar may be your best and only choice.

What are some things to look for in selecting a tree? First of all you want a tree that has needles of a good green color. You want a symmetrical tree—one shaped like an inverted cone with four good sides so that you can either set it in front of the picture window, in the corner or on the side of the room, wherever you please and have an attractive tree. A tree ought to add fragrance to the air at Christmastime. Branches should be pliable enough so they won't break easily, and yet not be heavy, coarse, and thick. You want a tree that holds its needles from the time you bring it into the house until you take it out. This usually is a matter of 1 to

❦   ❦   ❦

Lester E. Bell is *Professor* of Forestry and *Extension Specialist* in Forestry at the Michigan State University.

Plantation-grown Douglas-fir (above left) is a premium Christmas tree produced in the Pacific Northwest. The balsam fir (above right) was grown in Wisconsin and is a dense, compact tree that holds its needles well. Eastern white pine is at lower left. Black spruce at lower right has relatively poor needle-holding ability, but good color and fragrance.

3 weeks. The foliage should be relatively soft to the touch of youngsters, not stiff and prickly. And, of course, you want a tree you can find at local markets.

Most of the species desirable as Christmas trees have their local areas where they are best adapted or where they have grown natively, and people have become accustomed to using them. In the Pacific Northwest, the Douglas-fir reigns supreme, for it has been used traditionally as a Christmas tree there. In the Northeast—the New England States and upper New York State—the balsam fir has traditionally been one of the common trees available in local swamp areas, and it is used as a Christmas tree. Many local preferences, however, have been broken down in recent years by our better systems of transportation and marketing. Trees are shipped halfway across the Nation.

With the change in the Christmas tree industry from that of cutting wild trees or native trees to plantation growing, there have been changes in species used. Especially notable is the increase in Scotch pine. This tree is not native to the United States, but was brought here from Europe for timber growing and erosion control. But as plantation growers developed this species, it fitted itself remarkably well to our Christmas tree production.

Most Popular

Today, many Scotch pines are planted, grown, cultured, and harvested just for the Christmas tree trade. The U.S. Department of Agriculture estimates that about 27 percent of the 1964 output of Christmas trees in the United States was made up of Scotch pine. Second was the Douglas-fir with 22 percent of the total, and third was balsam fir with 12 percent. Other species commonly used made up lesser percentages of the total production.

One of the first questions prospective buyers ask is, "Where should I get my tree?" If you live in a large city or in suburbia, you may decide to go to a local Christmas tree lot established temporarily for the sale of Christmas trees during the November-December period. Or you may want to go directly to a Christmas tree farm where you will be permitted to select and cut your own tree. More and more of these places are available today, and it makes an excellent outing for the family. If you live in a smaller town, you may not have many choices.

What To Look For

Probably the first thing I look for is a tree with good, fresh, live green foliage that is soft to the touch, pliable, and yet not droopy. The second thing I look for is a tree that has good symmetry, straight stem, and good uniform taper. Since we use our tree in the living room in front of a large picture window, it has to have four good faces. I like to select a tree with a straight handle so we can put it in a Christmas tree stand and it will stay erect. I like a tree with twigs stiff enough so they can be easily decorated, yet still not sag with the weight of the decorations. And I like a full bottom whorl, as well as a uniform, well-developed upper tip. These are the main things that I look for. Of course, I usually take some of the children along and weigh heavily their desires in picking a tree for our home.

Once you've obtained a tree, here are a few additional pointers. Shake the tree well to get rid of dead needles and particles of grass and weeds before taking it into the house. For best results, make a fresh cut at the base of your tree—an angling cut at approximately a 30° to 40° angle, and then place the tree in a container of water. This is a good safeguard against the foliage drying out and becoming highly combustible.

Keep in mind that these trees are at a severe disadvantage, since they are put in heated rooms (70° to 75°) where low humidity exists (5 to 15 percent), and yet we still expect them to remain fresh, luxuriant, and green. Without water, they will become dry, brittle, brown, and combustible. A good sized and vigorous tree will use a quart or more of water daily. The water supply should be replaced each day in the container at the base of the tree.

Some folks have recommended putting chemical additives into the water to increase fire resistance, but the author has found plain tapwater is satisfactory. Season's greetings!

Water

How Our Cities
Meet Their Water Needs

HOWARD W. LULL

STAND at the top of the Newark, N.J., watershed and you can see the New York City skyline 30 miles away. Immediately downslope are 30,000 acres of municipal forest, a veritable wilderness set in the midst of the most densely populated portion of megalopolis, the 500-mile stretch of people, traffic, noise, and rooftops which runs from Washington to Boston. The Newark forest is a water forest. Water is its principal product—not its only one, but its most important.

New Haven has a 21,000-acre water forest, Hartford, a 20,000-acre one, and Boston owns the largest in the East, an 86,000-acre forest, which surrounds the Quabbin Reservoir.

All told, in the Northeast, there are around 400 municipal watersheds with far more than a million acres of forest land. The water from these watersheds serves about a third of the region's population of some 50 million.

In the West, the national forests furnish most of the water that supplies the cities and towns. Slightly more than 40 million acres of national forest land are used as municipal watersheds. More than 17 million people in almost 1,100 communities depend directly on these watersheds for all or a major part of their daily water supply. Notable are the 65,000-acre watersheds of Portland, Oreg., on the Mount Hood National Forest; the 147,000-acre watershed of Tacoma, Wash., on the Snoqualmie National Forest; and the Denver, Colo., watersheds on the Arapaho and Pike National Forests. Largest

municipally owned watershed in the West is the 66,000-acre portion of Seattle's Cedar River watershed.

The systems that connect forest watersheds to the cities' faucets furnish high-quality water—the reason for their being. Sparsely populated forests and associated wildland are stable environments, natural filters set into the water cycle between precipitation and streamflow. To a great degree, metropolitan areas have gone to the woods for their water. Very likely, water that reaches eastern faucets dripped from some forest tree on its way. In the West, chances are good that it came from a melting snowbank high in the forested Rockies, Cascades, or Sierras.

The municipal forested watersheds are special-use areas, and thus they get special treatment. John (Red) Heilman, Yale-trained forester on the Newark watershed for 30 years, puts it this way:

"Newark purchased the Pequannock watershed around 1900 simply to protect its water supply. Until the 1930's, no trees were cut unless they were dead. Even now we do little cutting. Water is our business: Average annual runoff in gross water value is worth 10 times or more the value of forest growth.

"The major objective of our management is the production of potable and palatable water that requires a minimum

    ʊ̃   ʊ̃   ʊ̃

Howard W. Lull is a *Project Leader* in watershed management research at the U.S. Forest Service Northeastern Forest Experiment Station in Upper Darby, Pa.

Water for the city—from the forest. Hogman Lake, Superior National Forest, Minn., is pictured inside the pitcher to show this forest-city relationship.

treatment. It costs the city about $7.50 per million gallons to treat the Pequannock water. Downstream along the lower reaches of the city-polluted Passaic, it costs $25 to $35, and during low flows it can cost $55."

Each municipal watershed has its own management problems. Baltimore, Md., for instance, has been purchasing land for the past 50 years around its three reservoirs and now owns about 17,000 acres. Louis G. Ningard, watershed supervisor since 1954, had for his task the cutting of all trees on the 3,100 acres inundated by Liberty Dam. Since then his job has been protection, planting, and careful harvesting of the reservoir forest. About 2,500 acres of shore-bordering open land were planted to trees. The forest was put under management. Logging is done by the wa-

tershed logging crew, and they operate their own sawmill.

But Lou Ningard considers his principal responsibility to be the maintenance of high water quality. In his words, "That's why the city bought this property, to keep the mud out of the water. All our logging is done with this in mind. Our logging roads are carefully located, and when we finish logging an area, we seed the roads and landings down."

Water supply has always been the chief focus of forest management on municipal watershed lands. Ralph C. Hawley, an early professor of forestry at Yale, in a working plan prepared in 1913 for the New Haven Water Supply Co., wrote: "The chief interest of the company is water, with forestry as a secondary consideration." The ultimate in this policy

105

was headlined in a 1954 story in *Colliers* magazine under the title "In New Hampshire Why Do Horses Wear Diapers?" The curious reader found out it was because the horses were skidding logs on a municipal watershed.

To cut or not to cut the trees on a municipal watershed is a question that has bothered many city officials, though by now the great majority of municipalities permit cutting. At one time, commercial cutting was not permitted on any of the municipally owned land within New York City's Croton watershed. As a result, pine plantations became exceedingly dense and developed evidence of stagnation and insect injury. Also, a no-cutting policy can sometimes reduce the yield of water.

Under longtime protection from cutting and fire, evapotranspiration (movement of water vapor from soil and trees to the atmosphere) will tend to increase, as Prof. Arthur Eschner, of the New York State University College of Forestry, showed in a 1965 study conducted in the Adirondacks—and water runoff will be reduced.

Controversy in the Seattle's City Council as to whether a large stand of commercially valuable timber on its watershed should be cut or not led in 1943 to appointment of a three-man study commission. The commission concluded that, in view of the extremely well-drained soil and natural storage capacity, there was little danger of erosion or excessive runoff from selective cutting. Also, they noted that revenue from logging would probably be substantial and could pay a large part of the administrative costs of the water department.

This problem is worldwide. A 1959–60 parliamentary inquiry in Victoria, Australia, as to the timber utilization on municipal watershed areas, concluded that controlled logging could be permitted under strict supervision.

The principal objection to the logging of municipal areas is the possibility that it would muddy the water. Research has demonstrated, however, that with care the watershed trees may be harvested without damaging water quality.

Waynesville, N.C., has profited by this finding. In 1948, with the help of the Tennessee Valley Authority and the State foresters, the town developed a timber management program for its 8,200-acre municipal watershed, and it has since grossed around $275,000 from timber harvesting. Under close supervision, loggers built 65 miles of road on the watershed without damaging effects. Water quality is as good as ever.

Manchester, N.H., has a forest management program on some 8,000 acres of its watershed land aimed at developing both high-quality timber and high-quality water. About 2 million trees have been planted and around 5 million board-feet of lumber have been processed at the city-owned sawmill.

Every scrap of wood is utilized down to the chips and sawdust. Timber and water management can be a good city business, when handled right.

Forest Service research during the past 20 years has also provided considerable evidence that cutting of small forested watersheds may increase the water yield. Clear-cutting of watersheds in West Virginia and North Carolina have produced maximum annual increases of 12 to 16 inches or 326,000 to 434,000 gallons per acre. In partial cuttings the increases were smaller and in proportion to the amount of timber cut. Under a sustained yield program of even-aged forest management, substantial increase may be secured from harvesting mature timber.

Snow is the key to municipal supplies in much of the West. Snow surveys at more than 1,000 snow courses permit accurate forecasts of municipal and irrigation water. Coordination of annual measurements is the responsibility of the U.S. Soil Conservation Service, a job that involves 19 State agencies, 80 private and quasi-public agencies, 11 different Federal agencies, and 20 municipalities.

U.S. Forest Service research has also discovered possibilities for increasing the water yield by manipulating forest cover in some of the snow zones of the West. In Colorado, for instance, cutting strips in a mature stand of pine, spruce, and fir has increased annual water yield from the snowpack zone on an average of 3 inches every year.

Soil Conservation Service snow surveyors at Ward Creek in California.

In California's snow zone forest, storage of the winter snow can be maximized by cutting a succession of east-west strips proceeding to the south. A wall of mature trees to the south creates maximum shade, and younger trees to the north minimize radiation of heat to the snowpack from the trees. Strip-cutting red fir has given an average annual maximum snow water content of 58 inches on April 1 compared to some 47 inches in the uncut forest. Progressive strip-cutting, as described above, would provide an additional 3 inches of water from this forest area.

Other Techniques

Cities may augment their water supplies by other means, including better use and re-use of the supplies they have. Reduction of water wastage in New York City from water mains and in unmetered domestic use would save 20 to 40 percent of total apparent consumption in that city. And in the metropolitan area of southern California perhaps 25 percent of the water used can be reclaimed at a moderate cost for both industrial and agricultural uses.

The coastal cities may satisfy their increasing water needs with desalinization plants. Currently there are plants in operation which can supply a million gallons a day of desalted water at a production cost of around $1 per thousand gallons (most of us pay between 25 and 40 cents per thousand gallons for water delivered to our faucets). By 1970–75, we may be able to construct plants that will supply 150 million gallons of water a day at a cost of 25 cents per thousand gallons. This excludes pumping, distribution, and storage charges which can total 20 cents per thousand gallons, a necessary cost because all the points are uphill from the sea-level plants.

There may be cheaper methods for augmenting the city water supplies. For instance, if desalted water could be produced and delivered for as little as 50 cents per thousand gallons, it would still probably be cheaper to obtain fresh water from a supply as far as 600 miles away.

"In other words," according to Abel Wolman, a leading authority on water

supply, "it would be much cheaper for New York City to pipe water 270 miles from the St. Lawrence River, assuming that Canada gave consent, than to build a desalinization plant at the edge of town." Mr. Wolman has a point.

Long-distance transport of water already supplies water to major segments of our population. Water supply systems of New York City, Los Angeles, San Francisco, and Denver are examples.

Los Angeles and around 50 southern California cities draw water from 2 distant sources: Owens Valley 340 miles to the north, and the Colorado River 240 miles to the east. And an even more distant source is in the process of being tapped, the Sacramento River 440 miles to the northwest. New York City has an aqueduct that taps reservoirs in the upper Delaware River 120 miles away. By transmountain diversions, Denver receives water from the upper elevations of the Arapaho National Forest.

San Francisco brings water 155 miles by aqueduct from the Yosemite National Park and Stanislaus National Forest. And there are now proposals to move water from the Snake River southward 800 miles to Lake Mead for distribution in the arid Southwest. In the main, these projects reach toward forested headwaters to supply the needs of the cities.

For further reading:
Anderson, H. W., *Managing California's Snow Zone Lands for Water*. Forest Service Research Paper PSW–6, Pacific Southwestern Forest Experiment Station, Berkeley, Calif., 1963.
Hewlett, John D., and Hibbert, Alden R., "Increases in Water Yield After Several Different Types of Forest Cutting." *International Association of Scientific Hydrology*, Vol. 6, 1961.
National Association of Manufacturers, *Water in Industry*. National Association of Manufacturers, New York, 1965.
Reinhart, K. G., Eschner, A. R., and Trimble, G. R., Jr., *Effect on Streamflow of Four Forest Practices in the Mountains of West Virginia*. Forest Service Research Paper NE–1, Northeastern Forest Experiment Station, Upper Darby, Pa., 1963.
Sherwani, Jabbar K., *Urban and Industrial Water Supply: Prospects and Possibilities*. American Water Resources Association, Urbana, Ill., 1965.
Water: Development, Utilization, Conservation, Roma K. McNickle, editor. Western Resources Papers, Univ. of Colorado Press, 1963.

This source in the Pisgah National Forest, N.C., helps supply Savannah, Ga., with water.

Small Watersheds Make a Big Splash

RALPH C. WILSON

TOURISTS, stay away at your own risk! Residents of the Ozarks foothills have swapped damaging floodwaters for a large fishing lake, a State park, and a topnotch waterfowl refuge. And they have beautified the lakeshore with dogwood and redbud plantings.

Who is benefiting from this fine swap? Well, tourists like you and me certainly are. But the folks from the Flat Creek watershed in northeastern Arkansas are reaping major benefits, too.

In any case, this is a prime example of how the recreation developments in small watershed projects are helping to meet the ever-rising demand for more public water-related recreation in our Nation.

Economic Gains, Too

Today, in the Flat Creek watershed, the tourists and residents alike enjoy boating, swimming, fishing, camping, picnicking, and a variety of other activities. Besides all this water-based fun, there are some solid economic returns. What's more, migratory ducks and geese by the thousands have a first-class stopping place.

But let me start at the beginning of a success story which really holds water.

The problem in the Flat Creek region of Lawrence County in the low, rolling foothills of the Ozark Mountains was "too much or too little."

Farmers had too much water. Flooding usually occurred about four times each year, damaging the crops, buildings, and roads and interrupting travel for school buses, mail and milk routes. Gullied lands in the upland section of the watershed contributed to the flood problem by filling the drainageways with sediment. Average annual losses amounted to about $60,000.

Yet nearby was the Arkansas Game and Fish Commission's 1,000-acre Shirey Bay-Rainey Brake Wildlife Refuge that often needed extra water to accommodate the more than 15,000 ducks and geese that stop over there daily during their migrations. These bottom and hardwood lands are ideal resting and feeding grounds for migratory waterfowl. But during years of low rainfall in late summer and early fall—a frequent thing—the area is dry.

A solution to this problem would be to get the water off the farmers' fields and store it until needed for the wildlife refuge. So the landowners—through the Lawrence County Soil Conservation District—and the Arkansas Game and Fish Commission teamed up as cosponsors of the Flat Creek watershed project under the Watershed Protection and Flood Prevention Act (Public Law 566). This is known as the Small Watershed Act.

Exit flood damages! Enter recreational opportunities unlimited!

In addition to a very intensive program of land treatment measures, particularly on the gullied lands, the watershed work plan included six reservoirs. One of these

Ralph C. Wilson is a *Recreation Specialist* in the Watershed Planning Division of the Soil Conservation Service.

reservoirs, around 15 minutes from the town of Walnut Ridge, is 645-acre Lake Charles, a multipurpose structure planned for both flood prevention and recreation.

Named after Charles C. Snapp, Walnut Ridge businessman and a former member of the game and fish commission who was instrumental in promoting and initiating the project, Lake Charles is rapidly becoming one of the most popular recreational spots in northeastern Arkansas.

Besides serving as a storage tank for the water to be released into the wildlife refuge, the lake is the focal point around which the Lake Charles State Park is now being developed. This was one of the first projects that took advantage of an amendment to the Small Watershed Act by Congress in 1962 which allows the Government to supply its technical and financial support to watershed project sponsors in developing public recreation facilities. Under the 1962 amendment, the U.S. Department of Agriculture—through the Soil Conservation Service—was able to pay up to 50 percent of the costs of enlarging the reservoir, purchasing additional land, and installing minimum basic facilities for recreation use.

Skier at another watershed in Arkansas, the Caney Creek Watershed, near Wynne.

$400,000 Spent

Approximately $400,000 is being spent on the development of facilities at Lake Charles to provide a wide range of water-based fun, including fishing, swimming, camping and picnicking, hiking, boating, sightseeing, and nature study.

Down along the south end of the lake, not far from the huge earthen dam which holds back the water, an attractive beach and swimming area complete with bathhouse and concession facilities is attracting thousands of bathers in every week during the summer months.

The lake has been stocked up with bass, crappie, bluegill, bream, and catfish by the game and fish commission. Thus far, few anglers have left empty-handed.

A public boat launching area has been provided, complete with ramp, dock, and bait and supply center. Rental boats and motors are available at the boat dock. As a concession to the fishermen, motors over 10 horsepower are not permitted by the game and fish commission. Other public boat docks and supply points will be constructed at a later date, many by private enterprise on a permit basis.

Family camping areas, picnic spots, hiking and nature trails, and a scenic overlook are all designed to provide full enjoyment of the picturesque setting of the Lake Charles development. A well-designed system of sanitary facilities and paved access and circulation roads and parking areas enhances use of the area.

Steps have been taken to preserve and improve the site's great natural beauty. Nearby youths were employed in the planting of dogwood and redbud trees around the banks of the lake. Within a few years, the lakeshore should be quite spectacular in early spring.

Although much of the work has been done, some of the planned facilities are still under construction. More "touches of beauty" are yet to be added. Upon completion, however, the recreation development at Lake Charles will be one of the most "developed" in all Arkansas. Considering the pride that the local folks seem to take in their project, it is quite possible that they will be adding on to it for some time to come.

When it's fully developed, the park is expected to attract about 200,000 visitors

111

each year. Peak season is between Memorial Day and Labor Day, with over 10,000 visitors during the Fourth of July weekend alone. However, the park and most of its facilities are open year around. The lake is partially drained in October after the peak visitor season, when the water is needed to flood the Rainey Brake area.

The big Lake Charles recreational development stands out as a testimonial to teamwork. The Bureau of Outdoor Recreation, the Forest Service, and the Soil Conservation Service all helped prepare the plans for the development. Approximately half of the construction costs of the recreation facilities (about $200,000) were provided by SCS, which also developed the overall project work plan. The Farmers Home Administration arranged for a low-cost $30,000 loan to help the sponsors pay their share of project costs.

State Bought Land

The land for the development was acquired by the Arkansas Game and Fish Commission at a cost of nearly $100,000. The commission also helped with some of the land clearing and landscaping and is responsible for management of the lake. The Arkansas Highway Commission relocated over a mile of paved highway, at a cost of about $70,000, to permit construction of Lake Charles at the most favorable location. It also constructed the paved access roads, parking areas, and shore trails. The Arkansas Publicity and Parks Commission built the caretaker's residence, shared in the construction cost of other improvements, and operates and maintains the State park.

Individual landowners, acting through the Flat Creek Watershed Improvement District, helped to raise the local share of project costs. Lawrence County did the beach grading and sanding job. A local banker supplied the sand. The local Rural Electrification Administration cooperative extended lines to service the area.

Like all small watershed projects, the development at Lake Charles is a local project. It was initiated, partly financed, constructed, and is operated and maintained by the local people. They also own structures built as part of the project.

The Boy Scouts and other youth groups, church groups, civic, service, and sportsmen's clubs have flocked to the Lake Charles area. Recognizing the great recreational potential of watershed lakes, some of these groups have started to look around for a place of their own adjacent to Lake Charles or on one of the other lakes in the Flat Creek project. Although such private groups are not eligible for cost-sharing assistance, they may receive technical help from the Soil Conservation Service in planning recreation facilities in and around small watershed lakes.

The recreation development at Lake Charles is providing many social and economic benefits. It has brought public recreation opportunities closer to the local population. It has enhanced community values by creating a better, more attractive place to live and by increasing land values. Although this development is still in its infancy, the influx of thousands of tourists to the area is giving a real boost to the local economy through increased demands for food, lodging, transportation, gasoline, fishing and hunting supplies, and for related sports and recreation supplies and equipment.

13,000 Watersheds

There are around 13,000 small watersheds of less than 250,000 acres each in the United States, of which about 8,000 need project action for flood prevention, erosion control, and the like. The U.S. Department of Agriculture believes that recreation developments could be incorporated in several thousand of these.

So, if your community would like to swap floods, drought, or erosion problems for beauty and such leisuretime pursuits as fishing, swimming, boating, camping, hiking, and picnicking—and at the same time give a boost to the community pocketbook—remember that this kind of exchange is not limited to Arkansas, "the land of opportunity."

And if you're a tourist looking for water-based fun, keep projects like the Flat Creek watershed in mind. More are being built all the time. State offices of the Soil Conservation Service can tell you where to find them.

Vermonters Play It Cool With Water Recreation

LEMUEL J. PEET

HALFWAY up the tall dimension of Vermont live 20,000 people who demonstrate a refreshing zeal for fishing, camping, hiking, skiing, for wildflower preservation, and for kindred pursuits. Others may take to outdoor enjoyment lightly or as the stuff of wistful dreams. But not the residents of the White River Valley's rolling hills and winding streambanks—they are fashioning their own special way of life.

For example, they think an abundance of cool, sweet water habitable for trout is almost as important as a plenitude of handsome, stanch homes for humans. Their maturing plan weighs the value of a heart-lifting view of a mountain on a scale just about equal to that applied to the productive enterprises now developing for family breadwinners.

And the many private investments in the newly launched recreation areas bear witness to the firm purpose of the valley dwellers.

Putnam Blodgett, Jr., put $37,000 into building a 15-acre lake on Roaring Brook atop the timbered slope in back of his dairy farmstead at Bradford. He added guest facilities to the farmhouse, a cluster of rustic cabins in the lakeside woods; also trails, toilets, cooksheds, stables, and a craft shop. Before he hired counselors and cooks, this dairyman had invested $50,000 in his recreation enterprise.

Such a venture might once have stirred local prophets of doom. Now, in the late 1960's, Blodgett's lively young campers in summer, succeeded by hunters in the fall, skiers in winter, and fishermen in the spring—document a vital theme in the story of the White River Resource Conservation and Development project.

Originally, Blodgett's was one of 35 recreation- and wildlife-oriented facilities to be installed in this 635,000-acre project embracing parts of 4 counties. Landowners soon proved they had many more ideas. Today, outdoor fun prospects run the gamut, from hunting wild boar to quietly gathering butternuts—from "schussing" down a ski slope to smelting one's own copper on an old mine site.

Specialists Help Out

Leading the agricultural interests in providing bases for such activities is dairyman Edson E. Gifford, Sr., chairman of the White River Soil and Water Conservation District. Head of the R.C. & D. Project Coordinating Committee is Sheldon M. Dimick, local banker. Lending their know-how to the effort are virtually all resource specialists operating in the 992 square mile area. They work at the elbows of 100 representatives from the valley's towns and villages, citizens from all the walks of life.

In 23 rural towns, the needed emphasis on recreation potentials literally stared planners in the face. From 3,200-foot

꽃 꽃 꽃

Lemuel J. Peet has been *State Conservationist* for the Soil Conservation Service in his native Vermont since 1943.

113

Mount Monastery in the west, to Blodgett's high pasture on the extreme east, every promontory looks out upon classic scenery. Yet, within a 500-mile radius live 50 million people. And the market for marginal farmland among vacation and retirement homeseekers was already fast livening.

Streams lace the countryside—including 400 choice miles of channel haunted by trout, bass, pickerel, and other gamesters. Retreating glaciers had left precious few acreages of impounded water.

Preferred frontage on the two outstanding lakes, Morey and Fairlee, had long since been snapped up.

Searching for recreation water, project planners inventoried 50 sites capable of impounding at least 20 acres apiece. Their potential totals over 1,000 added water-acres. A tempting 275-acre lake site was noted near Randolph.

The shaping of a water-abundant future quickly followed the start of project planning back in 1964.

As part of his 1,000-acre conservation plan, Webb Keefe, retired educator, installed a 4-acre pond for sportsmen at his newly built hunting and fishing lodge near Ely. It enhances a wilderness preserve which features imported Russian boar, as well as native deer and bear and other shooting quarry, too.

'Lake Champagne'

Elsewhere, dairyman Maurice La-France constructed a 2-acre pond on a clay site in his pasture. Improvements included a trucked-in sandy beach, a playfield, bathhouse, snackbar, bench-tables, and a picnic pavilion. The handsome area quickly became a community-wide attraction for the village of Randolph Center. LaFrance's user fees amplify his 175-acre dairy income. Tourists often stopped to inquire if they could camp beside his "Lake Champagne." The farmer was thus encouraged to prepare 30 tent and trailer sites. He has plenty of elbowroom left in which to expand upon his $15,000 investment.

A contractor, Robert Levasseur, too, joined the project's search for water development. He checked the R.C. & D.

inventory for suitable sites. A prime spot showed on an abandoned 80-acre farm owned by Phillip Kratky, of Royalton. The businessman readily warmed to Levasseur's proposals. Armed with a project-originated design, the contractor set his crew to work on the Fay Brook location in the town of Strafford. The completed dam holds 6 acres of water. It furnishes a scenic view for two new year-round residences plus several vacation homesites Kratky expects to develop.

Pond Building

Farm pond building operations begun 25 years ago by cooperators of the White River Soil and Water Conservation District picked up momentum—and in a new direction. Most of the 98 little bodies of water visible at the turn of the decade were designed for livestock or firefighting. Vacation land buyers brought along their own concepts of pond values: A liquid jewel to admire outside the picture window; a cool place to entertain weekend guests; a nesting, resting, or watering retreat for wild creatures.

Thus, the rate of pond construction jumped from 7 to 21 annually—in this era of resource project stimulation.

Locating more land suitable for sport, relaxation, new homes, and awakening industries also perplexed the White River leaders. In response, Project Coordinator Eugene C. Hanchett of the Soil Conservation Service is directing a high-speed survey of area soils. It defines each acre's capability for housing, factories, commercial, and recreation sites—or the entire spectrum of community wants.

Newer accommodations often blend in with the work-and-play atmosphere.

Swiss chalet-style, all-weather dwellings have begun to emerge from lofty footings amid trees on the skier-inviting face of Hawk Mountain at Pittsfield.

Twenty new year-round homes with spacious lots are taking shape on a plateau near Blodgett's camps and within sight of the majestic Connecticut River.

At Sharon, farmer George Ainsworth has set up a travel-trailer park on 5 of his 105 acres of dairyland. Steadily moving toward him and an eventual nearby interchange are construction crews shoving Interstate Highway 89 across the hills. To Ainsworth's and other project area enterprises, the Boston to Canada thoroughfare will mean potential customers at a rate three times the present daily traffic volume. A similar harvest is expected from Interstate Highway 91 being forged along the eastern edges of the project, bordering New Hampshire.

New Plants Open

Advantages of enticing employees to an area where it's possible to catch a fat, brown trout for dinner after work hours or to practice a few Christiana turns on skis during the noon break haven't been lost upon commercial and industrial leaders. In this setting, newer enterprises including a plastic parts firm, a wooden toy factory, a cable distributing terminal, and a parquet floor processing plant have added scores of jobs to the local economy.

"It's gotten so that I can't find any extra help to hire," says building contractor Kenneth E. Manning. Demand thrives for all-weather vacation homes at prices up to $25,000 a unit. This has boosted Manning's need to 25 workmen at season's peak. "Five or six men used to be plenty for me," Manning adds. "Our business is up 25 percent over the past 5 years. The trend is to spanking-new, winter-and-summer dwellings. We are running out of farmhouses to remodel."

Real estate agents such as Orville A. Curtis reflect a similar outlook. Curtis testifies, "In the past few years, just about 90 percent of my buyers have come from out of State—from New York, New Jersey, and central New England. Not long ago, I'd have 30 to 35 ready-built properties to show. These days, I've got to scratch for a handful!"

Project Leader Hanchett sampled the tax rolls of 11 selected towns. He found the nonresident versus resident property ownership ratio edging ever closer to the 50–50 mark. This changing state of affairs is measurable in a steadily broadening tax base. It has helped to pay for improved school buildings, new sewage treatment plants, and other services.

Local folks, themselves, are alert to their "backyard" resources. A good example is Pinnacle Ski-Ways. The 100-acre family-fun facility serves the White River Valley area. In a single year, local people chipped in $50,000, built four trails, two lifts, and a base lodge. Soil Conservation Service technicians helped them plan measures to correct poor drainage, erosion, and excessive icing on slopes. At the first snowfall, both young and old queued up for ski instruction.

People now outnumber the cows in this area once dominated by dairy farms. But the remaining cows and farms continually break and make milk production records. No one is writing off agriculture. "The intermixed landscape of farms, fields, forests, and villages is a kind of 'visual' resource the new people come here for," affirms Edson Gifford, Sr. He and other boosters among White River Soil and Water Conservation District cooperators say this fact dictates speedier planning. They're shooting for land conservation treatment at three times what the rate was in preproject days.

Many of the 1,200 landowners involved in district work have also become active project promoters. Their influence on a program aimed at balancing needs of land and people, within the decade, is expected to enhance 60,000 acres of crop and pasture fields and 33,000 acres of forest. It will spice a melting pot of aims containing town resource planning, farm management counseling, flood prevention, municipal water supplies, woodland product usage, and still more facilities for sportsmen, holiday residents, and retirees.

Local folks already note a heightened vitality which abundant outdoor recreation has brought to their economy. The future promises a heady array of benefits led by employment at the rate of 1,450 man-years on resources-related construction. This is the initial 5-year phase. In the same period, the project plan points to a $1.5 million increase in real estate value.

Meanwhile, Putnam Blodgett finds his time increasingly splintered between the needs of 80 milk cows and needs of campers and other recreation-bent guests. Economists analyzing his pay-for-fun enterprise say he has added a $24,000 net average increase to the local economy.

115

Waterfowl-Wildlife Refuges
Let Even Longhorns Horn In

JOSEPH P. LINDUSKA

TISHOMINGO, Chincoteague, Black-beard Island, Okefenokee—colorful names, these, and colorful places, too. They're a part of the farflung system of the national wildlife refuges, a chain of nature preserves which includes more than 300 units that totals nearly 29 million acres. The odds are there's a refuge near you, since all except 5 of the 50 States have at least one.

Many refuges lie astride the congested urban stretches of the eastern seaboard, the Middle West, and the Pacific coast. Mainly they offer sanctuary to millions of migrating waterfowl, but they have other values. People need solitude, too, and 15 million Americans found respite during 1966 in visiting these wildlife havens that can also be human refuges.

Most of them came to observe the birds or merely to wander around and escape momentarily the harassment of city living. Others satisfied a recreational thirst for hunting, fishing, or boating. The national refuge system offers all of these things and more.

Several refuges are unique because they make up the last stronghold for animals bordering on extinction. An example is the Aransas Refuge, located halfway down the Texas coast, 75 miles north of Corpus Christi. Here, on 47,000 acres of bays, estuaries, tidal flats, and sandy islands, visitors may see the whooping cranes, one of our largest birds and probably the rarest in North America.

This giant of a bird, standing 5 feet high and with a 7-foot wingspread,

winters only on Aransas and the adjacent lands. There you may see it—and a lot of other wildlife—from late October to mid-April, when each whooper begins its hazardous 2,600-mile trip to summer nesting grounds in the Far North.

The only nesting area which is now known (and only recently discovered) is in Wood Buffalo National Park of Canada's Northwest Territories.

Whooping cranes had all but vanished from the wildlife scene before establishment of Aransas. Fifteen lone survivors reported in during the winter of 1941–42, and things continued to be "touch and go" for the species for a number of years. The winter of 1965–66 saw 44 individuals on the refuge—hardly a thriving population but, nevertheless, one that's edging up instead of down.

The Key deer is another species that had dwindled to near extinction in the 1940's, but since then has been preserved for people to see. A remnant herd of 50 animals was faced with certain displacement—victims of intensive land development—when area acquisition to preserve their habitat was started. In 1966, the population numbered around 400 animals, most of them occupying the refuge lands on Big Pine Key in Florida. This diminutive race of whitetails is the smallest deer in all North America.

❀ ❀ ❀

Joseph P. Linduska is *Associate Director* of the Bureau of Sport Fisheries and Wildlife, U.S. Department of the Interior.

Whooping cranes fly across pond at Aransas Wildlife Refuge, Tex.

These are furtive creatures, but alert visitors to Big Pine Key regularly see the 40- to 60-pound midgets as they scurry through openings and across the roadways in their tropical setting.

Other refuges provide unusual recreational opportunities for people interested in the "offbeat" and the unusual. At the Salt Plains National Wildlife Refuge in Oklahoma, you may dig for selenite crystals. At De Soto National Wildlife Refuge in Iowa and Nebraska, you may pick the delectable morel mushroom, a species so distinctive that not even the rank amateur can go wrong. Sanibel National Wildlife Refuge in Florida is a mecca for those interested in rare and beautiful seashells; and at the Tamarac National Wildlife Refuge in Minnesota, there are settlers' log cabins and even Chippewa Indian burial grounds.

Would you like to see a real Texas longhorn, that distinctly American breed of cattle which has made famous the old Chisholm Trail and the Goodnight-Loving Trail, and that laid the basis for endless TV shows and "horse operas" a century later? The longhorns once numbered in the millions; today only a few thousand remain. You may see them at Fort Niobrara National Wildlife Refuge in Nebraska and the Wichita Mountains Refuge in Oklahoma, where relict herds are being maintained.

But more than preserving the rare, the unusual, and the endangered, the refuges mainly serve as a haven for the millions of ducks, geese, and other migratory birds. And this is what most persons come to see. If you are serious about bird watching—and sooner or later most people seem to develop this interest—you will do well to come equipped with binoculars and a bird guide. Much of the fun is in knowing and distinguishing the many kinds that are present in confusing variety. The activities and antics of the bird world are engrossing to anyone taking

Canada geese take off from a waterhole in south Texas where many of these geese spend the winter months.

the time to observe up close. A camera, likewise, will find good use in permitting you to record some of the unusual sights which you are sure to encounter.

Most of the Federal areas are staffed by biologists—individuals who sought out such jobs because of a great interest in the outdoors. These all are enthusiastic naturalists who can help you to a richer enjoyment of the world of nature. A stop at the refuge headquarters will yield suggestions on what to see and where, as well as helpful literature.

A few refuges are equipped with visitor centers where you can see displays that tell the story of the refuge, where there are movies or color slide shows of the area and its wildlife. Many have nature trails for walkers, with numbered posts keyed to descriptive leaflets. These explain refuge operations or identify some

118

of the unusual wildlife or plants. Still others, like the Seney National Wildlife Refuge in northern Michigan or the National Bison Range in Montana, have regularly scheduled auto tours.

If your hobby is fishing, you will find possibilities on many national wildlife refuges. Most of these areas have water on them—ponds, lakes, streams, and beaches. Wherever possible, on either a yearlong or seasonal basis, these units are open to fishermen. More than a fourth of all visitors come for this purpose.

Hunting, too. Nearly half a million people enjoy this sport each year on national refuges. Some are open to waterfowl shooting on a limited basis. On others, you may hunt for a variety of resident game such as deer, pheasants, quail, rabbits, and grouse. A few offer the unusual in hunting experiences. On Desert Game Range in Nevada you may pursue the elusive desert bighorn sheep; and on Chincoteague National Wildlife Refuge in Virginia exotic sika deer occur in sizable numbers.

If hunting on a refuge strikes you as being inconsistent with the purposes of protecting and saving, let me explain. Big game, if allowed to increase to an excessive degree, can be their own worst enemy. They overbrowse their range; then starvation ruins the herd. But even before nature balances animals to food supply, the destruction of trees and shrubs removes food and cover essential to many smaller animals as well. It's good management for the game—and to the sportsman's benefit—to crop big game judiciously. And most small game can't be stockpiled. If peak numbers in the fall are not reduced by hunting, nature again has a way of paring the flocks through disease, predators, and other means. Regulated hunting can put game in the hunter's bag that would otherwise perish from natural causes alone.

Refuges offer picnicking facilities ranging from the rudimentary base of a few tables and a colony of ants to the elaborate center with fireplaces, running water, comfortable restrooms—and two colonies of ants. Overnight camping is generally not permitted, since such public use is incompatible with wildlife needs of the area. However, camping facilities are to be found on some of the larger refuges, such as Crab Orchard National Wildlife Refuge in southern Illinois and the Wichita Mountains Wildlife Refuge in southwestern Oklahoma near Lawton.

Boating and water skiing are permitted the year around on several refuge lakes and seasonally on some others. Such facilities as launching ramps, swimming beaches, bathhouses, and concessions where meals or refreshments may be obtained are usually available on the area or else nearby.

By now you have probably concluded that the refuges are as variable as fingerprints. That's true. And that's why there is no fixed pattern of recreational development on the many units. Some refuges are so intensively used by waterfowl that just "looking" is the only recreation compatible with the job and the objective of wildlife management. On others, wildlife is localized or uses the area on a seasonal basis so there is "wiggle room" to share the ground and water with people, even including the "whoop and holler" of the water skiers. Where there's a question, wildlife has priority, of course.

Under the Land and Water Conservation Fund Act of 1965, visitors to most wildlife refuges are charged a nominal fee. Holders of the $7 "Golden Passport," of course, are admitted along with their carload of passengers to all the refuges as well as to the many other Federal installations. But if you do not have a Golden Passport, you may purchase a daily or a monthly entrance permit. All the refuges requiring a permit are plainly posted.

Wherever you live, it is likely you're within a fairly easy driving distance of one or more national wildlife refuges. Most highway maps show their location, but if you desire more detailed information, write the Bureau of Sport Fisheries and Wildlife, U.S. Department of the Interior, Washington, D.C. 20240.

And one more thing. When you visit Aransas for a look at the whooping crane, that largest and rarest of our migratory birds, don't refer to them as "whopping" cranes or as "big white buzzards." Phil Morgan, the refuge manager, is a sensitive type and deadly serious about his charges.

For further reading:
U.S. Department of the Interior, Bureau of Sport Fisheries and Wildlife, *Directory of National Wildlife Refuges.* WL–466, 1965.
——— *The National Wildlife Refuge System.* RL–1–A, U.S. Government Printing Office, Washington, D.C. 20402, 1964. 5¢
——— *National Wildlife Refuges—1965.* Resource Publication 1, U.S. Government Printing Office, Washington, D.C. 20402, 1965. 20¢
——— *Publications of the National Wildlife Refuges.* RL–406, 1965.
——— *Waterfowl Tomorrow,* Joseph P. Linduska, editor, U.S. Government Printing Office, Washington, D.C. 20402, 1964. $4.00. Available in Canada from The Queen's Printer, Ottawa. $4.00

A Texas longhorn.

The Marsh: Rev. Ainsworth's Community Legacy

PHILIP F. ALLAN

A PAIR of wood ducks squeak protests as we leave the woods road and climb the dam. On a magnificent May morning we scan the marsh where tree swallows swirl, dip, and sweep across last year's cattails. Mount Monadnock, which gives its name to geological counterparts throughout the world, towers to the north. The "Parade Ground," where the local militiamen once drilled, lies on the left. And on the rise to the right sit "The Manse" and the old church where the Reverend Laban Ainsworth had lived and preached 175 years ago. In between lies the marsh. The town is Jaffrey, N.H.

The work of a private enterprise, the F. W. Greene Estate, Inc., has created in this historic and beautiful landscape a community asset that cannot be measured in dollars. You will see why.

Although all the land now occupied by the marsh was once owned by the Reverend Mr. Ainsworth, it was sold at auction when he died in 1858. Later known as the Ethan Cutter Meadow, the land was reacquired in 1886 by Mary Ainsworth Greene and Rear Admiral Greene, her husband. It is now a part of the Greene Estate. There are five heirs who share and share alike, Theodore P. Greene of Amherst, Mass., Mrs. W. Ainsworth Greene of West Hartford, Conn., and Walter F. Greene and Norman and William Torrey, all of Jaffrey, N.H.

The story of this marsh really starts with the Reverend Mr. Ainsworth. In his day it was the custom of New Hampshire towns to provide for the livelihood of the ministry by furnishing land. The best farmland was not to be wasted on the minister by the thrifty Yankees, but there was plenty of rocky forest land; and that is mostly what the Reverend Mr. Ainsworth got. He made the best of it, however, and rented out the farmable areas during his lifetime. Some of this land changed hands in subsequent years before being pulled together again by the minister's descendants.

By 1905, farming became unprofitable. The meadow grew up to bluejoint, willows, alders, and red maples. A dry spell in the early fifties exposed the meadow streambed. Then, in 1959, some beavers moved in. They dammed the brook and, thus, set marsh development going.

I met Walter Greene and the Torreys in a fine old colonial house in Jaffrey. Together they told me the story of how a community marsh was built by the Greene Estate heirs. I judge that this is not a wealthy estate; and that conservation interests and community spirit, as well as financial contributions from the five families, played the major role in development of the marsh.

Norman Torrey—the Torrey brothers married Greene sisters—is a family his-

Philip F. Allan is *Regional Biologist* for the Soil Conservation Service with headquarters at Upper Darby, Pa. The northeastern State region he works in includes New Hampshire. Mr. Allan is a graduate of the University of New Hampshire and did graduate work there. He is the author of more than 100 publications.

torian. He produced photos, maps, and news items that told something of family and marsh history. Walter Greene, a former professor of biology at Syracuse, Springfield, and Beirut Universities, filled me in on wildlife of the area. William Torrey, appraiser and selectman of the town of Jaffrey, described details of construction and arrangements with neighbors whose land was somewhat involved. He, too, led us on a guided tour of the marsh in a huge, old mud-slogging Plymouth car.

As we rode up the hill to "The Manse," Walter Greene told how the beaver dam gave way, but set them thinking of a permanent pond and marsh. As a start, the area was cleared of brush and trees. Next, the heirs got in touch with Walt Nelson and Ken French of the USDA Soil Conservation Service office at Keene, who assist the Cheshire County Soil Conservation District.

Plans were prepared by the SCS men and OK'd by the estate for construction of a dam. The plans called for a large water control structure of corrugated pipe to handle normal flow through the dam.

Flashboards on the upstream side were to be installed to permit regulating the water level, and thus aid in growing food plants for waterfowl.

Island for Waterfowl

The plans also provided for seedings to cover exposed soil on the dam and in the emergency spillway; plantings of Tatarian honeysuckle and autumn olive in the marsh environs for wildlife food and for ornamentation; an island, to provide a safe resting spot for visiting ducks and geese and, perhaps, for nesting. Nature trails, too, were planned.

"It was all very well to plan," commented William Torrey, "but there were complications. Before we could proceed, we had to enlist the cooperation as well as the legal agreement of neighbors, for a part of the dam would go on the properties of Elmer Ford and Agnes O'Hare. And, then, some land belonging to other neighbors would be flooded."

In June 1963, the dam was finally built. "Luckily," notes Norman Torrey, "we found a bed of clay within a few feet of the damsite. And this made a good, tight, core wall for the dam. Another drought in that summer postponed the filling of the pond, but heavy rains fell on November 8 and soon water covered 20 acres. In almost no time there were lots of horned-pout and pickerel and townspeople started fishing." These old-time favorites of New Hampshire fishermen lag in popularity only behind the native speckled trout.

"We allow hunting, too," Norman told me, "and the local boys can trap muskrats and other furbearers."

Not only the pond and marsh but also most of the rest of the 220-acre estate is open to considerate use by the 3,200 residents of Jaffrey. For the bird watchers walking the trails, there is a host of migrant warblers, with a modicum of the resident species; and thrushes and fly-catchers; finches, sparrows, and gros-beaks; swallows; and many other interesting species of birds.

I talked over with Walter Greene the possibilities for use of the tract by schools for nature study. He assured me that there were almost unlimited opportunities, not only for schools but also Boy Scouts and similar organizations.

Although little such use has been made during the short span of its existence, the men all hoped for the estate to serve this purpose. Here, the town lad can see wood duck nest boxes in operation; visit beaver dams to see how those animals step the water down into the marsh; and find in the pine woods the scarlet, juvenile newts whose olive-colored parents loaf in the pond and steal worms from the hook of the horned-pout fisherman.

And for the girls there are ladyslippers, marsh marigold, and trout lilies. If they but will, the Scouts here can learn the wintergreen flavor of sweet birch sap; the feel of mud between the toes and of pine needles under foot; the delicious smell of the Mayflower or the not-so-nice skunk cabbage—both should be known! Down by the water's edge they will find what the New Hampshire oldtimers called the "stripéd adder," the harmless garter snake; in the ruin of Laban Ainsworth's barn, the "spotted adder" or milk snake

121

and, alongside an old stone wall, the racy black snake.

We reached a point in our tour where even William Torrey's durable Plymouth could not go because of the spring thaws. So we walked on over to the "Parade Ground." It has been plowed recently. The young seminarians from Ireland, learning to be missionaries at the nearby Queen of Peace Seminary, are growing potatoes there. In return for this community benefit, the Greenes and Torreys have willing workers when trails need clearing or shrubs need planting.

As an addition to his January 20, 1966, news story published in the *Monadnock*

Ledger, Norman Torrey described the quick response of wildlife to the building of the pond, marsh, and adjoining lands. "To the west of the pond," he noted, "lie a few large fields and several hundred acres of wilderness, an ideal area for recreation and for wildlife conservation. Beavers, muskrats, mink, and an occasional otter have taken over the pond, along with black and wood ducks, blue herons, occasional egrets, bittern, kingfishers, woodcock and snipe, pheasant, grouse, and numerous other birds. . . . The marsh is thus a boon not only to the Greene heirs, but to the whole community." I think he has a point.

Fields and Ponds
for Wild Ducks

WILLIAM W. NEELY

YOU CAN HAVE a place to hunt wild ducks—on your own land or by forming a hunting group and leasing some land.

If you own land which can be managed for ducks, not only can you have hunting for yourself and your friends, but you can also get income through the sale of shooting privileges.

But whether you own or lease land, techniques to attract ducks are the same.

In some sections of our country, the wild ducks will come into dry crop fields to feed. But since there is lots of cropland, you can't count on them coming to yours. The surest way of having ducks come to your land every year is to provide their food in the feeding condition they like best—in water. This is true anywhere.

You can provide the combination of food and water for ducks in several ways. One is to construct and manage a "duck-

pond." Another way is to impound water for only a part of the time.

A duckpond is a permanent impoundment. The water depth varies from a few inches on the edges to perhaps 6 feet or more in the deepest places. The duck foods that you grow are aquatic plants—the kinds of plants which live in water.

One good example is sago potamogeton (*Potamogeton pectinatus*). Many kinds of ducks like both the seeds and the vegetative parts of this plant. Sago will grow anywhere you have a pond with "hard" water, alkaline water, or water which is a little salty.

᭧   ᭧   ᭧

William W. Neely is a *Biologist*, Soil Conservation Service, Columbia, S.C. A significant part of his 28 years with SCS has been in management of wet lands for wildlife. He has assisted with the planning and establishment of many thousands of acres of duck fields and ponds.

If your pond water has low mineral content ("soft" water), you cannot grow sago potamogeton. However, it is likely you can grow either northern or southern naiad (*Najas flexilis* in the Northern States or *Najas guadalupensis* in the Southern States). These naiads grow similarly to sago potamogeton, but they are not quite as attractive food for ducks.

If your pond water is mildly acid or it has an organic stain so that you cannot grow either sago or naiad, then watershield (*Brasenia schreberi*) may be your best possibility for growing duck food. The seeds of this plant are particularly attractive to ring-necked ducks.

For brackish water ponds, widgeongrass (*Ruppia maritima*) provides a choice duck food which is easy to grow. See chapter starting on page 141.

You can produce even more choice and attractive food for ducks in a duck "field" than you can in a pond. A duck field is an area kept dry to cultivate crops for duck food and then flooded during the fall and winter to make the crops available to ducks. Since all of the water in a duck field is shallow, it is more frequently used by the species which most hunters prefer—the mallard, pintail, and black ducks.

A duck field requires some flatland that can be enclosed with a dike. If it is wet land, enough drainage must be established to grow the kind of duck food planned. A reliable source of water for flooding is necessary.

One instance is a flat area below a farm pond. Usually only a low dike is necessary. Install a pipe through the dike and a gate for water control and a ditch for drainage, if needed. Plant the field to a crop suited to the soil and climate and which is a choice duck food. For example, it might be browntop millet (*Panicum ramosum*).

In the fall, draw enough water from the pond to shallowly flood the field. Since gravity flow can be used, this is easy to do. About 6 to 12 inches is a good depth for flooding. If the flooding is over 18 inches deep, the field will lose part of its attractiveness to ducks that "tip" to feed, like mallards and pintails.

The same principles apply to duck

Golden retriever brings in a blue wing teal in field of flooded browntop millet. Rice Hope Plantation, Georgetown, S.C.

fields in other locations. You may have a flat crop field suited to growing corn that you can enclose with a dike to form a duck field. From experiences all over the country, this technique has proven to be highly successful in providing good duck hunting.

In most fields where corn will grow, you will have to pump in the water for flooding. This is not hard to do with the same kind of equipment which the farmer uses for irrigation.

If the land you plan to use for a duck field is too wet for cultivation and can't be properly drained, there are still some good duck foods which you can grow. One is Japanese millet (*Echinochloa crusgalli* and its varieties).

To grow this kind of millet, keep the field flooded until early summer to retard the growth of weeds and grass. Then let the water off the field and immediately broadcast Japanese millet seed on the wet soil. The seeds germinate rapidly without land preparation. Shallowly flood the field during the fall and winter in order to make the crop available to ducks.

In a similar way you can grow Japanese

123

millet around the edges of a farm pond for duck food. Lower the water level in the pond several feet in early July. Broadcast millet seed on the portions of the pond bottom exposed by the drawdown. Allow the pond to refill during the fall when the millet matures.

Smartweeds are native plants that you probably already have growing on your wetland field. The seeds are choice duck food. You can manage a smartweed field for ducks. In early spring, drain the field dry enough to burn the previous year's accumulation of plant debris. During the spring and summer allow livestock to moderately graze the field. Livestock will not eat the smartweeds because of the peppery taste, but will graze most other plants. With little competition, smartweeds grow vigorously and make a good seed yield. Flood the field in fall.

Where To Get Help

Other ways to manage duck fields and ponds are described in USDA Farmers' Bulletin 2218, listed at the end of this chapter. You can get help from your local soil conservation district or Soil Conservation Service office for planning and designing either a duck field or pond.

If you are interested in having a reliable income from your duck field or pond, you should try to provide the best hunting possible. Duck hunters will pay well for good shooting. As much as $25 a person for a single morning's hunt is not unusual. Fee hunting for ducks is common throughout the United States. With the increasing demand for outdoor recreation, more places to hunt will be needed.

There are three ways normally used for "selling" duck hunting. One is by a charge for each hunt. In return for a fee, the hunter is furnished a blind—and perhaps a guide and a dog for retrieving—for a day or part of a day's shooting. This is often done in the large irrigation reservoirs in Arkansas and in ricefields flooded after the harvest. It is probably the most profitable way of selling duck hunting today.

If you have hunted this way, you have likely seen that it has some drawbacks. One is that it takes a lot of the operator's time. Another is in dealing with the hunters. Most are strangers to each other. Some are experts, while some are on their first hunting trip. To the chagrin of the experienced hunters, the beginners are apt to blast away at ducks out of range and frighten off the flocks.

There is another way of selling hunting which you might rather use. This is to lease out your field or pond to a club or group of hunters for the entire hunting season. The facilities and the services you provide may be elaborate or simple.

Your lease should stipulate how often there will be any hunting (say, twice a week), that there will be morning shooting only, and the hunters must be out of the blinds by noon. This will protect your field from overshooting so that ducks will come back each year. Other than this, the club or group makes its own bylaws and rules and resolves hunter difficulties among the members.

If you are looking for a place to hunt, a third way may work best for you. Form your own hunter group among friends or business associates. Lease some suitable land and develop a duck field or pond yourselves. The shared cost can be reasonable. There are plenty of sites over much of the country. Many owners of these sites will be agreeable as they get a development which increases the value of their land without any cost to them, plus the income from your lease.

To help your duck field contribute to the overall welfare of our waterfowl, keep it flooded after the hunting season is over. The birds need your food and protection until they leave for their nesting grounds. It's good business for you too—many of the ducks will return to the same spot next fall.

Good hunting!

For further reading:
Neely, William W., and Davison, Verne E., *Wild Ducks on Farmland in the South*. Farmers' Bulletin 2218, U.S. Department of Agriculture, Washington, D.C. 20250, 1966.

Water Makes
the Desert Bloom

KENNETH K. BARNES

CACTUS and sun-bleached skulls are a familiar symbol of the deserts of the Western United States. The thirsty and exhausted pioneer pressing on toward water which proves to be only a mirage strikes a note of terror in all of us.

Today the vision out on the horizon might prove to be a metropolitan area of some 500,000 persons.

The deserts once feared by the '49ers are now home to 3½ million people. Half of these live in 6 metropolitan areas of over 100,000 population. The other half live in smaller communities, in irrigated valleys, and on sprawling ranches.

Wheel ruts of the stagecoach and the prairie schooner have been replaced by the four-lane, divided interstate highways. Where infrequent waterholes were once protected at gunpoint, swimming pools dot the suburbs.

Water has made the great difference. Water has made the desert bloom. This water was always there, but modern man's technology has controlled and exploited the water supplies to develop a boom in desert living.

The major portion of the States of Arizona, Nevada, and Utah are desert. The desert claims important portions of California, Oregon, Idaho, Wyoming, Colorado, New Mexico, and Texas. Major desert cities include Albuquerque, N. Mex.; El Paso, Tex.; Las Vegas, Nev.; Phoenix and Tucson, Ariz.; and Salt Lake City, Utah.

Geographers have arbitrarily agreed that a desert is a region which receives less than 10 inches of unevenly distributed rainfall each year. Only very specialized types of vegetation grow naturally in desert regions, as a result of the low rainfall coupled with high temperatures and a high evaporation. Much of the rainfall, particularly in summer, may come at high intensity, several inches in

Irrigation of lawns and gardens in desert areas sometimes has a bonus for the kids.

꣠   ꣠   ꣠

Kenneth K. Barnes is *Professor* and *Head* of the Department of Agricultural Engineering at the University of Arizona, Tucson.

125

just a few hours, and be lost to plants as a result of high runoff.

The desert is not "barren." It abounds with plants and animals. But the desert is inhospitable except to those plants, lower animals, and human beings that have specially adapted to it.

Plants adapted to the desert are called xerophytes. They use many tricks. Some drop their leaves when the soil dries and grow new ones when moisture again becomes available. Others, particularly the cacti, are water storers. They quickly take in the available soil moisture and control its release for use in the hot dry months that lie ahead.

Some plants have hairy leaves to shade

ISLANDS IN THE DESERT

There is a ski tow 20 miles from the city hall of the desert metropolis of Tucson, Ariz. In the Salt Lake City area, the annual rainfall at Saltaire 15 miles west of the post office is less than 12 inches, while 9 miles east of the post office it is 24 inches. Forty miles west of Salt Lake City, the annual rainfall is less than 6 inches; 20 miles to the east of the city, annual rainfall is 42 inches.

Mountain masses project to great elevations above the desert floor. At Tucson, the Catalina Mountains tower to 9,000 feet above sea level, 6,600 feet above the valley floor. The mountain mass of the Catalinas is only around 10 miles thick, and on all sides there is desert. At Salt Lake, the Wasatch Mountains rise 6,000 feet above the city.

These mountains, which are individually too small in area to show on a small map, result in sharp changes in climate as one travels for only a few miles.

The U.S. deserts are located in the geological region known as the Basin and Range Province. The mountains which border the desert valleys are frequently high enough to support dense forests of pine, fir, spruce, and aspen. The high rainfall of these mountains makes them humid islands in an arid sea.

leaf surfaces from sun exposure. Others turn their leaves to present a minimum surface exposed to the sun. Many other plant adaptations are found.

The animal dwellers of the desert are often nocturnal. They move about for feed at night and are seldom seen during the day. Many of these animals of the desert make their homes underground for protection against the daytime heat. Some small mammals of the desert need only that water which comes from the metabolism of dry food. They go through life without a drink of water.

Some Indians of the desert adapted

Water stored for irrigation is water stored for recreation too.

	1900	1920	1940	1950	1960
Albuquerque, N. Mex.................	6, 238	15, 157	35, 449	96, 815	201, 189
Bernalillo County....................	....	29, 855	69, 391	145, 673	262, 199
El Paso, Tex..........................	15, 906	77, 560	96, 810	130, 485	276, 687
El Paso County......................	24, 886	101, 877	131, 067	194, 968	314, 070
Las Vegas, Nev.......................	....	2, 304	8, 422	24, 624	64, 405
Clark County........................	....	4, 859	16, 414	48, 289	127, 016
Phoenix, Ariz........................	5, 544	29, 053	65, 414	106, 818	439, 170
Maricopa County....................	20, 457	89, 576	136, 193	331, 770	663, 510
Salt Lake City, Utah.................	53, 531	118, 110	149, 934	182, 121	189, 454
Salt Lake County...................	77, 725	159, 282	211, 623	274, 895	383, 035
Tucson, Ariz.........................	7, 531	20, 292	35, 752	45, 454	212, 892
Pima County........................	14, 689	34, 680	72, 838	141, 216	265, 660

their lives to utilization of native desert plant and animal materials. The Papago of southern Arizona is unique in his ability to make use of the desert plants for both food and shelter.

Still other Indians developed water supplies and an irrigated agriculture to make the desert bloom. The earliest and the most extensive Indian irrigated agriculture recorded disappeared mysteriously from the desert around A.D. 1400.

By A.D. 700, these Indians were developing a highly effective irrigated agriculture in the valleys of the Salt and Gila Rivers of Arizona. They developed many miles of canals and irrigated thousands of acres. In total, 125 miles of canals and 140,000 acres of irrigated land have been identified. However, it is doubted that all of this was used during the same period of time.

All these people and their irrigation economy disappeared, leaving only ruins with meager clues as to their ways of life and the reasons for their disappearance. The people are known as the Hohokam, a word in the language of the Pima Indians which means "those who have gone."

Why did they go? Water made their desert bloom. But some failure to control their water resources made their desert revert to arid wilderness. It is thought that an inability to store water during the dry years and to protect their fields and irrigation works from floods during wet years resulted in their doom.

Their disappearance was preceded by droughts in the 13th century and floods in the 14th, tree ring studies show.

With the coming of people of Euro-pean descent, the desert again began to bloom. Now major cities exist through the development of water resources. Salt Lake City, Las Vegas, Phoenix, Tucson, Albuquerque, El Paso, and many other communities, large and small, illustrate 20th century man's adaptation to the desert climate. He makes this adaptation not by devising schemes to minimize water use, but by developing water supplies dependable for year-round continuous use. But surely the Hohokam thought they had developed continuing dependable water supplies. Their 700-or-more-year period of success looms long against the brief 50- to 100-year history of modern man in the intensive application of water to the desert.

Each desert city and town has had its own history. There is perhaps no norm and no average which will adequately sum up the development of a desert city. The history of Phoenix, Ariz., is an example. It is a city of startling development, based upon a highly developed water supply. It is a living example of, "When tillage begins, other arts follow," in the words of Daniel Webster. It is the center of a metropolitan area of 900,000 people—located where in A.D. 1400 the Hohokam civilization disappeared apparently because of some failure of the water system which was the very basis of their life.

Modern Phoenix has grown from Jack Swilling's ditch. Swilling was a prospector and freighter who came to Arizona in 1862. As he traveled over southern Arizona he foresaw the potential of the Salt River Valley, now occupied by the Phoenix metropolitan area.

127

Roosevelt Dam, first of several dams on the Salt and Verde Rivers system, stores water for eventual use in the desert area downstream.

		Temperature, °F.				
Mean annual rainfall— inches		January			July	
	Annual Mean	Mean	Mean Minimum	Mean	Mean Maximum	
Albuquerque, N. Mex..........	8.8	56	34	20	78	93
El Paso, Tex. (Ysleta)*.........	7.0	62	42	26	80	95
Las Vegas, Nev................	4.6	66	45	32	87	105
Phoenix, Ariz. (Mesa Experi- mental Farm)................	7.8	68	49	34	88	104
Salt Lake City, Utah (Saltaire)...	11.9	52	27	20	80	91
Tucson, Ariz. (University of Arizona)....................	10.6	68	49	35	87	101

*Notes in parentheses are U.S. Weather Bureau designation of station of record.

During the fall of 1867, Jack Swilling completed the organization of a group of men, into the Swilling Ditch Co. These men commenced to dig a ditch which would carry water from the Salt River to their fields. Water from the new ditch was first used for irrigation in 1868. Irrigation grew, and in 1869 the hundred or so permanent residents named their new townsite Phoenix.

The phoenix is a mythical bird said to have risen to glory from the ashes of its own funeral pyre. These Arizona pioneers envisioned their community rising to glory from the ashes of the Hohokam civilization, and so it has.

No Storage Available

Swilling's ditch and those that followed brought over 100,000 acres under irrigation during the late 1800's. This irrigation was based on direct diversion from the flowing river. No storage was available in those years.

From 1897 to 1899, severe droughts occurred. In February 1900, a flood took out all the diversions on the river. The people of the valley came to recognize the need for upstream storage and control.

June 17, 1902, is a turning point in the history of the Salt River Valley. On that date Congress passed the National Reclamation Act. It was signed by President Theodore Roosevelt.

The Reclamation Act provided the framework for organization and financing which made the first dam a reality. And on March 18, 1911, the Theodore Roosevelt Dam was dedicated. There in person was Theodore Roosevelt himself.

The dam was built under an agreement made between the Federal Government and the Salt River Valley Water Users' Association. The association was successfully formed when in July of 1903 the owners of around 200,000 acres of land in the valley became shareholders. They pledged the production of their land to finance construction of the dam.

Additional dams have been constructed on the Salt and its major tributary, the Verde River. In 1966, storage available in the system totaled 2,099,400 acre-feet. The distribution system serves around 242,000 acres.

The dams store water from mountain snows, and summer storms. Methods have been devised to predict flow into the reservoirs weeks to months ahead. Controlled release of water can be made for irrigation and to provide reservoir storage to protect against floods. The drought and flood disasters which plagued the Hohokam and the early Phoenix pioneer should not happen again.

Crop, Lawn Needs

Phoenix has an average annual rainfall of 7.7 inches. Compare this with examples of the water requirements of several crops: Cotton, 41 inches in 8 months; alfalfa, 74 inches in 10 months; barley, 25 inches in 5 months; wheat, 23 inches in 5 months; oranges, 39 inches in 12 months; and cantaloup, 19 inches in 4 months.

More meaningful to the homeowner is the use of water by a bermudagrass lawn in the desert: 44 inches, April through October; in July alone, over 10.

129

Thus in the desert no farming and no gardening, no cool lawns, and no landscaping are possible without developed supplies of water.

The Phoenix area has developed water supplies for agriculture, but these water supplies made of Phoenix a sought-out place to live and work. Thus its population has exploded, jumping from 65,000 in 1940 to 522,000 in 1964. Perhaps a better guide to population growth are the county figures, from 186,000 in 1940 to a whopping 870,000 in 1964.

This very brief story of a desert city is unique and common as well. The other desert cities of the United States have enjoyed similar growth. Each has had its own start, its own pattern of growth, its own high points of history. But in each, water has made growth possible. Water has made the desert bloom.

For further reading:
Golze, Alfred R., *Reclamation in the United States*. The Caxton Printers, Ltd., Caldwell, Idaho, 1961.
Jaeger, Edmund C., *The North American Deserts*. Stanford University Press, Stanford, Calif., 1965.
Mann, Dean E., *The Politics of Water in Arizona*. The University of Arizona Press, Tucson, 1963.
Shadegg, Stephen C., *The Phoenix Story—An Adventure in Reclamation*. Stephen C. Shadegg, Phoenix, Ariz., 1958.
U.S. Department of Agriculture, *Climate and Man*, the 1941 Yearbook of Agriculture. Washington, D.C. 20250, 1941.
—— *Water*, the 1955 Yearbook of Agriculture. U.S. Government Printing Office, Washington, D.C. 20402, 1955. $2.25.

Fishin' Luck *Has* To Be Good on the Horseshoe Lakes

ROBERT E. McLELLAND

CRAPPIE have moved into shallow water"—"crappie spawning!" are common phrases which spread like wildfire throughout the Mississippi Delta area beginning in mid-March and continuing with an ever-increasing tempo.

Fishing fever, in epidemic proportions, is common from Memphis, Tenn., to Angola, La., and the old saying, "When you are too busy to fish; you're too busy" certainly becomes a true statement. With the first few warm days of spring, fishermen—men, women, and children from 8 to 80—converge upon the calm waters of these cutoff bends, or "Oxbow Lakes" as they are sometimes called, along the "Mighty Mississippi" for the only known cure for fishing fever. This cure is to catch a limit of slab crappie (also called white perch or Sac-a-Lait in Louisiana) in the shallow water along the banks.

I know. For the past 20 years I have fished some of these lakes, and the desire to "drown some minnows" is still as strong as ever, motivated mainly by the fact that you know you can catch fish.

With cane pole, line, sinker, medium-size cork, a small spinner above your hook, and a bucket of minnows you're in business, fishing either from the bank or from a small flat-bottom boat some 12 to 24 inches deep.

The native vegetation along the cypress- and willow-lined banks of these lakes

✻ ✻ ✻

Robert E. McLelland is a *District Supervisor*, Farmers Home Administration, Pine Bluff, Ark.

130

affords ideal spawning grounds and protective cover for the game fish—crappie, black bass, bream, and blue channel cat—which abound in these natural lakes.

When the willows begin to green up and dogwood is in bloom, you know it is spawning time for all species of these game fish. Variety adds to the excitement of the trip for when your cork suddenly disappears under the surface you set your hook and wrestle your fish to the top of the water—not until then do you know whether you have tied into old mossback black bass, channel cat, or slab crappie.

By May 1, the bluegill bream have moved into the shallow waters along the banks to make their spawning beds. That's the time for popping bugs (small floating lures), earthworms, crickets, and other common baits to serve their purpose. In my opinion, bream have more fight ounce for ounce than any other fish. I have caught limits of 50 bream using crickets and worms for bait, without moving the boat more than 30 yards from one breambed to another.

Fly fishing for bream with popping bugs and slow sinking flies is an unexcelled sport, especially when you can catch a big bream or miss a strike almost every cast. Your wrist and arm need a rest after an hour's fishing. Anyhow, it's your turn to swap places with your buddy who has been paddling the boat and who has hardly been able to stand the pressure—and couldn't without knowing his turn was coming. In fact, on occasion I have accused my partner of having run his watch ahead on me.

Since bream, unlike other species of game fish in these lakes, usually spawn more than one time during the summer—once beds are located they will provide excellent fishing until the fall.

Arkansas has only one kind of natural lake—horseshoe lakes. These lakes were primarily created when the floodwaters from the Mississippi River, seeking a shorter route, cut through the narrow neck of a meander which had grown overlong or when the river changed its course by crossing its natural levee to a paralleling tributary. Current is reduced in these old channels, and the river begins to deposit sand and silt in the quiet

water. The heavier particles are deposited near the ends of the lakes and eventually fill them to the extent that there soon is no water connection with the river, except during the flood periods.

Other lakes have been formed by the U.S. Corps of Engineers straightening the river, thus leaving the great bends as lakes.

These natural horseshoe lakes provide the sportsman with earlier fishing than the larger artificial lakes, due to their being more shallow. Thus, the water temperatures rise more rapidly in spring and are naturally replenished with adult fish and spawn from the overflows during the high river stages. These lakes are as fertile as the delta soil itself, and tests show that they can produce 900 to 1,000 pounds of game and rough fish per acre.

A number of these lakes are so remote that the use of a four-wheel-drive vehicle is required to reach them, while other large lakes are reached by hard surface and gravel roads, with boats and other facilities readily available for rent.

Millions of Crappie

Recreation plus—that's what you find on the horseshoe lakes. Picture a giant crescent set in fern green cypress. Bass—the big black fighters leap from a mirror of the sky, snagged on the sharp hook of the angler's line. Crappie, millions of them, waiting impatiently for the baited hook of the neophyte fisherman. Brown bodies flash golden health in the sun as swimmers cut the cool lake surface. Later, boats and party barges are dark images in the widening path of yellow moonlight.

This is yours for the asking whether you travel south from Memphis on U.S. Highway 61 along the east side of the Mississippi or along U.S. 79 and 65 along the west. You will not be far from a lake offering various types of recreation where local citizens, bait shops, and chambers of commerce will be more than glad to give you the needed information.

Two of the more popular horseshoe lakes in Arkansas are Horseshoe Lake near West Memphis and Lake Chicot at Lake Village in the southeastern corner of the State. Chicot is the largest natural lake in the State. These particular lakes are now cut off from the river and major floodwaters by the Mississippi River levee. They are State owned and managed by the State game and fish commission.

Lake Chicot, 16 miles long and three-quarters of a mile wide, attracts thousands of visitors and sportsmen annually from all over the United States.

Lake Chicot State Park, composed of 120 pecan-covered acres, is located 8 miles north of Lake Village, Ark., on the north 7 miles of Lake Chicot.

This park, only 7 years old, attracted over half a million visitors in 1965. Out-of-State overnight campers outnumbered State residents in the number of campsites rented, with as many as 18 States represented at one time.

Facilities include at present 12 ultramodern air-conditioned cabins and 4 house trailers. Each cabin accommodates four to six persons, with a private patio and charcoal grill, boardwalk, and dock. Rates—$8 for two people and $1 for each additional person, with linens furnished. Reservations for cabins must be made well in advance. Write to Superintendent, Lake Chicot State Park, Lake Village, Ark. 71653. Additional cabins and a 40-room lodge with a dining hall to seat 150 people are planned.

Camping fees are $1 per campsite per night with a 30-day limit. A total of 150 additional campsites are under construction. The other facilities planned include tennis courts, a baseball diamond, an archery field, and two more large pavilions for group activities.

The trailer park can accommodate 30 trailers with water and sewer connections. A parking area for 60 additional trailers with water, light, and sewer connections will be constructed. The campsites, on a first-come basis, provide water, electrical outlets, tables, restrooms, and charcoal grills. The picnic area boasts of 175 public picnic tables for outdoor use.

The other facilities include a cafe, tackle and bait shop, grocery store, boat rental, and fish cleaning areas. An olympic-size swimming pool is under construction. A playground for the children offers swings, slides, rides and bars, and a pen with native whitetail deer.

M. R. Causey, park superintendent, is an "Old Pro" when it comes to crappie fishing. His rig consists of a cane pole, short line (3½ feet), and a feathered jig. He has been park superintendent since the year Lake Chicot State Park opened, and he fishes enough to keep informed on where the fish are biting. He readily passes along this information to any of his visitors who request it.

The "Old Pro" displays a 2¼-pound crappie. M. R. Causey, the superintendent of Lake Chicot State Park in Arkansas.

Average Over a Pound

Mr. Causey explains that the jig is flipped near dead snags, brush, or green willows, and is kept moving. Crappie usually take this bait as it is going down.

He has caught crappie weighing up to 3½ pounds, with the average weight exceeding 1 pound.

The Arkansas resident fishing license is $3.50 per year for persons 16 or over. For nonresidents 16 or over the annual fee is $6, and a 14-day license is $3.50.

Following U.S. Highway 65 farther south into Louisiana you drive along beautiful Lake Providence. This blue 7-mile-long lake averaging a half mile wide offers public fishing docks, water skiing, sail boating, swimming, and boat rentals. Motels and restaurants along the shore have private lake facilities for guests.

Continuing south on U.S. 65 in Louisiana you will find other outstanding recreational areas—Lake Yucatan near Newellton, La., and Lake Bruin State Park near St. Joseph, La.

A Louisiana resident fishing license is $2 per year for persons over 16. A nonresident license for those over 16 is $5, and a 7-day license is $2.

In Mississippi, some of the more highly utilized lakes are Moon Lake in Coahoma County, Beulah Lake in Bolivar County, and Eagle Lake in Warren County. The Mississippi Game and Fish Commission reports that these lakes have been providing excellent fishing for many years.

The Mississippi resident fishing license is $3 for fishing with artificial bait or from a boat. A resident fishing from the bank with natural bait does not need a license. The nonresident fishing fee is $6 for an annual license, while a permit for 3 days costs $1.50.

If you lean toward water sports, with the emphasis on fishing, you and your family will enjoy the natural horseshoe lakes of the Mississippi Delta.

Try them and see what I mean!

Flood Plain Safeguards:
A Community Concern

GILBERT F. WHITE

AS TOWNS GROW and as rural areas are settled, they often wake up to find that overnight they have lost precious reaches of land along valley bottoms. Sometimes it is a subdivision which cuts up a tree-bordered channel. More often it is scattered houses or industrial plants which take over the lowlands. Once invaded, these corridors of water and bottom land, with their distinctive vegetation and bird and mammal populations, are destroyed for public recreation and wildlife use and can be reclaimed only at rather heavy expense.

Because the valley lands commonly are subject to overflow from their streams, they lend themselves in a unique manner to community action to promote wise use of land in the public interest. With a few rare exceptions, every stream gets out of its banks from time to time and uses its flood plain to carry the flows that it cannot accommodate in its normal channel. The hazard of flooding at any given elevation above the channel can be estimated with some confidence, but the year of occurrence cannot be predicted.

Often newcomers to a river valley are completely unaware of the risk of the stream rising far above its banks. Even old residents may not have experienced the great floods that' come on the average of once in 200 years, and yet may strike 2 years in a row, as in the Connecticut valley in the early 1950's.

Once it is recognized, the flood hazard may become the basis for community measures which will preserve open space for desirable recreation and for habitat protection.

Several types of regulation are used by public groups to guide the use of flood

᭙   ᭙   ᭙

Gilbert F. White is *Professor* of Geography at the University of Chicago. He was Chairman of the Task Force on Federal Flood Control Policy during 1965–66.

133

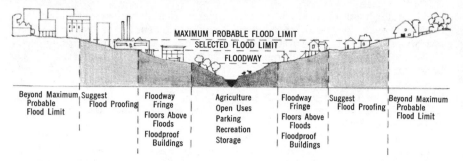

Beyond Maximum Probable Flood Limit	Suggest Flood Proofing	Floodway Fringe Floors Above Floods Floodproof Buildings	Agriculture Open Uses Parking Recreation Storage	Floodway Fringe Floors Above Floods Floodproof Buildings	Suggest Flood Proofing	Beyond Maximum Probable Flood Limit

plains. These include subdivision regulation, zoning, building ordinances, and channel encroachment restrictions. Some exist only on the statute books and are not applied. It takes a body of informed and concerned public opinion to support land use regulations.

Subdivisions may be permitted under rules that require the subdivider to leave the natural waterways clear of obstructions for drainage purposes or to dedicate strips of valley bottom for open space use. A number of California county planning boards, among others, now encourage any new development to leave the flood plains clear.

Zoning ordinances by counties or cities may restrict the flood plains to designated open uses, as in numerous sections of the Tennessee Valley or in Del Norte County, Calif. One Pennsylvania township permits agricultural, recreational, wildlife sanctuary, forestry, game farming, and public utility rights-of-way, and allows residential lots to include part of the flood plain zone so long as no structures are erected there.

In Anderson County, Tenn., the county zoned the land along the Clinch River and its tributaries and also the shores of the new Melton Hill reservoir.

City building ordinances may prevent structures from being constructed within the reach of ordinary floodwaters. For example, in several upstate New York towns residential use is permitted along flood plains so long as no structures are put in the way of floods: The houses are elevated above estimated flow lines and pleasant open space remains along the stream itself.

Many States, such as Indiana and New Jersey, now have regulations to prevent

the natural river channels from being obstructed unduly by filling, dumping, or construction. Not infrequently, a fill on one side of a valley will cause higher flooding on the other side or construction in a channel will lead to ponding of water upstream or to higher velocities in the stream. The State agencies use their police power to prevent this kind of damaging invasion of the flood plains.

Civic Groups Must Help

As with zoning and other regulations, effective policing of stream encroachment depends heavily upon the alertness and the persistence of citizen groups. State officers cannot be aware of all the places where valley filling is taking place. Subdivision plans need to be questioned by affected property owners. Zoning ordinances will neither be enacted nor enforced unless they have lively public support. Officials of Federal mortgage insurance agencies cannot always be informed as to where mortgages are proposed for new buildings in a hazard area.

People of the local community who know the flood conditions and the needs for the land must be prepared to speak up before the flood plain disappears beneath asphalt or brick.

The legal justification for stream encroachment, subdivision, and building regulations is generally clear. Wherever local zoning is authorized, the opportunity to make special provision for flood hazard is open—subject to State laws.

Nevertheless, it sometimes is argued that there is no solid legal basis for flood plain regulations. This argument usually is voiced by real estate operators who want freedom of action or by local officials who are unfamiliar with their own powers or with the practical experience of counties and cities in other parts of the United States.

Reviews of the legal experience with flood plain regulation may be obtained from the Tennessee Valley Authority.

But regulation should not be thought of as simply prohibiting the using of flood plains. It encourages wise use. It does not rule out uses that are in the public interest. Flood plain regulation has several purposes: To prevent any encroachment which would cause injury to others; to protect the health and safety of people who would be exposed to flood danger; to prevent the victimization of property owners who unknowingly might take on flood risk; to prevent public agencies from being saddled with the cost of bailing out or protecting people who locate in hazard areas; and to promote the general welfare of the community.

A reasonable regulation would permit intensive use of a flood plain where that would be in the interest of commercial growth, providing the structures do not increase the flood risk to others and are flood proofed—see chapter on page 146— to minimize public loss and personal danger. In some valleys, the soil deposited by previous stream overflow may serve best if preserved so that shallow ground water supplies are recharged when the floods go overbank.

The emphasis is upon making rational and conscious choices among the techniques which society has for dealing with flood hazards.

This is where the fact of flood dangers may favor a different kind of solution than for other, higher lands.

When the public expenses that result from exposing new property to flooding are taken into account, it may be found more desirable to hold the land in open uses than to develop it any further.

Or the desirable improvements may be in the direction of park or wildlife refuge management.

Essential to the planning and community decision leading to flood plain regulation is adequate flood information, including the heights of past floods, the probable extent of future overflows, and a map showing areas subject to flood. This should show the limits of whatever frequency of flooding can be determined. Starting at the streambank where water overflows every 2 or 3 years on the average, a cross section across a valley runs up to points beyond which water rises only once in a hundred years or even less frequently. But the infrequent flood may come next year bringing catastrophe.

The more detailed reports, such as those prepared by the Corps of Engineers in their Flood Plain Information Reports, as in Metropolitan Denver and Detroit, and by the Tennessee Valley Authority for scores of places in the TVA area, show several zones according to estimated frequency of flooding. They also give details on floodway capacity and constrictions. Certain of the maps prepared for the Soil Conservation Service watershed surveys indicate the boundaries of land subject to 25-year or 50-year frequency floods. Flood hazard maps published by the U.S. Geological Survey usually give the limits of the maximum flood of record (a solid fact where the zones are called into question in court) and give a basis for estimating the recurrence interval of different height flows.

Soil Survey Maps Used

In some places, the soil survey maps of alluvial soils are used as a rough delimitation of flood hazards, although alluvial soil—the product of past stream deposits—does not necessarily coincide with present stream overflow. The Lower Salford Township supervisors in Pennsylvania adopted the soil survey delineation of alluvial soils as a basis for setting a flood plain conservation district. And a new subdivision plan for Worthington— Green Valley near Towson, Md., used soil survey classification for designating lowland to be kept in open space.

In some regions, just the publication of the basic flood hazard report has a significant influence upon land development without any formal regulations. The maps of flood hazard prepared by the U.S. Geological Survey in cooperation with the planning agencies in the northeastern Illinois metropolitan area are used

135

by land appraisers and mortgage agencies. These maps also are a major help in the efforts of the Cook County Forest Preserve District toward acquisition of new park lands.

Federal agencies now use such data in their decisions on location and design of new public structures and highways and also in insuring of private mortgages.

Wherever streams overflow their banks the possible ways of dealing with flood hazard deserve to be taken into account in planning for wise use. Regulations by local agencies help to do this, and in many valleys may lead to open space uses which are not impaired by flooding.

Farm Ponds Add Up
to Oceans of Recreation

FRED P. MILLER and WILLIAM J. HORVATH

EVERY SUMMER thousands of city dwellers and suburbanites are replacing that drive to the ocean or lake with a trip to a farm pond as the paying guests of farmers across the Nation. A dairy farmer in Maryland's rolling Piedmont said of his pond, "From the standpoint of esthetics and family enjoyment, this is the greatest asset on my farm." Many urban people would agree that the farm pond is a potent recreational asset for them as well.

For farmers, the recreational benefits of a pond have often more than justified their investment. That is to say nothing of increased values from water conservation or providing water for the livestock, fire protection, wildlife, and from supplemental irrigation.

Farmers are not the only persons putting in ponds, however. The local Extension Service offices and the Soil Conservation Service offices are being contacted more and more often every year by people living in urban communities and in cities who have purchased a piece of land or a small farm "just out-of-town" and want to know how to build a pond for recreational purposes.

Let us consider some of the things a farm pond must have in order to become an enjoyable asset.

The swimming, fishing, picnicking, and the other recreational activities which millions of Americans are enjoying each year from farm ponds did not come about by simply digging a hole or damming a gully. Without an understanding of essential features of design and construction, it is unwise to undertake a farm pond as a do-it-yourself adventure.

You can obtain published information through your local office of the Cooperative Extension Service, the Soil Conservation Service, or soil conservation district.

These agencies can provide competent technical assistance or steer you to other State and Federal agencies which may help you. They can inform you of State and local health and water laws.

In many instances, cost-sharing can be made available through the USDA Agricultural Stabilization and Conservation

ψ ψ ψ

Fred P. Miller is *Assistant Professor* and *Specialist* in Extension Soil and Water Resources, Department of Agronomy at the University of Maryland.

William J. Horvath is *Executive Secretary*, Maryland State Soil Conservation Committee.

Service. State conservation agencies can help you stock your pond with fish and provide assistance in designing facilities for swimming, fishing, picnicking, landscaping, and maintenance. Sport fish for stocking may also be available from the U.S. Fish and Wildlife Service.

In selecting a site for your pond, be sure to consider the topography, soil type, and the water supply.

Topography or lay-of-the-land will influence the pond size and shape. Using these features to your advantage can greatly reduce the costs of construction.

An earthen embankment across drainageways or draws bounded by steeply sloping sides will make an ideal site. The steeper the slopes are, the narrower the pond. Ideally, steepness of the banks decreases above the damsite—allowing the water to spread over a wider area. Inlets and small coves enhance the configuration of your pond and provide sanctuaries for wildlife.

Take advantage of the existing trees to provide an esthetic setting. However, avoid flooding stumps and brush.

Do not overlook any unused swampy hollows, since they may be turned into a beautiful farm pond.

If the topography is too flat for impounding water in a natural draw, you can excavate a "dug-out pond."

A desirable soil type is essential for a successful farm pond. Since your pond is a vessel for holding water, it must be located on a soil containing enough clay to minimize seepage. A site that appears ideal may not hold water if sufficient clay is not present. Be cautious about constructing your pond on shallow soils where the bedrock is near the surface—especially limestone or rock containing fracture planes and joints.

Avoid sand, gravel, or organic deposits unless they contain enough clay to prevent excess seepage of water.

Sprayed-on asphalt liners and other materials can be used to seal a pond, but they add to your cost, and they may deteriorate or become damaged.

To keep your pond filled, you must have an adequate source of water. If the pond is to be "fed" by a watershed, the area should be of a sufficient size to maintain the water level, and yet not large enough to create a flood hazard or to wash nutrients from the pond. Ideally, the water level should never fluctuate more than 2 feet. Do not be tempted into damming continually flowing streams with large watersheds.

The size of a satisfactory watershed will depend upon the volume of the pond, the amount of rainfall, watershed topography, and use. A wooded watershed produces nearly silt-free water, but will yield less runoff than equivalent areas of cropland or pasture. Strict conservation techniques must be employed on cultivated watersheds to minimize the production of sediment. In several Midwestern States, a 10- to 20-acre watershed is adequate for each surface acre of water to be stored, but this ratio will vary with the local conditions and rainfall.

Do not overlook other water sources such as springs, artesian wells, underground drainage, or small streams. Dugout ponds in sections of very level topography are dependent upon underground drainage or high water tables. Always remember that a half-filled pond becomes an open invitation for weeds.

This pond, at Gordonsville, Va., attracts 20 to 30 boys and girls on good swimming days. The 1.8 acre pond is stocked with bass and bream for fishing. It also waters farm livestock and is used for fire protection.

The size of your pond will depend on the available site, the water supply, and intended use. Ponds that are smaller than a quarter of an acre in surface area are seldom very satisfactory. Fishing becomes less successful as the pond size decreases below one acre.

The larger ponds are, of course, more costly, and many States have maximum limits on the size of the pond and the watershed. Special construction permits are required if you exceed these limits. For family enjoyment, ponds from ½ to 5 acres are usually adequate—depending upon the local conditions and personal interests involved.

Water depth should be at least 8 feet for swimming and for fishing. A 1-acre pond should have about 25 percent of

Fishing has been good in this 20-acre farm pond at Madison, Ga. Submerged platform at the right background is used in regular fertilization program.

the area covered with 8 to 15 feet of water for successful fish management.

Deep water is required to minimize the effects of possible oxygen depletion during hot days in late summer and in winter when the pond surface is frozen. The depth requirement is less in the Southern States than in Northern States.

Avoid extensive areas of water that are less than 3 feet deep. Shallow water encourages mosquito production and the growth of aquatic vegetation which adversely affects fishing. The vegetation is a nuisance, even though it can be brought under control.

The best time to construct and complete a pond is in late summer or early fall. If swampy areas are to be utilized, they are usually driest at this time of year. Fall and winter precipitation will help fill the pond before weeds have become established. Fall is also a very desirable time for stocking fish.

If your pond is to be used for swimming, the diving raft or platform should be anchored solidly in at least 8 feet of water. Keep crossbars either well above or below the waterline to prevent them from being encased with winter ice and lifted from their base.

A clean beach area at least 30 feet wide should take advantage of natural scenic characteristics. A beach slope of around 15 to 1 is desirable. A layer of sand or of pea-size gravel 6 to 12 inches thick should cover the area and all the approaches. A grassy area around the beach will add to its beauty. Landscaping with trees, shrubs, and vines will help to provide privacy.

Other desirable beach features include an outdoor fireplace and picnic tables. These facilities can be used year around for activities ranging from picnics to ice skating parties. Electric lights, sanitary facilities, and other structures add to the enjoyment of the pond. Make sure that sanitary drainage flows away from the pond. Periodic water tests should also be made to guard against pollution.

A conspicuous sign stating the water depth is a desirable safety feature, and a life preserver ring with a nylon rope mounted in an easily accessible place is a must. Other safety equipment might

Winter fun on a farm pond at Arthur, W. Va.

include life buoys, boathooks, a ladder, and a red and white painted pole to use to haul a drowning person to safety.

And don't forget to check with your insurance company to analyze your degree of liability. Responsibility of the landowner varies in each State, but as a rule, the liability is reduced through the use of simple deterrents like fences, gates, and signs. Liability insurance is available.

Presence of the pond may also entitle you to a rate reduction on your fire insurance. You can check this out with your insurance agent.

Although the earmark of any good swimming pool is clear water, the water in a farm pond should be kept dark for fish production and weed control. This will not prevent its use for swimming.

Plants need light, but if the water is dark and fairly deep, the light is cut off and plant growth from the bottom of the pond is then discouraged.

Darkness in the water is usually caused by microscopic plants like algae which are consumed by microscopic animals. These animals are ingested by the larger aquatic organisms which are then in turn eaten by small fish, many of which serve as food for bass and other larger fish. Thus, the amount of algae regulates the quantity and quality of fish that your pond will produce.

As in the production of crops, your pond must be fertile to produce algae and good fish yields. Runoff from watersheds may contain sufficient fertility to support a fish population. If your water

Trout leap out of water as they are fed in Michigan pond, near East Jordan. Pond was converted from a barnyard into an income-producing recreation enterprise.

remains clear, however, fertilizer may have to be added. A general rule is that if you can clearly see your hand when your arm is immersed up to your elbow, you should add fertilizer.

Fertilizer recommendations are available from the State and Federal agencies.

Bass and bluegills are the most commonly stocked species throughout much of the country. To maintain a balanced population, approximately 10 to 15 bluegills should be removed for every bass. Trout require year-round cool temperatures and deep water. Information about types of fish, time of stocking, and fish management can be obtained through appropriate public agencies.

In landscaping your pond, fence off the entire pond area. Do not plant trees and shrubs on the dam and spillway. A tree-free shoreline will provide access for fishing and minimize leaf fall in the water. Maintain a healthy sod on these areas to check erosion and act as a final filter for incoming water. Keep the sod mowed and fertilized. Prevent silt from entering the pond by employing strict conservation measures, especially when the watershed is cultivated. Except for the beach area, maintain steep slopes at the waterline to discourage aquatic weeds.

A few ducks can assist in eating some surface pond weeds or scum, and they make attractive pond accessories.

The immense demand for outdoor recreation is a byproduct of our affluent society. City people are more than willing to pay for farm pond recreation.

Brackish Waters
for Sport and Profit

WILLIAM W. NEELY

IKE MANY Americans these days, you may be looking for outdoor space. It may be for your own recreation. It may be for profit in providing others with recreational facilities. With the increasing demands for land, where can you find such space?

One answer is through use of brackish waters and saline soils. There are not many competitors for this kind of land and water.

If you have tasted brackish water, you know that it has a salty and bitter taste. This very simple test tells you that there are limitations to the use of this kind of water. Wherever you find any brackish water, you can be sure that the soil accompanying it is also salty.

Many kinds of plants will not tolerate such soil conditions. Few things will grow for commercial farm crops. As a result, a large amount of our land is going unused for any present economic purpose. But this land may be quite well suited to recreational uses.

And no matter where you are in the United States, you are within a few hundred miles of brackish waters and saline soils. They are along the Atlantic, Gulf, and Pacific coasts—often extending 30 miles inland. This sort of soil or water also occurs in broad areas of the interior of our country, in the Midwestern and the Western States.

Your first thought of marshes for recreation will very likely center on hunting ducks or other waterfowl. But most of the coastal brackish marshes are covered with thick growths of cordgrasses or of needlerush. Neither will offer much to ducks. And unless you do something to make these marshes more suitable for waterfowl, you will find that you have pretty sorry hunting.

You can change a brackish marsh—either coastal or inland—into excellent duck fields and ponds. In many cases it is somewhat easier to do than with fresh water marshes.

An almost foolproof way to make a brackish area into a very attractive duck spot is to convert it into a widgeongrass pond. The duck hunters who do not own land have a particular opportunity to provide themselves with a place to hunt through widgeongrass ponds. Since so much of the brackish water portions of our country are going unused, it should not be difficult to lease a good location for hunting purposes.

Widgeongrass ponds are better suited to an arrangement of this sort than any other type of duck hunting development. This is so because they don't require regular on-the-site management.

Once the pond is established, only occasional checks are needed to see that it stays full of water and the water is brackish enough. Another advantage is that normally the initial costs will be

ψ　ψ　ψ

William W. Neely is a *Biologist* with the Soil Conservation Service at Columbia, S.C. One of his specialties is brackish marshes and the development of techniques to manage them.

141

the only significant expense which is incurred over a long period of years.

I have seen many examples of widgeongrass pond lease arrangements working well for both the landowners and the hunters. In these cases, the landowners did not have the ready cash to build a widgeongrass pond or else were reluctant to invest their money in one. In exchange for a rent-free lease for a specified number of years, a group of hunters put in the diking and water control structures.

The rent-free period varied to adjust for the cost of development of the site, but 5 years was average. At the end of this period, the hunters had the option of renting the widgeongrass pond yearly for an agreed upon charge.

Thus, the landowner had a capital improvement on his land without making any investment—plus a source of yearly income. And the hunters were delighted to have a place where they could hunt at a reasonable cost.

Low Dike Needed

To change a brackish marsh into a widgeongrass pond, you need a low dike to impound brackish water. You don't need deep water. Two feet is good. This depth of water will kill the cordgrasses or needlerush, and they quickly disintegrate. It is also deep enough to grow a good stand of widgeongrass.

Widgeongrass (*Ruppia maritima*) is a choice food for 15 species of ducks. It is a submersed plant (it grows beneath the surface of the water). Ducks eat the leaves, stems, seed, and even the roots. Widgeongrass grows in a wide range of water salinity, from just about fresh to even saltier than sea water.

For easy management, the most desirable salinity for a widgeongrass pond is about one-third the saltiness of sea water. This much salinity keeps out cattails and other fresh water plants which otherwise may be pests. Water saltier than one-third sea strength is all right, but is of no advantage. You won't need chemical tests to tell you if the salinity of your pond is all right. If it isn't, fresh water plants will begin to grow.

Then you can just let in more brackish water using either high tides or a pump.

Even without planting, widgeongrass will usually show up in a brackish water pond within a year or two. But you should not wait for that. Rake a few bushels of widgeongrass from a neighbor's pond or else purchase it from an aquatic nursery and scatter it across the surface of your pond. It doesn't take much to get widgeongrass started since it spreads very rapidly.

After the ducks feed in your pond all winter, it may appear that they have destroyed your widgeongrass. But don't be alarmed. There will be plenty of seeds and roots to establish stands for another year, you will discover.

It may be that the place you have to manage for ducks is not salty enough for a widgeongrass pond. Yet it is too salty to grow fresh water duck food plants. Or perhaps you cannot impound deep enough water in order to establish a widgeongrass pond.

You can still make a good duck field. In this case the duck food plant to grow is saltmarsh bulrush (*Scirpus robustus*). Ducks will eat the seeds.

One secret for growing a good stand of saltmarsh bulrush is a fluctuating water level. This is not hard to provide. Enclose the field with a dike and install a water level control device. During the spring and summer, gradually raise the water level from a saturated soil condition to a flooded depth of some 8 to 12 inches and back down to wet soil again.

Each cycle should take a month to 6 weeks, but the timing is not critical. Brackish water for flooding can be from the tides or from a pump.

During the fall and winter, hold the water level in your saltmarsh bulrush field around 12 inches deep for good duck feeding conditions.

Brackish wet lands have been successfully developed for other sorts of hunting. Fields for snipe shooting can be developed, and managed, at relatively low costs. If you have tried snipe shooting, you know that the snipe's fast, zigzag flight makes of it an extraordinary game bird indeed.

Good snipe fields have been made in

locations ranging from fresh water to those where the water was as salty as half of sea strength. Here again, water control is the basic requirement. The dikes and pipes for a snipe field usually do not have to be as large as for duck fields and ponds. Enough drainage is needed so that the field can support farm machinery. A reliable source of water for flooding the field is required.

The principal foods for snipe are wormlike animals in wet soil. You can encourage the production of these animal foods by disking the field in the early fall of each year. The native vegetation thus turned into the soil makes humus favorable to many of the animals of snipe diet. At the same time, the ground in the field is left in the bare condition which the birds like the best.

After you disk your field, shallowly flood it with water. Puddled is perhaps a better term. Water will have to be let into the field rather often for it to stay puddled all through the fall and winter.

Wild Goose Browse

Coastal lands infrequently flooded by brackish water usually have native stands of marshhay cordgrass (*Spartina patens*). The tender new growth of this plant is good browse for wild geese.

Fields of marshhay cordgrass can be easily managed as wild goose pastures. Burning during late summer is all that is required. The fire removes the tall vegetation and results in tender green shoots during the fall and winter months.

There is increasing interest in the possibility of using brackish marshes in the Southeast to grow commercial crops of shrimp. While this practice is in the trial stage so far, it appears feasible.

Shrimp spawn offshore, but the young move into brackish marshes in coastal areas to spend the first few months of their lives. If these young shrimp are held in salt water ponds constructed in the marshes, they will rapidly grow to a marketable size.

In our South Carolina trials, we have stocked ponds with young shrimp by letting water flow into the pond during high tides through a specially designed water control structure during May and June. At that time the young shrimp are about the size of mosquito "wiggletails," and they are swept into the pond with the flow of water.

By late October or early November, the shrimp are about 6 inches long and ready for harvest. This is done by draining off the pond through a long, inclined screen in the water control structure. The shrimp are thus strained from the water and can be raked into baskets at the end of the screen.

Sport Fishing

Sport fishing is another use of brackish water ponds. These ponds are built in salt marshes similarly to shrimp ponds. Stocking with fish is done by filling up the pond with water from a nearby tidewater creek. Wild fingerlings are numerous in the creeks and are swept into the pond with the inflow of water.

Since the desirable sport fish species spawn at different times in late winter and spring, water is let into the pond at intervals to bring in several kinds of fingerlings. The fingerlings grow to fishing size in a few months.

It is unlikely that any of the kinds of salt water sport fish will spawn in the pond. This is not of much concern since fingerlings can be stocked as needed.

You can get help in planning for all of these uses of brackish waters from your local Soil Conservation Service office. Such assistance will be particularly helpful in choosing suitable sites and in the design of dikes and of other water control structures.

By making them more productive of fish and wildlife, brackish marshes can help fulfill our increasing need for outdoor recreation facilities. At the same time, user fees can provide income.

Perhaps your librarian can get you a loan copy or photostat of the following publication, which gives more details than are covered in this brief chapter: *Saline Soils and Brackish Waters in Management of Wildlife, Fish, and Shrimp,* by William W. Neely; Transactions 27th North American Wildlife and Natural Resources Conference, pp. 321–335.

Ponds Bejewel the Land

M. L. DuMARS

AS THE AIRLINER began its descent for a landing at Kansas City, I gazed out casually—then, all at once, intently. Spread out on the dark velvet of the land below was a dazzling display of jewels.

Far as eye could see, gems of sparkling light rivaled the springtime solar splendor they reflected, flashing an invitation to the world to admire their untold wealth.

For these jewels were no ornamental stones, but ponds of water—more precious still. They were a showcase representing the hundreds of thousands of ponds that the men of my generation have installed on age-old gift-of-nature sites to improve their land and their living.

As seen from my plane window, the faraway dots of light and the nearby dashes signaled as if in code that this was a beloved and cared-for land.

They signaled, too, the conservation-mindedness of the United States public, which has shared the cost of constructing well over 2 million ponds on the farms and ranches of the Nation in just three decades. This is a striking average of over 650 for each county.

In conservation terms, a pond's major meaning is grass, the protective cover. On semiarid rangelands, well-spaced watering places enable cattle and sheep to graze vast areas not otherwise accessible to them. They need not overgraze and destroy part of the range while other grass is unused. Where rains are more plentiful and crops are grown in abundance, a pond for livestock water enables a farmer—on a practical basis—to convert a sloping, erosion-prone field into pasture.

Thus, a pond becomes meat and milk,

leather and wool. What's more, the grass-covered field holds onto its soil when the rains pound down and wash topsoil from unprotected land into rivers, lakes, and harbors. So the pond that means grass also equates with soil—soil that would otherwise no longer exist.

The metastasis of a cancerous gully etching lesions in the earth can be stopped and healed by a well-placed dam and through soil-conserving vegetation on the surrounding watershed.

Droughtproofing of a farm is almost impossible, but ponds help greatly in the dry spells that occur everywhere. In the usually well-watered Northeast during the prolonged drought that reached disaster proportions in 1965, many dairymen had to haul water long distances for their cattle—an expensive, discouraging act of desperation. Those who had impounded water on their land were especially thankful. The 4,300 ponds that they had constructed in just the last 2 years before the severest phase of the drought held a year's supply of water for 380,000 cows, which is more cows than there are in Vermont and Massachusetts together.

Irrigation water also comes from ponds on many farms, especially where the irrigation needs are comparatively small and infrequent. In one recent year, more than 5,000 farmers constructed dams for irrigation purposes alone.

As in bygone days, a pond is often the

ৠ ৠ ৠ

M. L. DuMars is *Director* of the Information Division in USDA's Agricultural Stabilization and Conservation Service.

old swimmin' hole and the fishin' place, and today it is more than ever prized as the safe substitute for a polluted stream. The typical farm pond is free of industrial waste products, and the careful farmer protects it from chemical pollution as he controls crop pests. Fenced to keep livestock from entering the water and damaging the dam, the good farm pond is relatively free of animal contamination.

Properly managed, it is free of damaging concentrations of algae and weeds—still but not stagnant, enjoyable for both swimming and fishing, a good place for children to learn to row a boat, a landing spot for ducks, an attraction for other wildlife, a quiet place for a picnic, a pleasant sight for the passerby. More than one farmowner has found his pond so attractive that he has changed his house-building plans and located within sight of the water.

Fire-conscious farmers have pooled work and money to build ponds near roads as sources of water for firefighting in many communities. Of course, a pond near the farm buildings is a special protection against destructive blazes.

The dam serves in place of a bridge across a low place on a growing number of country roads. In some counties and townships, the officials responsible for roads and bridges allocate money for the construction of a wider dam than would be needed by the farmer or the group of farmers who are building the dam for conservation purposes.

Ponds possess a luxurious quality for many of us who grew up in relatively dry places such as my native plains of Kansas. For many of us, water sports were unheard of. Few people bothered to fish the little holes along the banks of the trickling rivers. There was hardly any place a boy could learn to swim. At times he earned a parental scowl if he wasted half a dipper of cistern water by taking more from the bucket than he wanted to drink. Today

Pond on farm near Grafton, W. Va.

in that home territory, there are man-made lakes and ponds that dot the landscape like a heavenly galaxy on earth.

The Nation's rapid addition of ponds is doubtless due in part to people's liking for ponds and higher income with which to indulge their desires. However, public policy has played an important part. The public encourages farmers to construct ponds for conservation purposes by paying part of the cost, by providing the services of engineers and other technicians, and by providing credit to farmers who cannot get commercial credit. The cost-sharing is administered by the Agri-cultural Stabilization and Conservation Service, the technical services by the Soil Conservation Service, and the credit by the Farmers Home Administration.

Some States also help stock ponds with fish, and farmers can get from SCS and State agencies practical information on methods that enable them to get maximum use of their ponds and to guard against siltation and other hazards.

This information is widely used, for the landowner typically takes pride in his pond. It is a jewel not only as seen from the sky, but also as treasured and displayed by its owner.

Flood Proofing

JAMES E. GODDARD

O WNERS of flood plains properties can drastically reduce flood losses by use of flood-proofing measures. The costs are often surprisingly small compared to the expected savings.

Thousands of residences, commercial buildings, and industries on the flood plains sustain some degree of flood loss every year. Huge losses are suffered to structures, equipment, and stored products in both urban and rural areas. And the amount of these losses is growing.

Our rapid growth of population has increased the pressure to use lands that are convenient to the centers of growth. Consequently, many flood plains have been developed which should have been left in open space for recreation, agriculture, or for other uses which flooding would not seriously damage.

Flood control programs have provided partial protection for a large number of flood hazard areas. But it is not possible to protect all areas. The size of the problem measured both physically and in dollars of cost is too big. And flood control isn't physically practical for some areas.

Floodwaters affect buildings in varying ways. A horizontal force acts to crush the structure walls. Water pressure can force water through cracks, small openings, and even through some types of walls, thus causing the buildings to leak. The buoying or floating effect of the water may lift the building enough to permit the momentum or power of the moving water to slide the structure from its foundation. And erosion or scouring by swiftly flowing water tends to undermine the foundation itself.

Flood proofing is an action you yourself can take to make your own buildings watertight and to adjust the contents or location of your buildings to minimize

ϙ   ϙ   ϙ

James E. Goddard was Chief of Local Flood Relations, Tennessee Valley Authority, Knoxville, Tenn., through 1966 and is now a consultant with the Corps of Engineers, Washington, D.C.

146

flood losses. It also includes actions to protect roads, streets, lawns, fields, livestock, and your family from floods.

Flood proofing is especially effective in areas where the depths of floodwater are not great. It is also most effective where the floodwater velocities are slow and for areas flooded for only short periods.

You may think that you do not have a flood problem because there is a flood control dam upstream or because the river or stream channel near you has been enlarged. Don't be too sure. Few flood control projects provide complete protection. You can usually increase your individual protection by flood proofing your buildings and property.

Another false belief is that future floods will not be any higher than those of the past. Do not be misled by such beliefs. Contact your city or county engineer—they can often obtain information for you, or at least advise you, concerning future flood heights to be expected.

Maybe your activities require buildings located upon the banks of rivers and streams. These may be pumphouses for water supply, warehouses for temporary storage of goods being shipped by barge or boat, or buildings for water-related recreation. Buildings for such activities can be flood proofed to provide a reasonable degree of protection from the floods which you should expect.

There are three main types of flood proofing. One consists of the permanent measures for permanent protection, such as permanently closed openings in outer walls and installation of automatic valves on the sewerlines.

A second consists of temporary measures prepared in advance, but put into effect only following flood warnings or forecasts. An example would be a sewer valve which you would close by hand. Another would be a window or a door equipped with a removable cover which you would put in place only when flooding was actually expected.

The third type consists of emergency measures which you would improvise during a flood or carry out according to plans made prior to the flood. Examples are temporary removal of personal property, merchandise, or equipment and rescheduling of shipments to reduce the amount of commercial stocks, industrial products, produce, stored grain, or other items that would be damaged.

A study of flood proofing and possible actions that could be taken was made by John R. Sheaffer in 1960. His report, titled *Flood Proofing: An Element in Flood Damage Reduction Program,* is Research Paper No. 65 of the Department of Geography, University of Chicago, Chicago, Ill. An *Introduction to Flood Proofing* was prepared by the Center for Urban Studies, University of Chicago, for the Corps of Engineers and the Tennessee Valley Authority and published by those agencies in 1967.

Waterproofing Walls

One common adjustment is to seal the basement or other masonry walls with waterproofing compounds to prevent or reduce leakage. Such applications can be made on interior and exposed sides of walls at any time. Use of tarred paper and asphalt-based paints, available at any lumberyard, on the exterior sides of walls below ground at time of construction is good. An alternative is to provide drainage or pumping facilities. Sometimes a combination will be the least costly to you.

Your buildings may have small windows or other openings near the ground. Years ago they may have provided light or air to the basement rooms, but they probably are seldom used any more. They can be sealed permanently with materials through which water will not seep. Or you might use glass block to replace the windows. These would provide light and still not break due to water pressures.

"Sandbagging" is a well-known emergency protection. But this doesn't really mean that sand is required. Plain dirt is usually better. Yet it is still a good idea to be prepared by having cloth bags stored in a convenient location so they can be promptly filled and placed where needed. If you haven't provided for such bags, use any cloth containers that have a fine mesh. Bags of flour, fertilizer, cement, or feed can be used for sealing small openings, but this is, of course, more expensive than using earth.

Removable bulkheads or covers are the most effective way of sealing doors and windows. These bulkheads can be made of wood, steel, or aluminum. They should be built for fastening to bolts set in the frame of the opening. Neoprene or some other type of gasket should be used to make a tight seal. Bulkheads should be stored near the opening with necessary nuts in sacks which are attached to the bulkheads themselves.

The bulkheads can be permanently installed inside many display windows in a way which will not affect the exterior appearance. They may be hinged from the top of the openings and then lowered into position when they are needed.

Watertight caps with gaskets can be fitted on storage tanks. These tanks, and other floatable storage such as lumber, should be anchored in order to prevent them from floating away. Frame structures especially should be well anchored because they will float off their foundations more readily than masonry buildings. This can be done by bolting the tanks or the structures to thick concrete footings or bases which are designed to withstand the water's floating effect.

Creosote Timbers

Creosoting of timbers that will be exposed to floodwaters will protect them from rot. If waterproof cements are used when installing asphalt tile or linoleum, repairs after flooding will cost less.

During all floods there is a fire hazard. Electric power can be shut off, gas jets or valves can be closed, and open flames can be doused. Where you need power, even during the flood, locate the control panels and incoming powerlines above any expected flood levels.

Power to electric appliances should be turned off before they are flooded. After flooding, the appliances should be thoroughly cleaned and dried before being used again. Rugs and other furnishings should be cleaned promptly after flooding.

Erosion of lawns and of fields can be decreased through proper placement of trees and shrubbery.

Fences and hedges can be arranged so as to reduce the speed and thus the eroding effects of rushing floodwaters. Your county engineer, agricultural agent, or city engineer can advise you. Natural dunes along coastal areas should be retained because they provide fine protection against tidal action.

Roadbeds can be given greater protection by reducing the scouring action of floodwaters. Culverts and other openings should be large enough to handle most floods without overflowing and washing away the highway fill. Trees or shrubs can be planted or heavy rock placed on the slopes of road fills to resist washing. Where the fills are affected by groundhogs, gophers, or by other rodents, the rodents should be destroyed.

If you live in a flood plain or if you have equipment or other removable properties in the areas subject to flooding, you should have a plan to remove valuables in times of emergency. Some goods and equipment can be lifted to higher levels in the same structure. You should be prepared with the necessary materials to build platforms or to strengthen supports of available shelves.

You should know which roads flood at various flood heights to assure your safe escape from areas that are expected to be flooded to great depths.

Grain and other perishables should be stored at levels above the floods or in structures that are flood proofed. Storage of major quantities should be at elevations above any reasonable flooding.

Where the depths of flooding are not expected to be great, homes and other structures in flood hazard areas can be raised. They can be jacked up and their foundation walls raised at reasonable cost. Sometimes buildings can be moved to sites which are above the anticipated flood heights.

If you are building a new home, locate it free from flooding or design it to withstand any flooding with minimum losses.

In rural areas, there should be openings in the structures and in the surrounding fences or walls which will permit access to higher land for the livestock and for removing equipment.

The best time, and most economical way, to flood proof is when you build your home or other structures.

148

The Constant Fight Against Pollution

JESSE LUNIN

RECENT droughts in the Northeast have reminded us that water shortages can occur even in humid areas. This was apparent in the summer of 1966 as one traveled and saw stunted corn and other crops, brown pastures and lawns, and wilting shrubs. The imposition of restrictions on the use of water for watering lawns and for washing cars, and the possibilities of even more drastic curbs, has made urban dwellers as conscious as rural residents of water problems. In New York City, restaurant patrons have had to request water in order to have it served with their meals.

America is in no immediate danger of "running out of water." People in the arid West have always been aware that water is a precious commodity and must be conserved. In the humid East, an apparent abundance of water led to complacency until recently when two factors created concern over our water supply. First, the periods of drought from 1961 to 1966 in the Northeast affected crop production and depleted the surface and ground water supplies. Secondly, attention was called to the rapid increases in the rates of pollution of these waters resulting from increased urban and industrial expansion. As a result, there is an increasing awareness of the need for conserving both the quantity and quality of our Nation's water supplies.

Water is a renewable resource, but it is not inexhaustible. Nature's hydrologic cycle assures us of a never-ending renewal of our water supply. When water is used for municipal, industrial, or for agricultural purposes, it is not destroyed, but generally finds its way back into our water supply. This used water is changed; it now carries some waste materials. These contaminated waters are often dumped into larger bodies of water or are disposed of on land. In the latter instance, evaporation concentrates some of the wastes on the soil surface, whereas water moving through the soil will eventually carry some of the wastes down into the ground water supplies. Eventually, all water evaporates and later returns to the earth as rain or snow in a relatively pure state, ready for another use.

Through this never-ending cycle, there is just as much water in this country now as there ever was; but the amount does not increase. However, our explosive population growth and the rapid agricultural and industrial expansion that goes with it have caused our water needs to soar. By withdrawing water from streams too rapidly and by depositing too much waste too quickly, we have in some instances upset the balance of nature's built-in renovation processes for conserving water. As a result, some of our streams and lakes have become "wet deserts"—there is still plenty of water in them, but it is water so polluted that it supports almost no life at all.

૭ ૭ ૭

Jesse Lunin is *Chief* of the Northeast Branch, Soil and Water Conservation Research Division, Agricultural Research Service.

149

It has been estimated that the largest total dependable fresh water supply this country can ever hope to have is about 650 billion gallons per day. Today, we use almost 400 billion gallons of water a day. By the year 2000, we will need more than 1,000 billion gallons per day. Obviously, to meet such needs, we must preserve the quality of every gallon of water so that it can be safely reused several times over.

Just what is water pollution? It is the presence of any substance or material that renders the water unsuitable for any given purpose. However, what may be considered a pollutant for one specific use may not be true for another use. For example, drinking water must be of higher quality than that used for irrigation. When dealing with the problem, we must consider the multiple-use aspects of our water resources, and the fact that pollution of a small stream will ultimately affect the water quality of a large lake or river. For this reason, we must understand the source and types of various pollutants encountered and how they relate to the various uses of water.

Major Sources

The major sources of pollution are (1) sediment resulting from agricultural or construction activities, (2) municipal sewage, and (3) industrial wastes. Sediment has often been accused of being the No. 1 pollutant of our streams and rivers. Certainly it is the oldest adversary in the centuries-old battle against water pollution. It has been said that a history of the human race could be written in mud. Civilizations have collapsed because of their inability to cope with this menace.

Sediment affects us all in many ways. First, it represents the loss of another major natural resource, the soil. The sediment content of water impairs its value for municipal and industrial uses and necessitates costly treatment prior to use. Deposition of this material in lakes and reservoirs decreases their storage capacity. This can be corrected in some instances only by expensive dredging operations. Deposition in streams and rivers may alter their course and result

in streambank erosion and navigational hazards. And sedimentation in drainage ditches greatly reduces their efficiency. During floods, sediment deposition is responsible for costly damage to farmlands and other personal property.

Past records show that agriculture has been the greatest offender in contributing to sediment pollution because of poor farming practices. But now, however, through the efforts of agricultural research and the action agencies, good soil and water conservation practices are being developed and applied and are greatly reducing the soil loss from agricultural lands.

Intensified housing construction in urban areas and highway development, however, are causing a rapid increase in the sediment load of streams and rivers in many areas. The need for increased conservation practices in urban and industrial development is urgent.

Aside from the soil losses, agriculture's contribution to the water pollution problem may arise from two sources. First, the use of certain agricultural chemicals, such as pesticides, which may find their way into water supplies either in a dissolved form or adsorbed on sediment particles. The second source arises from waste disposal problems associated with concentrations of livestock as in feedlots. Impact of these sources on the overall pollution problem is being evaluated, and corrective measures are being developed through agricultural research.

Municipal sewage is of relatively recent origin as a pollutant. It was first brought to the public attention in the 19th century by a London physician who showed that that city's cholera epidemic had been caused by just one sewage-contaminated well. Even though the contamination of drinking water by disease germs has been nearly eliminated in this country, hundreds of communities are still discharging raw sewage into streams and rivers.

When we consider that this sewage contains effluents from toilets, hospitals, laundries, industrial plants, etc., then the potential of the pollutants as a health hazard is apparent. Sewage-contaminated water cannot, of course, be used for home consumption or irrigating food crops.

The problem of municipal sewage disposal is complicated by the fact that, years ago, most cities combined their storm and waste disposal sewers. Many of these combined systems work well, but others cannot cope with sudden heavy rains. When such storms occur, water mixed with sewage may flood and disable treatment plants unless bypassed, untreated, into a stream. In either case, the people may have little protection for several days from these wastes which may contain disease germs.

Even if adequately treated to eliminate the health hazard, sewage is esthetically undesirable because of odors and colors produced. Detergents have posed a particular disposal problem. Although there is no indication that they are injurious to health, they can cause foaming, which can clog treatment plants and, at the least, spoil the scenic beauty of streams.

One consequence of pollution, usually resulting from the discharge of either raw or treated sewage wastes into water sources, is an increase in nutrient levels in these waters. These higher nutrient levels result in a rapid increase in the biological population of the water. Excessive respiration and decomposition of aquatic plants deplete the oxygen content in these waters causing decay which, in turn, may produce an undesirable taste, odor, color, and turbidity. Increasing nutrient contents may also result in an increase in more undesirable species of aquatic life. All these factors make the water unsuitable for domestic, industrial, and recreational purposes. Many examples of this may be cited, such as Rock River in Wisconsin and Lake Washington near Seattle, Wash.

Rural and suburban residents should be aware that septic tanks and cesspools are a potential source of pollution to ground water supplies. This is especially true in the suburban areas with a high population density and with no municipal sewage disposal and treatment system available. An example of this is in Long Island, N.Y., where, in some areas, sewage disposal is accomplished by cesspools. Soil research is furnishing guidelines for more effective and safer use of systems such as these.

Pollution can put an end to body-building water sports for young "swingers" like this boy at Pine Grove Mills, Pa.

Urban and recreational areas are also plagued with solid wastes like paper, beer cans, and bottles, which are not readily decomposed or broken down. These frequently find their way into our streams and reservoirs. They are unsightly, although not necessarily a health hazard to our population.

Industry is also a great contributor to the pollution of our water resources. Considering the large variety of industrial operations, effluents may contain excessively large amounts of acids, oils, greases, dissolved salts, various organic chemicals, and suspended animal and vegetable matter. In some instances, the treatment of effluents can minimize the pollution hazard, but very often this is simply not economically feasible.

Many industries require a substantial quantity of water for their operations, and then it is essential that the resulting effluents be properly treated and disposed of, so as not to pollute the water downstream from the plant.

Wastes from the synthetic chemicals industry are particularly troublesome. Some are highly toxic to fish and aquatic life. Many do not respond to treatment.

151

The long-range effects on man of these new synthetics are unknown. Although the concentration in most waters is now low, it is imperative that we find a solution to meet water requirements of this rapidly growing industry.

Other specific sources of water pollution are far too numerous to permit a detailed listing here. Each specific source of water pollution must be evaluated not only as an individual case, but in terms of its contribution to the overall pollution of our larger bodies of water.

Integrated Approach

The water which flows into a lake or from a river into the ocean reflects everything that happens on the land within the drainage basin, or watershed, of that lake or river. Correction of a pollution problem in a river must, therefore, consist of an integrated approach that will include corrective measures for all sources within the river basin.

Most river basins contain large areas of agricultural lands. The degree of pollution from livestock and agricultural chemicals will vary in different parts of the country according to the type of agriculture being practiced. Contamination of waters by industry will also depend upon the types of industry located within the basin as well as upon the degree of industrial development.

Urban pollution, primarily from sewage disposal, will vary with population distribution and concentration and the degree of effective sewage treatment.

Studies of the Potomac and Delaware River Basins are now being conducted to determine the various sources of water pollution so that corrective measures can eventually be developed.

Water problems during the future will become more intense and more complex. Our increasing population will tremendously increase urban wastes, primarily sewage. On the other hand, increasing demands for water will decrease substantially the amount of water available for diluting wastes. Rapidly expanding industries which involve more and more complex chemical processes will produce larger volumes of effluents, and many of

these will contain chemicals which are either toxic or noxious. To feed our rapidly expanding population, agriculture will have to be intensified. This will involve ever-increasing quantities of agricultural chemicals. From this, it is apparent that drastic steps must be taken immediately to develop corrective measures for the pollution problem.

There are two ways by which this pollution problem can be mitigated. The first relates to the treatment of wastes to decrease their pollution hazard. This involves the processing of solid wastes prior to disposal and the treatment of liquid wastes, or effluents, to permit the reuse of the water or minimize pollution upon final disposal. Industry has applied such water treatments as screening, lagooning, filtration, deep well disposal, ion exchange, distillation, biological digestion, incineration, and many others to reduce their contribution to water pollution. In each case, the potential pollutant is disposed of in a manner which will minimize or eliminate the pollution hazard.

A second approach is to develop an economic use for all or a part of the wastes. Farm manure is spread in fields as a nutrient and organic supplement. Effluents from sewage disposal plants are used in some areas both for irrigation, as an additional source of water, and for the nutrients contained. Effluents from other processing plants may also be used as a supplemental source of water. Many industries, such as meat and poultry processing plants, are currently converting former waste products into marketable byproducts. Other industries are exploring potential economic uses for their waste products. In addition, some industries are studying means of modifying their industrial processes so as to minimize waste production.

Water pollution abatement must be a coordinated effort on the part of all contributors within a watershed, but each contributor must resolve his own problem. Agriculture has made great strides in reducing soil loss through research and development of better conservation practices. Improved fertilizer technology and the development of more efficient fertilization practices are minimizing loss of nutrients from the soil. The development of debris basins and settling ponds is helping to improve the quality of our water resources. Research on pesticides, and alternate methods of pest control, should eventually minimize this hazard.

Municipalities, in conjunction with State and Federal agencies and industry, are seeking new and improved methods of sewage and waste water treatment to handle the increased volumes expected in the future. The various industries are studying their disposal problems in an attempt to reduce their contribution in the future. In many areas, legislation is attempting to control pollution from urban and industrial expansion.

The State and Federal Governments are combining their efforts to make our water supplies clean and safe.

Every man, woman, and child has an obligation to cooperate in this great effort.

The Potomac: Problems, Potentials of George Washington's River

CARL J. JOHNSON

FROM the time of George Washington, our Presidents have been interested in the Potomac. But not before February 1965 did a President take a positive stand on the total watershed and its future.

In a "Message on the Natural Beauty of our Country," President Lyndon B. Johnson stated that the Potomac should become a model of both conservation and beauty for the Nation.

The President directed the Secretary of the Interior to develop a plan to "clean up the river and keep it clean," to protect the natural beauty of the river and its basin, to assure a supply of water from the river and other sources to meet municipal needs in the basin for the decades ahead, to provide adequate flood control, and to give maximum recreational opportunities to people who live along the river or its tributaries and to those who visit the river basin.

Judging from the Potomac Interim Report to the President, published a year later in January 1966, the Interdepartmental Task Force, established to develop the plan, has decided to first draw up a master plan for recreation. The plan apparently will provide for recreational use and for continued natural beauty by requiring high levels of water quality and public control of access to the river and its major tributaries, through easement or ownership of the flood plains and the shoreline. The final edition of the Task Force's report to the President was to be published during the summer of 1967.

For the Potomac to become the model conservation and recreation success which the President expects, the quality of the water in the river must improve significantly. Not only must there be more rigid limitations on the amounts of organic pollutants entering this river, but sediment—a continuing abuse to water quality—must be kept out of the Potomac by more effective erosion control measures.

While it is difficult to characterize a plan which is as yet incomplete, the main thrust of today's model plan for the

ψ ψ ψ

Carl J. Johnson is *Executive Director*, Interstate Commission on the Potomac River Basin.

235-917 O - 67 - 13

Potomac is abundantly clear. The plan is an expression of demand—primarily a demand for the water-based recreation which already has been mentioned.

And this recreation requirement stems principally from the pressing needs of the Washington, D.C., region where two-thirds of the basin's 3.5 million population lives without many satisfactory opportunities for outdoor recreation. While offending accuracy somewhat—for the sake of simplicity—one can yet fairly say that the model plan represents but another chapter in a lengthy catalog of demands which, in this century, Washington, D.C., and its suburbs have placed on the water and the land resources of the farflung Potomac Basin.

Served Three Masters

Starting with George Washington and ending up with Washington, D.C., the Potomac in its time has served three masters. The first two of the significant "users" were also famous abusers of the river. Likewise, the Washington metropolitan region, which is today the prime user of the Potomac, is also today its greatest polluter. In the history of the Potomac it appears that major abuses are inevitably linked to major uses.

The Potomac in George Washington's day was the only medium of transport of economic significance. The aristocratic Tidewater society which the first President represented was one largely engaged in raising crops—mainly tobacco—for export to the Old World. Since little was known and less was done about land erosion by Washington and his fellow plantation owners, much of their soil was lost to the river. The loss of soil proved to be the loss of the lifeblood of this early society, the resulting sediment destroying fish life and hampering navigation.

Opportunity subsequently moved upstream, and during the next century the Potomac served the mining industry—rather than agriculture. Coal was discovered in Georges' Creek in 1808, and Washington's dream of a navigational link with the West was sought through the building of the Chesapeake and Ohio Canal extending from Washington on up to Cumberland, Md. During the year 1907–08, the most productive mine in the world operated in the Georges' Creek Valley—the No. 7 Mine of the Consolidation Coal Co. with an average output of 5,700 tons per day. Like Tidewater agriculture, the underground exploitation upstream lasted for about 100 years.

Coal mining peaked out in about 1910 with a temporary revival during World War I, leaving a heritage to the river of pollution: Not sediment as in Tidewater —but the destructive acid mine drainage which still inhibits the using of the North Branch waters. The Chesapeake and Ohio Canal could not counter the competition of the growing railroad industry, and barge traffic was halted in 1924.

In post-World War II times, major economic opportunity lies again on the estuary, at Washington, D.C., and today the Potomac is primarily in the service of this emergent "World Capital." Agriculture is now lodged upstream, while the river's limited number of industries reside principally along the North Branch and along the Shenandoah. Washington, where the principal economic opportunities lie, is by far the single greatest user of water in the basin.

For a start, Washington and its suburbs constitute a large water supply demand— 300 million gallons per day on the average, which was three-fourths of the river's flow in the summer of 1966. What comes out, must go back. Hence, the city is converting a large percentage of the Potomac's flow to sewage. Although this sewage is treated by conventional methods, the untreated fraction or residue still remains formidable.

The number of pounds of biochemical oxygen demands which the metropolitan treatment plants put in the Potomac during an average day is at least three times the load discharged by all other treatment plants in the basin.

Finally, Washington is placing a growing outdoor recreation demand on both the river and its watershed lands.

The Potomac commences at Fairfax Stone in the Appalachian highlands of West Virginia and western Maryland. Cutting through the valleys and ridges, it makes its way across the Great Valley, through the Blue Ridge and the Piedmont Plateau. Just above Washington it tumbles over Great Falls to Little Falls, where after a 266-mile trip, it meets the tide and forms a major arm of Chesapeake Bay. Once at sea level, near Washington, D.C., it moves slowly another 117 miles to Point Lookout, where it enters the main channel of Chesapeake Bay.

Jefferson Quoted

As rivers go, the Potomac is not large. What it lacks in size, it makes up in beauty. It is a fitting subject for a major national conservation and beautification effort. Its passage through the various geological provinces has created spectacular scenery. Of the vista from the famous rock which bears his name at Harpers Ferry, Thomas Jefferson wrote:

"The passage of the Potomac through the Blue Ridge is perhaps one of the most stupendous scenes in nature. You stand on a very high point of land. On your right comes up the Shenandoah, having ranged along the foot of the mountain a hundred miles to seek a vent. On your left, approaches the Potomac, in quest of a passage also. In the moment of their juncture they rush off together against the mountain, rend it asunder, and pass off to the sea."

The average flow of the river, measured over a 30-year period, is 11,100 cubic feet per second (7.2 billion gallons per day), adequate for all basin needs far into the future. However, the flow in the Potomac is far from uniform. Its fluctuations between peak and low flows are greater than any other major river in the East. For over a month during 1966 only a little over one-half billion gallons per day came over Great Falls, just above Washington, while in 1936, some 275 billion gallons roared down upon Washington in the course of a single day.

The watershed of the Potomac contains 14,679 square miles located in West Virginia, Virginia, Pennsylvania, Maryland, and the District of Columbia; 11,580 square miles of this lies in the nontidal section above the District of Columbia. Average rainfall annually amounts to 38 inches, 55 percent of which comes between April and September.

Hey, where's the boat! It's there all right, even if you can't see it. The turbulent North Fork of the Potomac's South Branch offers exciting challenges to experienced kayak boaters like these near Petersburg in West Virginia.

Sherando Recreation Area in the George Washington National Forest, Va.

During the period 1896–1942, the runoff, measured at Point of Rocks, Md., averaged 13.2 inches per year which was about 35 percent of the rainfall.

Except for Washington, most of the Potomac Valley is rural, containing about 1 million people. But heavy industry has settled and uses the river in western Maryland and in the headwaters of the Shenandoah, the major tributary.

Agricultural endeavor is built around livestock and dairying, fruit production and poultry. Some farm operators are seeing the opportunity to develop outdoor recreation on their properties. This will undoubtedly grow as success by one farmer stimulates another.

Around 50 percent of the river basin is wooded area. Two national forests—the George Washington and the Monongahela—plus the Shenandoah National Park, containing Skyline Drive, account for nearly 600,000 acres of this forest land. These Federal parks along with a substantial number of State forests, parks, and hunting areas—particularly in Maryland and West Virginia—provide a base for the substantial recreation industry in the Potomac's upper basin.

The North Branch of the Potomac in western Maryland and in West Virginia contains the only exploitable coal seams in the basin. While during recent years mining operations have contributed little to the economy of the region, they have contributed heavy loads of sediment and mine acid pollution to the streams.

Sediment, the product of soil erosion, is serious over the entire basin. It has been estimated that about 2.5 million tons annually move down the river through Washington and settle out in the sluggish tidal estuary of the Potomac.

Just a single weekend of heavy rain has brought as much as 100,000 tons of sediment into the Potomac. This amount of topsoil, stacked on an area equal to the base of the Washington Monument, would tower 245 feet above this tallest structure in the Nation's Capital.

The Washington region, itself, is the basin's most "productive" source of sediment. One-fiftieth of the overall land area of the basin, this urban region is nevertheless responsible for just about a fourth of the sediment tonnage to reach the Potomac estuary each year. Soil disappears from the metropolis at six times the rate it is shed upstream. Urban sediment is a problem which could be largely resolved with tools already at hand; tools which have been developed and promoted by the U.S. Department of Agriculture for use on America's farmlands.

Soil conservation districts cover the entire Potomac watershed, except for the District of Columbia. These districts—with assistance from the Soil Conservation Service and other Federal and State resource agencies, have made considerable progress in stemming erosion from farmlands. Recently, the Northern Virginia Soil Conservation District and the Montgomery County (Maryland) Soil Conservation District have turned their attention downstream to erosion control on the basin's urban and suburban lands and are providing technical assistance to builders and local planning units.

Watershed treatment that emphasizes the control of erosion and sediment wisely makes up a very substantial part of the emerging Interdepartmental Task Force plan to make the Potomac a model of conservation. Such emphasis will lay a solid foundation for the extensive system of parks and recreation areas, scenic and natural preserves, hiking and auto trails, and wild rivers and lakes envisioned for the enjoyment of people living in and visiting the Potomac Basin.

Waste Treatment Rises

Some twenty-five years ago virtually no wastes, sanitary or industrial, were treated before being discharged into the Potomac. At the end of 1966, according to the Interstate Commission on the Potomac River Basin, 97 percent of the sewered population was to be provided with secondary type waste treatment facilities. Major industrial plants provide similar degrees of treatment for their waste water currently.

The problems of pollution are the most visible and dramatic along the Potomac at Washington. Here the river receives its single greatest load of treatment plant effluents. Here, too, the river meets the tide and proceeds slowly to the bay. Residual wastes from metropolitan treatment plants, deposited in this part of the river, are virtually stranded. These residual wastes get diluted only moderately and at times of low flow, hardly at all, due to the ever-increasing water supply demand which is met by withdrawals just above the Nation's Capital.

Even allowing for substantial amounts available from other sources, the run of the river will not meet expected water supply requirements. So artificial storage will be required. Waste water treatment for this vast population will demand real ingenuity, plus methods of waste treatment not yet known if the tidal estuary is to remain a useful reach of the Potomac for recreational pursuits and as a possible source of drinkable water.

Tidewater Outlook

As for the future, the only substantial industry in the Washington region is expected to be National Government.

The outlook for the Tidewater region is not clear. Outdoor recreation would seem to have the brightest future here, because of the region's proximity to the river and the Chesapeake Bay. Industrial development will probably be in the area of commercial fishing and fish processing, boat repair, and service facilities. Most, if not all, of these enterprises are dependent upon clean water, over which Tidewater has little, if any, control.

The lower Potomac is renowned for its finfish and shellfish. This fishery already supports a relatively large industry, whose future depends upon the maintenance of the water quality and salinity at least on a par with the present levels. An extension of the Washington metropolitan region downstream could wipe out this industry. While the States of Maryland and Virginia are aware of this, pressures for so-called development are severe and will increase.

With relatively cheap and undeveloped land that is scenically attractive, and lying within the boundaries of the developing east coast megalopolis with its millions of recreation seekers, the potential for growth of outdoor recreation is great in this Tidewater region. While there are opportunities for private shooting preserves, hunting, tent camping, and similar forms of recreation, sport fishing and recreational boating will be the major

157

opportunities for the recreation industry. The outlook for the upriver regions is a continuation of an agricultural community. If the development follows the precepts of the President's model plan, not yet in final form, the region will also surely have a fast-growing recreation industry, but will have little to offer the manufacturing industry, particularly that segment with a demand for water.

The overwhelming need for quantities of clean water for the Nation's Capital and the desire to maintain the natural beauty of the river will undoubtedly take precedence over industrial development along the upstream reaches.

Accessible to Washington, Baltimore, and Philadelphia recreation seekers, public recreation developments upstream will provide a fertile foundation for private recreation enterprises ranging from hunting and fishing and camping opportunities to motel and hotel accommodations.

A few enterprising landowners have already recognized the opportunities and are providing overnight accommodations for sportsmen, farm vacations, and campsites. A fortunate few who own the shoreline around small watershed reservoirs have developed camping, picnicking, and swimming opportunities.

So we see a continuation of a pastoral scene along the upper Potomac—hopefully with sparkling streams, clean streambanks, pleasant surroundings, and improved highways designed both for the motoring public and for the relatively sparse population of residents. Hopefully this will be a region attractive to the younger retiree who is seeking pleasant, moderate cost living space, plus an opportunity for seasonal employment, or the establishment of a small business.

A model river? It could well be that in eastern megalopolis, the Potomac, both Tidewater and "upstream," will become an oasis, neither seeking nor attractive to industry and commercial life—truly the model of conservation and beauty for the Nation which the President desires.

The Waterweed Nuisance

F. LEONARD TIMMONS

WATERWEEDS—about 150 different kinds of them—are endangering our use of outdoor water resources. Most of you who fish, swim outdoors, operate a motorboat, or irrigate crops are acquainted with the nuisances caused by some of these weeds.

Nearly everybody shares in the inconvenience and losses caused by weeds that interfere with the flow of water to be used for irrigation, electric power, or domestic and industrial purposes. We are also concerned about weeds that prevent or reduce the flow of drainage and floodwaters from rural and urban areas.

Algae, and especially some microscopic plankton forms, produce objectionable odors and tastes in drinking water. Some kinds are toxic to fish and others may result in "swimmer's itch." Excessive growths of these algae make the water green, "soupy," and quite undesirable for swimming purposes.

Dense growths of filamentous algae—

🌾 🌾 🌾

F. Leonard Timmons is *Leader* of Weed Investigations in Aquatic and Noncrop Areas, Crops Research Division, Agricultural Research Service, with headquarters at the University of Wyoming in Laramie.

158

threadlike plants without roots, leaves, or flowers—reduce fish production and interfere with fishing. They often plug irrigation sprinkler systems and siphon tubes. Some filamentous algae grow on concrete walls and bottoms of outdoor pools and on rocks in ponds and streams. They create slippery and hazardous conditions for waders and swimmers.

Submersed weeds—rooted plants which grow mostly under water—are even more troublesome in recreational waters. Dense growths may make fishing, swimming, or boating impossible. Eurasian watermilfoil is seriously damaging shellfish and other commercial and sport fisheries along the Atlantic coast.

Emersed waterweeds—plants that root at the bottom and extend most of their foliage and seed heads above the water surface—are most troublesome along the banks and shallow water edges. These weeds prevent access to and from the open water of ponds and lakes. They also greatly restrict or prevent waterflow in drainage canals.

Emersed weeds provide ideal breeding places for mosquitoes and hiding places for snakes. Thickets of tall emersed weeds like the cattails and phragmites are the favorite nesting and roosting places of the starling and other "blackbirds" which are nuisance birds in many cities.

Large floating waterweeds, like waterhyacinth and waterlettuce, are common in Southeastern States where they often make the waterways and lakes unusable. Windstorms and heavy rains force the floating vegetation against bridges, dams, and other structures causing washouts and flooding. Such weeds, especially waterlettuce, also provide ideal breeding places for mosquitoes.

When waterweeds decay rapidly underwater, they use much of the oxygen dissolved in the water and many fish suffocate. Some aquatic vegetation that decays in or out of water produces objectionable odors and tastes.

Owners of waterfront homes along bays, estuaries, or inlets along the Atlantic coast, from Virginia to Massachusetts, know well what a nuisance decaying sea lettuce and other marine algae can be. The plants grow on the bottom of tide-water areas to depths of 25 feet or more. When broken off, the dislodged plants are deposited by tides and winds along the shore, around piers, boat docks, seawalls, and other obstructions on the shoreline. The decaying masses of vegetation give off hydrogen sulfide gas, which discolors lead paints, tarnishes silverware, copper or brass fixtures, and has an obnoxious odor of rotten eggs.

Beneficial Functions

Many aquatic (water) plants perform beneficial and essential functions. A suitable biotic balance in "living" water is not possible without any aquatic plant growth. Algae and the submersed plants convert inorganic constituents of water—nitrogen, phosphorus, etc.—into organic matter. During growth, these plants remove carbon dioxide from water and add the dissolved oxygen that is necessary for the survival and growth of fish and other aquatic animal life. Plankton (free floating) algae are a major source of food for many species of fish, shellfish, and zooplankton and are the basis for the food chain of most fish species.

To encourage plankton algae growth in fishponds and sometimes to control submersed weeds, an inorganic fertilizer should be applied at an appropriate rate and time. See USDA Farmers' Bulletin 2181, *Waterweed Control on Farms and Ranches* for full information on control through fertilization.

Some aquatic plants, such as plankton algae, are a nuisance in certain situations and beneficial in others. Widgeongrass, wild celery, many pond weeds, and smartweeds are troublesome in fishing, swimming, and boating areas. However, they provide valuable feed for ducks, geese, and other waterfowl in marshes and in similar habitats.

The control of aquatic weeds is complicated by the presence of the beneficial aquatic plants and the troublesome waterweeds in one and the same area, and the dual beneficial-harmful nature of some plants. A decision must be reached as to which are to be protected and which controlled. If selective control is not possible, a choice has to be made whether

159

to endure the nuisance weeds or sacrifice the beneficial plants.

The fight against waterweeds—underway since 1900—is being extended and intensified now with all the available weapons, some old and many new.

Deepening the edges of a pond, lake, or reservoir until the water is at least 2 or 3 feet deep and filling in marshy spots along the bank will prevent or reduce growths of emersed weeds. This control is improved if the water is naturally darkened by organic acids, suspended clay, or plankton algae growth.

If possible, water management should be used to control waterweeds. Complete drainage of a pond or canal permits the bottom to dry for a few days and at the same time temporarily controls most submersed and some emersed weeds. Draining and drying, plus plowing or burning and freezing, will eliminate the cattail and most other emersed weeds. In larger reservoirs or other impoundments where complete drainage is not possible, periodic drawdown of the water level for 5 feet or more may result in similar control.

Shading the bottom mud with a black plastic sheeting for at least 3 weeks early in the growing season will control submersed weeds, filamentous algae, and some emersed weeds. In shallow water, keep the plastic on the bottom with weights. In water 5 feet deep or deeper, maintain the plastic at or preferably below the surface with lines and poles. Obviously, this method is possible and practicable only in the small, highly valued swimming and fishing areas of ponds, lakes, or tidal water shorelines.

The biological control of waterweeds by insects, snails, diseases, and several kinds of fish offers promise for the future. However, much more research is necessary before we can make extensive and safe use of any of them.

Early waterweed fighters developed many kinds of mechanical control devices that are available. These and some modern machines include handtools, weed cables, chains and saws, draglines, crushers, underwater power weed cutters, and hydraulic jets.

Mechanical control is possible in many situations and need involve no direct hazards to fish, wildlife, livestock, or humans. However, these methods are slow, expensive, and often laborious. Usually they produce only partial and temporary control. Also, the mechanical methods often increase the spread of submersed weeds. The cut or dislodged vegetation left in water is often moved by currents or wind action to locations where clogging of grates, pumps, and siphons, and damage to structures result. Accumulations of such vegetation along the shorelines will often harbor midges, flies, and mosquitoes.

Control of waterweeds with herbicides is far easier, much faster, usually longer lasting, and frequently less expensive than mechanical controls. The treated weeds, except floating types, usually die in place and then decay slowly.

Herbicide Progress

We have made considerable progress in discovering and developing effective herbicides for controlling most of the weeds in and on water. Except for sodium arsenite, most of the herbicides registered in 1966 for controlling waterweeds in one or more situations have a low order of acute oral toxicity to humans or to other warmblooded animals. Several do not harm fish at concentrations necessary to control the weeds.

However, the use of most herbicides for waterweed control is regulated and restricted. Many herbicides are not permitted in water to be used for irrigation or for drinking.

Much research is needed to determine the persistence and effects of herbicides and their chemical breakdown compounds in water, bottom mud, fish, shellfish, aquatic plants, and crops irrigated with treated water. Such information is urgently needed to insure maximum utilization of our water resources. An adequate number and variety of effective, safe, and approved herbicides will be needed to supplement other methods in winning the fight against waterweeds.

Copper sulfate at 0.1 to 0.5 part per million by weight (p.p.m.w.) controls plankton algae. Filamentous algae are killed by 1 p.p.m.w. (1 p.p.m.w.=4.3 pounds of pentahydrate crystals per acre-foot of water). At these concentrations, copper sulfate usually does not injure bass or bluegills, but it will kill trout. Concentrations of up to 4 p.p.m.w. (1 p.p.m.w. of copper) are considered safe for humans in drinking water.

Numerous herbicides are registered for control of the other types of waterweeds. Complete information on the weeds controlled, application rates and procedures, and precautions in use is given on the label of each package. Always read the label and follow instructions carefully.

Most submersed weeds can be controlled without injury to fish by applying diquat, dichlobenil, endothall (potassium or sodium salts), fenac, or sodium arsenite. Some of these also control filamentous algae, and dichlobenil controls chara (muskgrass or stonewort).

Sodium arsenite—extensively used to control submersed weeds since around 1930, but under rigid State regulations—is violently poisonous to humans and to other warmblooded animals. It is still used extensively in some States, but its use is now prohibited or discouraged in many States or localities.

Acrolein, aromatic solvents (xylene), and dimethylalkyl amine salts of endothall will control submersed weeds, but also kill fish at recommended application rates. They should be used only where saving the fish is relatively unimportant.

Granular or pelleted formulations of 2,4-D and silvex control watermilfoil, waterchestnut, and certain other submersed weeds. Certain esters of 2,4-D and silvex are toxic to fish at the recommended application rates.

Many emersed and floating waterweeds can be controlled by foliage spray applications of 2,4-D or silvex or 2,4,5-T. Avoid drift of spray or volatilized fumes of these herbicides onto nearby sensitive desirable vegetation.

Use silvex for the hard-to-kill alligatorweed and pickerelweed.

Duckweed, water-hyacinth, and water-lettuce are also controlled by diquat.

To control cattails, sedges, and aquatic grasses in drainage ditches and marshy wasteland, spray with dalapon.

For more complete information on the control of waterweeds see USDA Agriculture Handbook No. 332, *Suggested Guide for Weed Control,* 1967, pages 55–59, or Agriculture Handbook No. 269, *Herbicide Manual for Noncropland Weeds,* 1965, pages 52–57.

Waterweeds are not only a nuisance to the individual owners and users of outdoor water resources. They are also a national problem of major importance. The need for control becomes more and more serious daily. Surveys indicate that weeds are an increasing problem in our 170,000 miles of irrigation canals and 190,000 miles of drainage canals and ditches; also, in our 42 million acres of inland fresh water surface (including estuaries but excluding the Great Lakes).

Infest Ponds, Reservoirs

Most of our 2 million farm ponds and small reservoirs are infested with weeds to some degree. All the shallow areas of lakes, reservoirs, streams, and waterways 10 feet deep or less are subject to the growth of most submersed weeds. Some weeds, like elodea, will grow in clear water at depths of 25 feet or more.

Increasing growth of waterweeds—caused by nutrients in sewage, farm and industrial wastes, and other effluents from our increasing population—are rapidly reducing the usefulness and value of our inland waters. For example, the estimated 90,000 pounds of nitrogen and phosphorus compounds that each day enter the Potomac River below Washington, D.C., are believed to contribute to the rapid increase of plankton, milfoil, and sea lettuce. The 100,000 acres of Eurasian watermilfoil in Maryland in 1965 was twice that observed in 1961.

As our national water problems become ever more critical, so does our fight against waterweeds. To maintain a continued supply and movement of water of a desirable quality for use will require a maximum individual effort, alike by owners and users of water resources. Moreover, it will require our united effort through Federal, State, and local government agencies to prevent and control aquatic weeds.

Water Safety
Is Up To You

RALPH E. PATTERSON

WHAT terror strikes the heart more than to hear a piercing cry of "HELP!" from someone in distress in the water. If you were the only person nearby, would you know what to do? This chapter will tell you. By knowing and using these common safety rules around the water you will not only be safer, but will enjoy the water more.

Safety While Swimming

• Learn survival floating. "Drownproofing" is a relatively new, easy, and very effective method of staying afloat for long periods of time. Because two-thirds of drownings occur within 15 feet of the bank, dock, or boat, the ability to just stay on the surface for a few minutes will usually be long enough for rescue. The technique of drownproofing will be discussed later on.

• Learn to swim. Children should attend swimming classes as soon as they are old enough to enroll. Most communities have swimming and lifesaving classes available. If there are none in your area, then see your local American Red Cross, YMCA, or YWCA to get some started.

• Never swim alone. Swimmers should always use the "buddy" system and keep a constant check on each other. If your buddy is out of sight for an instant, locate him immediately. If he is in trouble, the seconds count. Small children should always be accompanied by an adult.

• Swim at a safe bathing place. Never swim in polluted water. There should be no glass, cans, trash, or debris in the swimming area. The lifeguard or a good swimmer should check the bottom to see there are no quick cutoffs or deep holes. A lifeguard should be on duty during all of the swimming periods.

• Before diving, make sure the water is deep enough and has no hidden objects. Also, be sure no swimmers are in the immediate diving area.

• Don't swim when overheated, overtired, or right after eating.

• Don't jump into very cold water. Enter it gradually. This prevents shock to your body.

• Know your ability and stay within it. Swim only where you are sure you can get back to land or a boat. Distance over the water is misleading. Waves or a sudden gulp of water may panic even a very good swimmer.

• Take a boat along for distance swimming in open water.

• Never push anyone into the water. Never force anyone's head under water unless they are expecting it.

• Never run along the edge of a pool, irrigation ditch, or stream. The walking surface around a pool should be relatively rough to prevent slipping when wet.

• Do not permit children to use inner tubes or inflated toys in either deep or flowing water.

• Get out of the water during a storm.

꘏   ꘏   ꘏

Ralph E. Patterson is an *Agricultural Engineer* and *Safety Specialist*, Federal Extension Service.

162

• Call "HELP" any time you are not sure that you can swim to safety. But never call "HELP" unless you really mean it.

Drownproofing

With the lungs full of air the body will normally float just below the surface. If the head is kept tilted slightly forward, water will not enter the nose, even with waves passing over the head. The body, arms, and legs are completely relaxed between breaths, as if floating in space. Only a small amount of energy is required to just raise the mouth out of the water long enough to get a breath. Thus, with some instruction and practice one can learn to stay afloat for hours.

The accompanying diagrams show the basic steps in drownproofing.

Men generally tend to float with a more stooped position than the girl in the diagrams. Shaking the arms, hands, legs, and feet will help you to relax as you drift and float face down in the water.

Why don't you team up with your buddy and try this system yourself?

Cramps—Don't Panic

Cramps are the involuntary shortening of muscles, frequently painful. They are usually caused by cold water, poor coordination, nervousness, tension, or a combination of these factors. If the muscle is permitted to shorten and become hard, the cramp may continue for several

HERE'S HOW TO DROWNPROOF YOURSELF

Take a deep breath, relax in the water with your arms and legs dangling until you want another breath.

When you want a breath, not when you need one, put your arms straight out in front from your shoulders. Spread your legs for a scissors kick.

Raise your head until it is nearly vertical, push down with your hands in a keyhole pattern, and bring your feet together. Exhale through your nose.

When your chin is even with the surface, open your eyes wide, open your mouth wide, and then inhale through your mouth.

Relax and you will settle in the water again. If you feel you are going too deep, give a slight push downward with your hands.

163

minutes. However, the obvious thing to do is act immediately to prevent the cramped muscle from shortening.

In water, as on land, at the very first feeling of a cramp, the affected muscle should be stretched as far as possible. Since a muscle will give a twitch or two before the actual cramp occurs, there is time to stretch the muscle as much as possible before the cramp reaches a serious state. About half of cramps occur in the calf of the leg and tend to bend the knee and straighten out the foot. Thus, the corrective action is to straighten the leg as much as possible and bring your toes up toward your knee as far as you can.

Rubbing the cramped muscle vigorously will also help by increasing the circulation and thus defeat the cramp. Likewise, if the cramp occurs in the arm, hand, foot, toe, or finger, straighten the affected part at the very first twitch. Occasionally a thigh muscle will cramp. Hold the leg extended as far as possible and rub, knead, and work the muscle with the hands to relieve the cramp.

Get out of the water and let the muscle rest for a while.

Stomach cramps have caused even expert swimmers to drown. Use the same method as with other cramps. At the first sign of a stomach cramp, arch the back backward as far as possible, thus stretching the affected stomach muscle. Hold this stretched position as long as the cramp persists. Do not panic. Stomach cramps are rare, and if treated instantly at the first twitch should cause no significant danger. With the drownproofing technique, anyone can float as long as necessary to relieve a cramp—it is not necessary to use both arms and both legs in order to surface for a breath.

Mouth-to-Mouth Resuscitation

If a person has been under water just a short time, do not assume he is dead. This is a doctor's decision. The following procedure has saved many lives. The author demonstrated this technique on television, and 10 months later Mrs. David Graham of near Clearfield, Pa., saved the life of her 22-month-old son, Billy, because she had seen the program and applied mouth-to-mouth resuscitation immediately. You, too, may be called on to save the life of someone. The following steps should be used in an emergency:

1. Start resuscitation at once, because every second counts!
2. Send someone for help.
3. Put the victim on his back.
4. Remove any foreign matter from his mouth with your fingers.
5. Place one hand under his neck and lift while pushing the top of his head back and down. This will put his head in a chin-high, open-mouthed position.
6. Pinch his nostrils together with your fingers to prevent air from escaping.
7. Place your mouth firmly over his mouth and blow until his chest rises.
8. Stop blowing, remove your mouth, and let the air come out.
9. Repeat—blowing up his lungs about once every 5 seconds until natural breathing resumes. For a child, use less air and blow up the lungs every 3 seconds.

If the victim is a small child be careful not to blow too hard into his lungs, as injury may result. Also, the mouth can be placed over the child's nose and mouth both, when they are small.

If air does not enter the lungs, raise the chin higher or pull it up with the fingers. An obstruction in the throat may be dislodged by turning the victim on his side and slapping him on the back between the shoulder blades. Again wipe out the mouth. Continue until the victim is revived or until a doctor determines that further efforts are useless.

Build a Safety Post

All ponds, pools, lakes, and swimming areas should have water safety devices, first aid equipment, and emergency instructions available. The "safety post" or "rescue station" is simple, inexpensive, but adequate for most nonpublic swimming areas. As usually recommended, it consists of an 8-foot post with a minimum of 2 feet in the ground. This may be steel or wood and round or square. Onto this post is fastened a bracket or a couple of large crossed nails to hold a 12- to 14-foot bamboo or other light pole used for reaching victims close to shore.

A life buoy or ring with 50 feet of light rope with a knot in the end is also hung onto the post. This is used by stepping on one end of the rope and tossing the life buoy beyond the victim, then pulling it back within his reach. Stepping on the rope end or getting a firm grasp on it will keep the rope from being pulled out of your hand when thrown.

The safety can on the top of the post contains a small, but adequate first aid kit. To the outside of the can are cemented instructions for emergency procedures, for first aid, and mouth-to-mouth rescue breathing. These instructions are waterproofed with a clear lacquer to protect them from the weather. The instructions may be obtained in card form from the American Red Cross.

An inner tube kept inflated may be substituted for the life buoy, but is not as satisfactory since it cannot be thrown as far as a standard life buoy or ring and may become deflated. Some 4–H clubs and Future Farmers of America chapters have built rescue stations. The cost is small, but the rewards may be enormous.

Rescue Procedure

If a person in trouble in the water is within reach, securely brace yourself and extend a hand to him. Or wade out to him, if possible. You can extend your reach with a pole, a board, or an article of clothing. Otherwise, throw a life buoy beyond the victim, holding securely to the end of the rope, and then maneuver it back to him. If he is even farther out, use a rowboat and have the victim hold on to the stern of the boat or board from the stern. If the boat has a motor, be sure that the propeller is stopped before the boat reaches the victim.

As a last resort, call for help, and then swim to the victim, approach from behind, and pull him in with your hand under his chin, pulling on his shirt or hair if necessary. Do not let the victim grab you around your arms or waist, as a person in panic will do. If the victim is unconscious, begin mouth-to-mouth resuscitation as soon as you possibly can and keep him warm.

If you see a person go under water,

ARTIFICIAL RESPIRATION

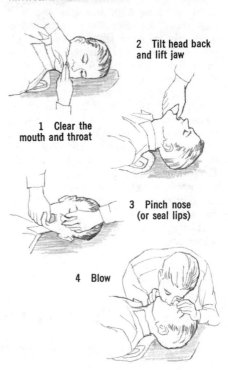

2 Tilt head back and lift jaw

1 Clear the mouth and throat

3 Pinch nose (or seal lips)

4 Blow

be sure to line the spot up with a mark on both the shores, preferably from two points, so as to locate the spot and save precious seconds in locating his body.

Boating Safety

Knowing and obeying safe "rules of the road" are as important on the water as on the highway. Courtesy is the best and most basic rule.

Powerboat operators should learn good seamanship. Courses in small craft are given by the Power Squadron, Coast Guard Auxiliary, and Red Cross.

Know the operation and capabilities of your boat. Practice maneuvering under all foreseeable conditions. Do not exceed the rated load or horsepower capacity of your boat. Be sure there is at least one U.S. Coast Guard approved life preserver aboard for each person. See that children keep their life vests or jackets on at all times. Carry all other safety and operational equipment recommended for your size and type of boat.

Step carefully into small boats. If you must move around, stay low. Be sure powerboats are properly ventilated. Immediately wipe up any spilled gas. Of course, do not smoke during refueling or immediately afterward. Always start your engine with the rudder or outboard motor set for straight forward travel and move slowly away from the dock. You are responsible for the wake of your boat, so reduce speed when you're passing bathing beaches, canoes, other small boats, and docks. Avoid sharp turns at high speeds. Keep alert for other boats, especially when you are towing skiers. Someone besides the boat operator should watch skiers at all times.

If caught in a storm, head into the waves and reduce speed. When you can't make headway against a strong sea or if your engine or motor quits, trail a sea anchor or bucket from the bow (front) to keep you headed into the waves. Don't swim from a boat unless it is tied up, anchored, or there is someone aboard who can operate it.

In an emergency, signal other boats or flash an S.O.S. toward the horizon every 15 seconds. S.O.S. is three short flashes, three long flashes, and three short flashes. If your boat capsizes and doesn't sink, stay with it until help arrives.

Much more information is available from the Outboard Boating Club of America, 333 N. Michigan Avenue, Chicago, Ill. 60601 and the American Water Ski Association, Seventh Street and G Avenue, SW., Winter Haven, Fla. 33880.

Ole Swimmin' Hole
Goes Modern

BERNHARD A. ROTH

SEVEN miles south from Christian Musser's farm in the heart of the Pennsylvania Dutch country, there's the city of York. It has 60,000 people. Were all of them to migrate to the farm at a given signal, the spectacle would be impressive. It would also illustrate the amount of traffic entertained at Musser's farm pond in the past two decades.

Firemen on outings, family reunions, Boy Scout and Girl Scout campouts, church groups with picnic hampers, visiting farmers munching sweet corn while studying the crop fields—they troop to the pondside virtually all year long.

When called on, Chris Musser and helpers serve hamburgers, "real Dutch" chicken-corn soup, barbecued chicken, and baked corn-in-the-husk. To one and all he serves generous portions of rural hospitality. Besides the fun of playing host, he reckons the pond rewards him in at least three other ways. There's the income from group rentals; homegrown and home-cooked meals bring up to $2 apiece; and take-home sale of farm produce is stimulated by pond visits.

Why does a modest, soil conservation district-built body of water draw more people than any five-alarm fire? Chris says, "I can't explain about these city

꙰   ꙰   ꙰

Bernhard A. Roth is a *Public Information Officer* for the Soil Conservation Service assisting 15 Northeastern States from the regional technical service center at Upper Darby, Pa. He has written extensively on outdoor recreation as a byproduct of conservation.

166

people. Maybe they come here to see the soil and water which are underneath all of their roads and buildings!"

Recreation Magnet

But York County agency officials have their own version. They say the southern Susquehanna Valley neighborhood is simply bursting its population seams. Developed recreation space has fallen far behind the demands. Thus, nearly any patch of land near water has magnetic force for pent-up urbanites.

Added magnetism at Musser's includes the vigorous farm family activities plus good country "chow and cheer" which enhance the pond background.

Like the other conservation ponds now built and still a-building, Musser's has a unique history. It could begin, in the imagination, with eons of geologic upheaval. Ultimately, there was a swampy hollow for an early Mennonite farmer named George Gross to worry about. Gross sold his farm—and the hollow—to Chris Musser's grandfather, Christian, way back in 1904.

Next in line, Chris' father, Jacob, grew tired of roping and hauling cattle out of wet spots. When Chris was big enough to swing a pick and spade, father and son dug 1,300 feet of trenching, by hand, and inserted tile drain lines.

They dried out several acres of formerly seepy hillside. Water still drowned the bottom of the hollow.

There it sat—too thin to farm and too thick for fishing—until Melvin L. Blish of USDA's Soil Conservation Service came along. Blish, assisting the newly organizing York County Soil Conservation District, had worked with other strong-minded Mennonite farmers and restrained his optimism on approaching Chris Musser to talk about conservation.

But, as the SCS man tells it today, "Chris grabbed the farm conservation planning idea as though it were second nature to him, and I guess it really is. Revised land use, crop rotations, contour farming, protected waterways—and so on—Chris took right hold of the whole system and made up a complete plan for his farm. But the first time I suggested converting that mucky hollow into a pond—man, oh man, did I run into a stone wall!"

Nowadays, Musser picks up the train of Blish's reminiscing with a twinkle, "Yes, I thought a long, long while about the $1,000 or so which I figured a good pond would cost."

When Chris did decide to go ahead, local contractor H. P. Williams charged him only $810 for the job.

As designed by Blish, the pond was to require 740 feet of diking, 30 feet broad at the base, and 20 feet at the top. It would be fed by springs in the bottom plus the drainage from the hillside tile. Surface runoff would be totally diverted. The pond would cover almost 2 acres.

"I went out to see how they were getting along the first day," Blish recalls. "It was so wet the 'dozer and pan were sinking faster than the dike was going up. I suggested they wait a month." Completed in August, the pond was full with 3 million gallons the next March.

Seeded to lush, durable grasses and hedged with multiflora rose, the area was initially a haven of retreat from farm chores for Chris, his wife, Anna, their twin daughters, Mary and Martha, and five sons, Christian, Gordon, Paul, Alvin, and Glenn. Choice moments were those free for fishing, for swimming at the graveled beach, or for just watching the sunset colors fade across the water.

First inkling of the pond's community importance came from members of the nearby Manchester-Mount Wolf hockey team. They asked Chris' permission to practice on the "biggest expanse of ice for miles around." Moreover, they suggested he hang a tin can on a gatepost for their loose change. To this, the farmer readily agreed, and the pond then began earning income for Musser.

The following summer, Chris was hosting a combination social-and-serious meeting of area landowners on fishpond management. A sudden thunderstorm pounced upon the group. Soaked to the skin, they raced to the farmhouse 800 feet away. Archie Hug, county agricultural agent, had a rueful suggestion: "Chris, it's too late to help us now; but why don't you stick up a shelter down

167

there? I'll bet you'd have all sorts of folks eager to come out here—willing to pay their way, too."

Musser had a quick flashback to the hockey team experience. "At that moment, the idea of making the pond part of the farm cash register really began to jell. I started out small with a shelter and a few simple facilities. Then, as the word-of-mouth got around, I saw groups get larger and more frequent. I added accommodations to suit—a little of this and a little of that."

The "this's" and the "that's" are now quite considerable.

They include: A metal-roofed pavilion with bench-tables to seat 100 people served by a well-equipped kitchen; a covered, 18-foot-long, cinderblock barbecue pit; two large outdoor fireplaces to supplement the kitchen; a small refreshment stand; toilet facilities; piped-in spring water and outlets; electrical service for appliances, night lighting, and house-trailer usage; and a collapsible 16- by 24-foot stage used by entertainers and speakers.

Additional items include the 800-foot oiled access road, ample parking space, and a softball diamond. Maintenance of the grounds and facilities is largely supplied by local groups. They barter their labor for use of the pond.

Income derives from rentals at $5 per group weekdays—$15 per group weekends and holidays. Larger returns come from the majority of users who request a fabulous Dutch farm treat at the pondside. Rental rates are then scaled to the nature of the meal.

Patronage has long since reached the saturation point. Usually there's a waiting list. The roster of "regulars" reads much like a directory of service, church, fraternal, industrial, and agricultural organizations for the county as a whole.

And it's not all business. Youngsters in the vicinity are welcome to try their fishing luck on the abundant bass and bluegills. Twenty troops of Boy Scouts from the York-Adams Council and Girl Scouts from several towns are accommodated for their annual camporees and the practice of outdoor skills.

Volunteer fire companies of the area are encouraged to test their equipment regularly at the pondsite. In 1965, the test proved to be the real thing. A brush fire raged in the nearby hills. Hydrants could not supply the tanker-trucks fast enough. The latter shuttled from the fire to the Musser pond water until the blaze was finally contained.

10,000 Visits a Year

Son Paul and his family have just taken over the farm operation. Chris has finally had a little time to analyze the pond's true values. The basin plus the adjacent facilities cover about 7 acres. "These acres wouldn't have paid off in crops," Chris says, "but they have given us years of income, thanks to the pond. I think maybe we've gotten even more income, indirectly, from it as a 'sales promoter' for our turkeys, hogs, beef cattle, eggs, and much of our field produce. I guess you'd call it good 'public relations.' "

Mel Blish has since been promoted to the position of area conservationist for the Soil Conservation Service at Clarion, Pa. Looking back, he muses: "I think it's clear that Musser's pond enterprise was 'way ahead of its time. I can name dozens of landowners and agency people who were influenced by what they saw at Musser's.

"It was the first multiple-purpose pond in York County."

The 10,000 visitors who now come annually to find relaxation beside its shimmering depths indicate the pond will continue to reflect a bright picture of recreation potential for years to come.

Warm Water Ponds for Panfish

HOMER S. SWINGLE

SINCE early colonial days many Americans have had a yearning to discover an isolated fishing hole, known only to themselves, where fish could be caught readily and where fish tales grew the tallest. Since 1 in every 4 men and 1 in every 11 women in the United States participate in the sport of fishing, secret fishing holes of this type have become difficult to find in our public waters. The well-managed warm water fishpond is a nearly perfect answer to their dreams.

Only within the past quarter century has research developed the procedures and know-how necessary to make investment in these dreams a reasonably safe investment. During this period, more than 2 million farm and community ponds have been constructed and operated to produce a multitude of stories about both "the fish that got away" and other high points of the day's fishing.

A successful pond begins with correct location, good planning, and correct construction. Bulletins giving construction details are available, among them Alabama Agricultural Experiment Station Circular 95. Other publications can be obtained from the U.S. Department of Agriculture and from State fish and game divisions. Local Soil Conservation Service technicians and the county extension chairmen know local soil conditions; they are the best source of advice during this stage. They can help prevent costly mistakes such as locating the pond where soils will not hold water, where there is too much or too little water, or from

an inadequate spillway design and other problems. Since fish are ready for stocking in the fall or winter, planning should be aimed at having the pond ready for stocking during the fall months.

Since we will be stocking small fish of desirable species, we do not want other fish present to eat or to compete with them. Prior to stocking, wild fish should be eliminated within the pond and barriers constructed to prevent fish migration into the pond from either downstream or upstream. Adequate barriers to fish migration are a part of pond construction. Also, to minimize trouble with wild fish, it is best not to begin impounding water until after the first frost in the fall. This insures that wild fish, even if present, cannot spawn prior to introduction of the desired species.

Warm water ponds are those in which the summer temperatures rise above 80° F. in the top 1 foot of water. These temperatures occur in pond waters in lowland areas from the southernmost part of the United States north almost to the Canadian line. In warm water ponds, the principal fish raised are the bluegill and

ꙮ   ꙮ   ꙮ

Homer S. Swingle, *Professor* (Fisheries) at Auburn University, has been in charge of fisheries research at the Agricultural Experiment Station, Auburn, Ala., since 1934. He was U.S. representative on pondfish culture at three Pacific Science Congresses. Dr. Swingle served as president of the American Fisheries Society in 1958 and was chairman of an FAO Symposium on Pondfish Culture in 1966.

169

the largemouth bass. Fingerling of these species for stocking ponds are available from hatcheries of the U.S. Bureau of Sport Fisheries and Wildlife and from many State hatcheries operated by State fish and game divisions. The redear sunfish, channel catfish, or bullhead catfish are often present as supplemental species. These supplemental species usually are available only from private commercial hatcheries, but this is not always so. Warm waters are required for reproduction and growth of these species.

When to stock: As soon as fish are available from the hatcheries and fish food is available, the ponds should be stocked. Since bluegills feed on water insects which become abundant within 1 month after the water is impounded, these fish may be stocked in the fall or early winter. Early fall stocking is best since they will grow rapidly during the fall months, slowly over winter, and again rapidly the following spring. Fall stocking gives maximum growth of bluegills before their spawning period, and early spawning in the next spring or early summer.

Largemouth bass are usually stocked in May or June, after the bluegills. Since bass feed upon small fish, they often eat the smaller bass unless large numbers of small bluegills hatch shortly after the small bass are stocked. If bass eat bass, too few may be left to keep bluegills under control and to prevent overcrowding. For this reason, stocking bluegills late in spring or in summer is undesirable because it delays their spawning and results in poor bass survival.

Where stocking of bluegills late is unavoidable, the answer for better bass survival is to stock around 1,000 fathead minnows per acre in February or March. These will spawn before bass are stocked and surround each bass with its favorite food—which is small fish.

How many to stock per acre: Since we are trying to raise fish to catch, we stock the maximum number of bluegills that will grow to a desirable size (3 to 6 ounces) by the time the pond is open to fishing. How many is this? Fertile land yields fertile water, making a productive pond; poor land yields poor water, making a poor pond. Consequently, the num-

Channel cat delivered by Fish and Wildlife Service truck to stock pond near Coolidge, Tex.

ber of fish we can raise per acre of water varies with the richness of the land in the watershed unless we apply fertilizer directly to the pond.

With unfertilized ponds, the correct number of bluegills to stock may vary from 100 to 1,500 per acre, and we would have to know the relative fertility of each watershed. However, by adding fertilizer we can make the waters produce fish more uniformly. The amount of fertilizer we should add will vary from less than 100 pounds per acre in richest watersheds to a maximum of 1,500 pounds in the poorest. In these fertile waters, we can grow 750 to 1,500 bluegills per acre to a desirable size; the average fertilized ponds are stocked with 1,000 bluegills.

Bass Stocking Rules

With largemouth bass we usually follow the same criterion. The correct number to stock is the maximum number that will grow to a desirable size, about 12 to 16 ounces within 1 year. We also want enough bass to eat most of the small bluegills so that there will remain just enough to replace the bluegills we harvest each year. This is usually the same number of bass as the maximum we can grow to a desirable size, 70 to 100 per acre in a fertilized pond.

However, if we desire to grow large bluegills in our pond, we may wish to have more bass per acre, even though they may not exceed 6 to 8 ounces within the first year. Extremely large bluegills (0.5 to 1.5 pounds) result from bass so crowded that practically all small bluegills are eliminated every year as they hatch in the pond, and from severely restricting the annual catch of both bluegills and bass.

Pond weeds may provide such dense underwater jungles that bass cannot catch the small bluegills. For other reasons also we want either to eliminate these weeds or to keep them under control. Weeds piercing the water surface shelter mosquito larvae, and mosquito bites are not the bites we expect to enjoy when we go fishing. Luckily, if we keep the pond well fertilized, the microscopic plants we produce prevent weed growth except in the shallow water. Both biological and chemical methods of controlling aquatic weeds are given in a USDA bulletin, *Waterweed Control on Farms and Ponds,* Farmers' Bulletin 2181.

Fertilizer needs vary from superphosphate alone in old ponds or those in rich watersheds, to a complete fertilizer (8–8–2) and lime in less fertile waters. Information on pond fertilization is given in USDA bulletin *Warm Water Ponds for Fishing,* Farmers' Bulletin 2210. No fertilizer is presently recommended for shallow, fertile ponds where snow cover remains over ice for extended periods. Fertilization in such cases is believed to increase the danger of winterkills of fish from low oxygen.

The new pond should not be fished until approximately the first of July, 1 year following the stocking of the largemouth bass. The delay is to allow the bass time to mature and to produce the first spawn of young in the pond: Young bass are then present to replace those caught out. If no young bass can be found by June of that year, 50 to 100 small fingerlings per acre should be stocked.

When a pond is first opened to fishing, fish can be caught quite rapidly, partly because of the high weight of harvestable fish present and partly because of their inexperience with lures and baits. Excessive fishing during this period can result in the removal of so many fish that it will be very difficult to maintain good fishing in the subsequent years. Rapid removal of most of the big bass is especially harmful, since these fish must prevent overcrowding by eating most of last year's crop of small bluegills. For best results, not over 20 pounds of bass per acre should be removed during the first summer of fishing.

In the fertilized ponds, the bluegill-bass combination can maintain an annual harvest of approximately 150 to 170 pounds per acre, which should include not over 30 pounds of bass. Only an exceptionally well-balanced population in the most fertile ponds can produce annual yields of 200 pounds. If the pond is to be operated to produce large bluegills, then the annual catch should be restricted to not over 100 pounds of bluegills and 15 pounds of bass per acre.

Trip Through a Watershed—
the Poteau River Project

TARLETON JENKINS

FROM THE NORTH U.S. Highway 71 curves over an instep of White Oak Mountain, nudges Waldron Lake near the dam, and jogs with Square Rock Creek on into the wide, tree-canopied valley of the Poteau River.

Along this highway thunder the great tractor-drawn stacks of logs for the sawmills of Waldron, Ark., and the mountainous loads of crated chickens for the poultry plant. Along it, too, roll the trailers, the campers and the burdened autos of the vacationers, the usual river of people in rubber-tired motion.

Where the highway skirts by the lake there is a turnout for the traveler. The lake is brimming now, a pleasant scene. But in the winter of 1962–63, the people of Waldron used to drive out to this point to see how much lower the level of their water supply had fallen. That was a winter of crisis, of near disaster, of prayer. It was also a winter of decision and action by the people of the Poteau River watershed.

The highway, passing the State Highway 28 intersection, slants on to Waldron, population 1,758 (1960 census), the bustling center of the valley's commerce. It is a neighborly, hello-Joe town, its bonds of fellowship more closely drawn now by the long, demanding task of developing a watershed plan.

Through the town's midsection the trucks of logs and chickens rumble, the ones bearing logs turning to the east, those with chickens to the west. From the sawmills when the wind is right come the sour-sweet smell of the new-sawn pine, oak, ash, and gum, and the whine of the saws. Here is stacked enough lumber to build a city, with a steady flow of timber from the slopes to keep taking its place.

The throbbing of the engines at the poultry plant is a symphony now to the ears of the businessmen, particularly to G. W. Henderson, the postmaster and the president of the Waldron Chamber of Commerce.

Shut down this plant, Mr. Henderson explained, and you have cut an artery of the community's life. The poultry plant must have water—750,000 gallons of it a day, as much as is used by all the rest of the community. When the city's supply fell so desperately low, the plant closed. The 375 men and women employed by the plant were idled. Trucking of poultry from the 200 farms in the area stopped, as did the return flow of cash—$22,000 each week for birds and eggs. The payroll of $20,000 a week stopped as well.

The mayor, W. A. McKeown, a former lumberman and hardware dealer, admits the city was in trouble with its water supply nearly gone.

"We would have lost most of our industry," he recalled. "As it is, we now can look forward to growth. We have plenty of water, no more problems there.

ῼ　ῼ　ῼ

Tarleton Jenkins is *Assistant Director*, Information Division, Soil Conservation Service.

We also have a new hospital, splendid schools, and a good supply of quality labor. We need an improved airport and a country club—other things employers are interested in when they consider a plant site. We will get those."

The abundance of water comes from the new lake which is a part of the Poteau River watershed protection and flood prevention project carried out with the help of the U.S. Department of Agriculture. It appears as site 5 on the watershed maps prepared by the Soil Conservation Service engineers. The lake is a broad expanse of clear, sparkling water, 2,100 acre-feet of it for Waldron's use. (An acre-foot—43,560 cubic feet—is a unit of water equal to an acre's surface area 1 foot deep.) In addition, the lake will hold temporarily nearly 3,700 acre-feet during heavy storms to guard against flooding.

Paul Whittington, the SCS work unit conservationist in Waldron, showed the lake proudly to a visitor.

"People like to drive out along here just to look at it," he said. "It's a reassuring sight, especially when you've seen the way things were for a time without it."

You can drive along the dam to where the automatic pumps up on the tower take water from the lake to the city's new water plant. The tower also functions in time of heavy rains to draw off floodwater and ease it into the stream course below.

Any account of the development of the Poteau River watershed project is sure to include the name of "Brother" Evans.

The Reverend John E. Evans, sighting the visiting car, slipped the clutch of his tractor into higher gear and came bouncing over to the Evans farmyard.

Lean and wiry, his hair white and close-cropped, Brother Evans is—as he had wanted to be—a country minister. He came to the valley 27 years ago, bought farmland near the Poteau River downstream from Waldron, and soon had two rural congregations.

Membership on the Poteau County Soil and Water Conservation District's board of supervisors was an almost natural consequence for Brother Evans. And when he found his farm cut off periodically by the flooding Poteau River, his interest turned to flood prevention.

"We had been bothered in this watershed about three times a year on the average by floods," he related. "And there was a lot of interest in the watershed in securing a project. When I learned that the Poteau was considered for one of the pilot watershed projects in 1953 but missed out, I was really upset. We resolved not to miss again."

Development of the project plan was an almost painful affair. The people of

Boating is a popular family sport on many of the Nation's watersheds. This scene is in Kentucky at Lake Malone, Mud River Watershed.

Waldron were bent on swift action to provide a water supply. A flood prevention plan in conjunction with the building of a dam for storage was, to many citizens, less important and could wait.

Way to a Sound Plan

"We just had to sweat it out," said Brother Evans. "When the people learned the real benefits of a watershed project, they became interested in developing this kind of a plan. We are now getting protection from floods, which have been very costly to us—often costly to the people of Waldron—and we have the problem of a water supply for Waldron solved, too."

To Brother Evans, the struggle and dissent involved in the development of a watershed plan are a normal and even valuable part of the process.

"In this way you eventually arrive at a sound plan, with all aspects taken into account, both immediate and long range," he said. "I would be wary of any such plan drawn up quickly, with everyone in constant agreement."

B. S. Hinkle, who served Scott County as its agricultural agent for 31 years and then served repeated terms in the State legislature, is the man who influenced consideration of a new element in the watershed plan—a lake for recreation.

"I found a site on Jones Creek in the 1950's," he recalled. "I thought it would make a recreation lake, which we have needed here. The State game and fish commission approved it. When the U.S. Fish and Wildlife Service took a look at our proposal, they recommended an even larger project—about 1,000 acres.

"We had the survey made and got options on the land. Then the watershed project came along, and it looks as if we will have a wonderful lake there, with fishing, boating, water skiing, and plenty of space for people to picnic and camp. The Forest Service will help with this last. You know, I mean to have a boat on that lake. I like to fish."

Down on State Highway 28 the community of Bates hoped to share, too, in the watershed development. A leader in the community's effort is Everett Sanders who, with his brother Elvan, runs a sawmill near the highway. There was coal mining around Bates years ago and the community hummed. The 2-story brick school building near the Sanders home housed more than 100 pupils. The building is unused now.

Sanders is a member of the local committee on area development. Objectives are road improvement, a community building—and water.

Water is of very poor quality in Bates. It comes from shallow wells, and is charged with minerals. Water heaters and other appliances are damaged. Mrs. Sanders and most of the other housewives prefer to drive the 13 miles into Oklahoma with their weekly washing—rather than to use the well water.

The communities of Cauthron and Weeks, too, could benefit from a water supply in the flood prevention site near Bates on Shadley Creek, known as site 10 in the watershed project. The residents hope that the project can include a 30- to 40-acre lake with about 1,000 acre-feet for the communities' use.

"Several kinds of small business will be interested in us here if we have water," Sanders commented.

A county survey for needed water and sewage development is in prospect.

18 Dams in All

The Poteau River watershed project has moved ahead with unusual speed, possibly as the result of the momentum generated by a town's need for water. Active in support of the project have been its sponsors, the Poteau River Soil and Water Conservation District, the Le Flore Soil and Water Conservation District in Oklahoma (into which the watershed project extends a short distance), the Arkansas Game and Fish Commission, the Poteau River Water Improvement District, and Waldron.

In the project plan, all told, are 18 floodwater detention dams with a stretch of channel improvement for the river. When the work has been done, a rain such as fell in 1960—causing the most damaging flood in recent years—will result in little or no harm. The project,

174

with other proposed watershed projects in the area, is part of the plan developed under leadership of the Soil Conservation Service for a Resource Conservation and Development project designed to enable the local population to bring the economy of an eight-county region closer to its potential.

If the residents of the Poteau valley needed a new stimulus in carrying out their watershed project, it may have come in the spring of 1966 with one of the intense rains the area can expect that time of year. It totaled 8 inches.

"We would have had plenty of trouble without this project," said Mayor McKeown. "But as it was—well, it merely contributed to our water supply."

And Brother Evans, who in years past was marooned by the river's flooding, was able to cross the Poteau and meet his flocks right on time.

A Drink From the Desert

RAY D. JACKSON and C. H. M. van BAVEL

FEW desert travelers today are like the hardy prospectors of years gone by. People of all ages and from all walks of life go to the desert for recreation. The desert is beautiful and interesting, but to the unwary traveler who finds himself stranded without water, it can be a nightmare—and a killer. Lost, thirsty, with nothing but cactus for company, he may think it impossible to find water.

Actually the Ancient Mariner's words "Water, water every where, nor any drop to drink" are usually true, even in the desert. There is, almost always, water in desert soils and always in living plants; the trick is to get it! With a piece of plastic film, a person can build a simple solar still and get a drink of water from the desert soil and plants.

All the necessary parts for the "survival still" can be carried in a pocket. These parts are a piece of clear plastic film about 6 feet square; a second, but smaller, piece of plastic film, aluminum foil, or other waterproof material to use as a container; and a plastic drinking tube.

To make the still, dig a bowl-shaped pit about 3 feet across and about 2 feet deep in the soil. Use the small piece of plastic film or aluminum foil to make a container in the center of the hole. Put the drinking tube into the container and bring it out of the pit.

Arrange cut pieces of cactus or other plant material in the pit around the side of the pit, and spread the clear plastic film over the top. Place soil around the edge of the plastic to hold it down, and then put a rock about the size of your fist in the center of the plastic. Push downward on the rock until it is about 1 foot below the soil surface. The rock should be directly over the container. The still is now complete; just wait awhile for a drink. (See photos on next page.)

If the sun is shining, water droplets will form on the bottom side of the plastic film in about 30 minutes. In about an hour the droplets will start running toward the point of the cone and fall into the container. In 3 to 4 hours about

꽃   꽃   꽃

Ray D. Jackson is *Research Physicist*, U.S. Water Conservation Laboratory, Soil and Water Conservation Research Division, Agricultural Research Service, Phoenix, Ariz.

C. H. M. van Bavel is *Chief Physicist* at the laboratory.

(left) Slicing a cactus to expose the water-bearing inner pulp.   (right) Cactus slices placed around container which can be made from heavy aluminum foil, plastic film, or any water-proof material.   One end of the drinking tube is in the container.   The pit now is all ready to be covered with the plastic film.

half a pint of water will be in the container. During the day, about 2 pints of water will collect; during the night, about 1 pint is a typical yield.

Most clear plastic films will work in a solar still. However, some types are considerably better than others.

The film should be clear, strong, and wettable. Being wettable means that waterdrops that form on the underside of the film will cling to the film as they run to the point of the cone. On a non-wettable plastic, the drops will form, but many fall off before reaching the point of the cone, thus reducing the amount of water which is caught.

Polyvinyl fluoride films are satisfactory for these purposes.

The still works well in desert areas where sunlight is abundant and where there is some water in the soil or where

Edge of plastic film is securely weighted down with soil all around rim of pit.   Rock is placed in center and pushed down to form the film into an inverted cone.   Rock must be directly over container.   The solar still is now complete.   Wait for a few hours, and then you can take a drink.

176

fleshy plant materials such as cacti are available. However, it works equally well on an ocean beach or in areas where water is abundant, but polluted. In an area without vegetation and without any water in the soil, the still could be used to purify water from body wastes, engine coolants, or other undrinkable sources.

When deciding where to locate a still, dryness of the soil, availability of plant materials, exposure to sunlight, and ease of digging a pit should be considered. It should be exposed to sunlight all day.

If the soil is damp, or plant material is available, build the still where it is the easiest to dig. If the soil is very dry and no plants are available, it should be located in a streambed or depression where water may have accumulated after a rain. On an ocean beach, the pit should be just above the high watermark so sea water is plentiful in the sand, but the still is not damaged by waves. Near a polluted pond or stream, the pit should be dug at a point where the soil is wet, but where water does not accumulate in the pit and spill into the container.

The amount of water produced by a single survival still is not enough for continued survival in a hot, dry climate. Under extreme conditions, about 1 gallon of water per day is necessary to maintain life. Two stills would nearly meet this requirement, and one still could provide sufficient water to prolong life until rescued. It is well known that panic caused by thirst drives people to wander to an almost certain death within hours. A modest, but dependable, source of water could prevent these tragedies.

More Crawfish
for the Gourmet

CARL H. THOMAS

CRAWFISH are good to eat, fun to catch, and provide income to many people in Louisiana. So . . . "you get a line and I'll get a pole". . . .

Crawfish tails have been a seasonal delicacy in Louisiana for many years. Early historical writings relate stories of crawfish abundance and of tasty dishes. Natural Louisiana swamps once provided enough crawfish for the local people. But with more demand, less rainfall, and competing land uses, the crawfish supplied from the unmanaged areas became undependable.

Through the efforts of technicians of the Soil Conservation Service, Louisiana Wildlife and Fisheries Commission, and Louisiana State University, procedures were developed whereby commercial and recreational crops of crawfish can be grown on purpose.

Since 1963, thousands of pounds of live crawfish a day have been moved out of flooded fields in south central Louisiana during early spring and summer. Hundreds of people have gained employment from the fishing and processing. Eating places serve more people, most of whom drive many miles to eat crawfish, and wetlands development for crawfish has

꽃 꽃 꽃

Carl H. Thomas is *State Biologist* with the Soil Conservation Service in Albuquerque, N. Mex. He served as State Biologist with SCS in Louisiana from 1957 to 1966.

become a big, new conservation practice.

Landowners, rice farmers, and businessmen like Bert Gilbert, Roland Faulk, Ashby Landry, Elmer Naquin, John Ruppert, Alphe Simon, and many others pioneered the crawfish farming efforts.

Steps To Follow

Rotation of crawfish with a forthcoming rice crop is one type of crawfish field. This type begins with an area of native pasture—an idle ricefield in rotation growing grass—and the procedure generally follows this sequence:

1. In early spring the field is plowed.
2. About May 1 the field is replowed and the rice planted.
3. The growing rice is flooded with water about 4 to 5 inches deep from May 15 to August 1.
4. Most ricefields are harvested between July 15 and August 15. Fields are dry at this time.
5. Between September 1 and November 1 the field is reflooded for crawfish.
6. The crawfish are harvested between January and June.
7. Water is maintained during the period of September through June.
8. Water is removed from the field, and it reverts to native pasture until rice is planted next season.

The remaining crawfish burrow into the soil to escape enemies and to obtain moisture. The irrigation of rice once in 2 years provides sufficient moisture to maintain this resident population. Even though crawfish are native in south Louisiana ricefields, unsuccessful attempts to raise a commercial crop have occurred on land that had not been planted to rice in 4 or more years because of lack of water. On such fields it may be necessary to stock adult crawfish at the rate of 5 to 10 pounds per acre, in water, during the month of May.

The water should be a minimum depth of 6 inches at all times, and about 18 inches is deep enough to grow crawfish. Deeper water makes the harvest more difficult. Strong outside levees around ricelands make water-holding easier.

Raising crawfish in rotation with rice is only one method of commercial production. Another way is to build a levee around a piece of land which shows signs of native crawfish and manage for a crop every year. This way, you are actually just guaranteeing what nature does every so often. And it can be either wooded swampland or open land.

The sequence of events in growing crawfish on land every year is as follows:
• Establish a suitable water control system—levee and drainpipes.
• Let native grasses grow to provide food for the crawfish. Fertilize if you find it is necessary.
• Flood the area with water 6 to 18 inches deep between September 15 and October 1.
• Hold water on field throughout the fall and the winter.
• Beginning December 1, set test traps to see if crawfish population is ready to be harvested.
• Drain field about June 15 and repeat the procedure outlined above.

With these management procedures, harvest usually begins in late December or January. Weather influences the starting time of harvest. A warming trend is needed in late winter to stimulate feeding, growth, and movement to traps.

The crawfish harvested in December, January, and early February are usually larger ones, 10 per pound. These are adults which survived from the season

Viki Faulk of Crowley, La., displays large red swamp crawfish taken from a field near her home. Six of this size weigh a pound.

before; and include a few large but immature individuals from early-hatched eggs. Most eggs hatch in October, and the young reach large size by March.

The harvest is conducted in various ways. Some farmers contract their fields to commercial fishermen for a set fee per pound of crawfish harvested. Others fish the field themselves and sell directly to the public or to wholesale buyers. Still others allow the public to fish at so much a pound, or a combination of these methods is used. Retail prices usually begin at 35 cents per pound live weight and go down to a low of 10 cents depending on what the supply is.

A well managed and diligently harvested field yields between 400 and 1,000 pounds of live crawfish per acre. This production is accomplished only with heavy fishing and if all crawfish 15 or more grams in weight are harvested.

Types of Traps

Most commercial crawfishermen now use the standard cylinder-type or funnel-entrance trap. Catfish heads, gizzard shad, buffalo fish, carp, and beef melt are the baits commonly used. The bait is placed in the wire cage, and crawfish enter through the funnel.

The old bait is removed each time the trap is checked and fresh bait is added. It is important to have the bottom of a funnel-entrance trap on flat ground so the crawfish will crawl in, not under, the entrance. A well baited and placed trap will catch ¾ to 1 pound in 6 to 8 hours. The trap is usually checked in the early morning and late evening.

The common crab or crawfish net is used by sports crawfishermen when the crawfish are "really biting."

A person should check the nets every 10 to 15 minutes since the crawfish find this bait quicker.

Crawfishing is fun, and safe for the whole family. I talked to two ladies crawfishing one day between Crowley and Jennings, La. They told me they were having so much fun they had forgotten to eat their picnic lunch.

Water on the ricefields is not so deep as to offer a threat to the smaller folks. People of all ages can walk the rice paddy levees with the small wire-supported crawfish nets, poles, buckets, and bait. And it is quite a thrill to lift the net when 10 to 20 large red crawfish are holding to the piece of meat used as bait.

Ways To Cook Crawfish

You can eat crawfish in a number of ways. Three pounds of the boiled ones, served with tomato flavored sauce on the side, makes a meal. Crawfish bisque, crawfish étouffée, and crawfish salad are popular dishes. Gumbo and pie are delicious also. Seafood specialty houses serve crawfish year around, and regular eating establishments in southern Louisiana add them to the menu by demand during the season, February through June.

The meat in the crawfish tail is all that is eaten. However, the "fat" (liver) is used as seasoning. The larger crawfish have smaller percentages of tail meat. When 8 or 10 crawfish weigh a pound, there is only about 9 pounds of tail meat per 100 pounds of live crawfish.

In average size crawfish, 25 to 30 per pound, there is 14 pounds of meat per 100 pounds of live crawfish.

Recipes for cooking crawfish are easily found in almost any southern Louisiana cookbook.

Crawfish used to be available only to local Louisiana folks, but now they are cooked and packaged commercially under a number of brand names. The processing plants are both on the farms and in the towns. A large processing plant was built near Breaux Bridge, La., in 1966. Here, the crawfish are cooked, packaged, and frozen for sale to retail outlets. Thousands of pounds of live crawfish are used daily in the Breaux Bridge plant.

Crawfish are providing recreation for many people, giving the landowners additional income, increasing employment, and improving land use. The stimulation of business to local cafes, hardware stores, and sporting goods stores, and the increase in tourist trade are other benefits. So you see, the lowly crawfish is no longer lowly in Louisiana!

A Bright New Day for Weyers Cave

CECIL W. ROSE and ROBERT A. HOLLEY

SOON you won't see water wagons, cistern pumps, or weatherbeaten outhouses in Weyers Cave.

And it won't be too long before good clear water from a new system will gush out of kitchen faucets throughout this north Shenandoah Valley community in historic Augusta County, Va. This county—once one of the largest in the Nation—originally extended all the way to the Mississippi River.

Things are looking better for Weyers Cave residents along with the residents of some 30,000 other rural communities that are now lacking modern water and sewage facilities.

This is because of the USDA Farmers Home Administration's rural community facilities program under the Aiken-Poage bill, enacted in October 1965. Chances are now good that each year more than 1,400 communities with a total of about a million residents will for the first time begin benefiting from water and sewage disposal systems which millions of city residents have been taking for granted for years.

It is this program in action which is keeping Weyers Cave from joining the steadily growing list of dying towns. Soon, with a flip of the switch, excellent spring water from a centrally located supply will flow at a rate of over a million gallons a day.

This will update the living conditions of some 500 Weyers Cave people more than anything that has happened since the railroad station opened in 1872.

In seconds after the switch has been flipped in this town that was looted and burned out during the Civil War, fresh, clean, sparkling water will rush out of the pump through chlorinating equipment and into a shiny new storage tank on a nearby hill.

From there it will flow by gravity to serve the community's needs. This is indeed a great milestone for 120 farm and other rural families, for the businessmen, and for the students in the local elementary school.

Good running water will be available in almost unlimited supply for the first time since the town of Weyers Cave was founded in 1804. Add to this the unexpected bonus from having a brand new sewage system, and then it becomes evident why the Weyers Cave people are now filled to the brim with enthusiasm.

Gone forever is the need for residents to rely upon shallow wells subject to pollution from overflowing septic tanks. Gone also is the need for patching tar-streaked cisterns and the need to pump out aged septic tanks.

Things are truly different now. For the undertaker has been cheated out of burying another American town.

This came about through the untiring

※ ※ ※

Cecil W. Rose is a *Civil Engineer*, Association Loan Division, with the Farmers Home Administration.

Robert A. Holley, an *Information Specialist* with the Information Division, Farmers Home Administration, died in June of 1967.

work of some farsighted Weyers Cave civic leaders which had resulted in the approval of a USDA Farmers Home Administration grant and loan. These funds made it possible for the borrowing Weyers Cave Sanitary District to take much needed action—action that would cross Weyers Cave off the list of some 30,000 communities which lacked modern water supply and sewage disposal facilities.

Dice's Spring—for many years this town's only source of water—is being enclosed and a pump installed. The other construction includes a 300,000-gallon storage standpipe and the laying of some 4 miles of 6- and 8-inch pipeline.

Building of the sewage disposal system will solve a longtime problem, one that halted construction of new homes and business buildings for many years.

Because of the area's impervious soil, septic tanks—the town's only waste disposal method—have been unsatisfactory. An estimated 80 percent of these septic tanks were not working properly at the time the Farmers Home Administration grant and loan were approved.

So it is no wonder that the residents of a town that was at one time the valley's leading livestock and hay shipping center are thankful that during the past several years they had managed to keep its name on the map.

Although the Weyers Cave Sanitary District—a public body—was the official applicant for the grant and loan funds, five businessmen named to a Ruritan Club planning committee are credited along with the FHA county supervisor, Donald Spencer, with doing the needed organizational work which led up to the financing of the facilities.

This group, headed up by Chairman Loren Miller, paint manufacturing firm sales representative, started in earnest in September of 1964 to cure a stagnated town. The members were Cletus Houff, Houff's Transfer Corp. president; Harold Roller, local dairyman and Shenandoah Valley Milk Producer's Association executive secretary; Harry Driver, Weyers Cave Bank cashier; and George Schreckhise, Schreckhise Nursery manager.

Three years later, with the greatly needed community facilities all assured, three of these men—along with FHA County Supervisor Spencer and President Joe Shiflet from the spearheading Ruritan Club—expressed high optimism concerning the town's future.

"Financing construction of this water supply and sewage disposal system has really been a matter of life and death to the Weyers Cave community," explained Schreckhise. "The facilities were urgently needed. Residents could not get permits for sewage disposal, and without them there was no point in anybody planning to build a home in the community. This town is destined to expand two to three times its present size due to its good water and sewage systems."

Needed for 30 Years

Banker Driver emphasized that the community has been in need of these facilities for more than 30 years, with conditions becoming more acute as the population increased.

"Community expansion is now practicable. A new 3,000 student capacity Virginia State Industrial College is set for occupancy near Weyers Cave by September 1967," Driver said.

"This will mean that scores of new homes will have to be built for the teachers and others. The lack of water and sewage facilities has been the only factor holding back community growth."

Transfer Corp. President Houff said completion of this FHA-financed project will make it possible for employees of his and other firms to build homes close to their places of employment.

"Weyers Cave—located in the county's center and only 12 miles from the Staunton, Waynesboro, and Harrisonburg trading centers—may well soon be one of Augusta County's fastest growing communities," points out FHA County Supervisor Spencer. "An airport has been constructed near here. It and the proposed State industrial college will have a big impact on the area when in full-fledged operation."

Ruritan Club President Shiflet agreed that the community's growth can't do anything but soar in the light of present prospects made possible by assurance of the new water and sewage disposal systems for this Virginia area.

Weyers Cave will soon not only be a more comfortable place to live, but a more beautiful one. Nurseryman Schreckhise reports that the availability of water will mean more landscaped yards and green lawns throughout the community.

It is too early to report the full impact of the two Farmers Home Administration-financed projects on this small Virginia town. But what happened in Tennessee's Warren County when adequate supplies of fresh water became readily available gives one a good idea of what the future holds for the farm and other rural residents in the Weyers Cave region.

When the Farmers Home Administration 3 years ago made $1.3 million in loans to five Warren County, Tenn., communities for financing construction of much needed modern water systems, things began to happen.

Like spokes from the hub of a wheel, pure water systems now fan out from the McMinnville town water system in every direction.

These miles of waterlines provide a pure water supply to over 6,000 rural residents throughout the Irving College, Lower Collins, North Warren, Centertown, and Viola water utility districts.

Four Plants Built

That was only the start of the Warren County rural development success story.

Four industrial plants whose facilities cost around $550,000 to construct have located in the area since installation of the new systems. And they will soon be employing close to 400 area people.

Some 260 new homes costing over $3 million have been built in the area of the five Warren County communities. Another 390 houses have been remodeled at an expenditure of over $34,000.

Seventeen small businesses, including coin-operated laundries, a horse training stable, garages, service stations, nursery packing barns, and the like have started since the Farmers Home Administration-financed water system came into being.

182

⚘

HOW TO GO ABOUT IT

Here is how projects such as the ones at Weyers Cave, Va., and in Warren County, Tenn., come about:

Applications for financing a proposed water or sewage disposal system through the Farmers Home Administration can be made at any of the USDA agency's 1,600 offices by towns and villages with populations up to 5,500 people and by water districts or organizations operating on a nonprofit basis.

To be eligible a loan applicant must:

• Demonstrate that needed credit can't be obtained from other sources at reasonable rates and terms.

• Show that the water or sewer system will benefit rural people.

• Possess the legal capacity to borrow and repay the money, to pledge security for loans, and to operate the facilities or services which are to be installed with the loan funds.

Funds may be borrowed to install, to repair, or to expand rural water supply and waste disposal systems. This includes funds for reservoirs, pipelines, wells, pumping plants, and for filtration and treatment systems.

Funds also can be obtained to refinance debts, to pay engineers and attorneys, and for acquiring rights-of-way and easements.

A borrower's total indebtedness for such loans cannot go over $4 million. The maximum term for these loans is 40 years, and the interest rate cannot exceed 5 percent.

All of the loans must be secured in a manner which adequately protects the Government's interest. Bonds or notes pledging taxes, assessments, or revenues will be accepted as security if they meet statutory requirements.

A mortgage will also be taken out on the organization's facilities when State laws permit this.

In addition to loans, grants may be obtained, when necessary, to defray up to 50 percent of the construction cost.

⚘

A total of some 190 families in the five-community area have purchased around $31,500 in appliances, now that these communities have an adequate supply of running water for the first time.

New community buildings valued at over $500,000 have been built. This includes a church, a post office building, a wing on the school building, two recreational centers, and an addition to Irving College.

Other steps include the purchase of land for $500,000 by the State for a park at Rock Island and purchase of its first fire-truck by the town of Viola.

This all took place since the first of the five Farmers Home Administration-financed water systems started the water

flowing to both farm and rural residents.

All of this worked to create new jobs and payrolls in the county. Then there are the untold benefits resulting from more adequate fire protection and the availability of fresh water for schools.

Indeed, the future is becoming much brighter as the years pass for the some 30,000 rural communities lacking modern water and sewage disposal facilities.

If you live in a waterless or sewerless community, you can obtain the details of how this program might be obtained by calling on the USDA Farmers Home Administration office which serves your county. There are more than 1,600 such offices serving every rural county in the States and in Puerto Rico.

Land Management for City Water

E. BRUCE JONES, RICHARD LEE, and JOHN C. FREY

WATER is steadily becoming more and more scarce around our cities. There the demand for large supplies of water is concentrated in small areas. The snow and the rain which fall in the urban area provide little usable water per person or per industry. Thus, many cities must look beyond their boundaries for clean water supplies.

Clean water is essential to life itself. Obvious as this fact may be, we are apt to forget just how much water we actually use. Each man, woman, and child in the United States uses, on the average, 44,000 gallons per year. It is estimated that the average water consumption per person will rise about 50 percent during the next 35 years.

Based on a daily requirement of 120 gallons, the average price that you pay for

water is about 5 cents a day, or $18.25 per year. Because there is not enough available in all places to satisfy all the needs, water—like many other economic goods—has begun to command a price. And its price is determined, in the final analysis, by supply and demand.

Although there may be various sources from which a city may obtain its water

The authors are all from Pennsylvania State University and are associated with the Institute for Research on Land and Water Resources.

E. Bruce Jones is *Assistant Professor* of Meteorology and *Assistant Director* of the Institute. As Assistant Director, he is in charge of the Water Resources Center.

Richard Lee is *Assistant Professor* of Forest Hydrology and is associated with the Institute.

John C. Frey is *Professor* of Land Economics and *Director* of the Institute.

supply—like streams, lakes, reservoirs, or ground water—the ultimate source is the atmosphere. Of the 30 inches of snow and rain which fall on the United States in an average year, 21 inches are returned to the atmosphere through evaporation and transpiration. This water is partly used to support forests, cultivated crops, and native grass. The remaining 9 inches, which is the manageable supply, drains from the land surface or becomes part of ground water seepage. Of this amount, about 3 inches is withdrawn for human use, and 6 inches flows directly into the oceans by way of streams.

Major Water Sources

The major sources for the Nation's water supply are our rivers and creeks. These furnish 75 percent of the water used by cities, towns, and for irrigation on farms, 90 percent of the fresh water industry uses, and nearly all water used to generate hydroelectric power.

All streams, regardless of size, begin as a mere trickle in some headwaters area, commonly called a watershed. Some watersheds are small and within a few miles from the water consumers. Some large watersheds supply water to users over 1,000 miles away. For example, in the high mountains of Wyoming, Utah, and Colorado rises the fountainhead of the Colorado River, which supplies some of the water needs of the population in southern California, Arizona, and in sections of Mexico.

Large or small, in your own backyard or far over the horizon, all watersheds basically perform the same functions—catching huge amounts of rain and of snow and converting them to streamflow. Precipitation in the humid Eastern United States averages about one-tenth inch daily. Arid and semiarid Western States receive perhaps a third that amount.

A precipitation of one-tenth inch is no more rain than that which falls in a light shower. However, it adds up to 11.3 tons of water per acre or 1,740,000 gallons per square mile. If collected in a "catch basin" the size of an average rooftop, this amount would fill as many as eighty to a hundred 1-gallon buckets.

The fraction of total snow and rainfall required for home and other non-industrial city needs is very small. A city with a population of 100,000 in the Northeast would require a catch basin of a mere 6 square miles if all of the precipitation were recovered. Normally, 400 persons can be sustained for a year by the recovery of an inch of precipitation from 1 square mile of watershed.

In the orderly disposition of water in the watershed, every piece of ground—a square foot, an acre, a square mile, a complete drainage basin—performs a vital hydrologic function. That this function can be changed by man's use of land has been shown by history and many recent experiments and experiences.

A city with a population of 100,000 requires 12 million gallons of water a day for its domestic needs. Although this may sound like a vast amount, if you were to spread 12 million gallons of water over a 10-square-mile watershed, the depth would be hardly great enough to measure—less than a tenth of an inch. A growing forest can consume twice this amount during a single day.

The type of surface which catches the snow and rainfall determines the amount of water available for municipal use. If the watershed is heavily vegetated, plants may consume a large portion of the precipitation. City dwellers, for the most part, are dependent on these vegetated watersheds for clean water and have a big stake in keeping them green.

Paving Technique

At the other extreme, an artificially paved watershed will give practically 100 percent runoff. This technique, although rather unusual, might be used where there is a demand for water that cannot be met otherwise.

Other management practices to help increase the water harvests are being developed. Clearcutting oak forests on deep soils in humid North Carolina provided enough additional water per square mile the year following cutting to support 6,800 city dwellers. It is important to note, however, that every watershed is unique and must be treated

184

individually. Thinning lodgepole pine stands on shallow soils in the Colorado Rockies reduced the amounts of water used by the trees, but the operation did not add significantly to the overall yield of the watershed, a study showed.

Population and industrial pressures in the Northeast United States are creating

———————————————⚘———————————————

MUDFLAT BLUES

Careless use of watershed lands has, in the past, resulted in soil erosion, foul streams, and a waste of the water supply. The promiscuous taking of crops, lumber, and minerals has blotted out beauty and has left some areas open to the ravages of duststorms and floods.

Such thoughtless dissipation of watersheds feeding a city can sap its water sources and cause the added expense of providing reservoir space for the needed surplus water. For example, if 1 inch of soil were scraped off the top of a 250,000-acre watershed and dumped into a river, almost 1 billion cubic feet of top soil would be either carried into the sea or trapped behind a reservoir. In a reservoir, this amount of mud would displace just about 7 billion gallons of water—enough for the domestic needs of a city of 100,000 for almost 2 years.

But with skillful land management of this very same watershed, roads could be built, timber harvested, livestock and wildlife could graze, and you could enjoy recreational activities with no loss of soil or vegetation significant enough either to upset the balance of the water cycle or to pollute the water.

———————————————⚘———————————————

a strong urban demand for water. Guidelines have been developed for timber harvesting to increase the water supplies. Should the value of land for water collection and storage surpass its value for timber production, replacement of trees with grass or similar water-conserving plants may become necessary.

Research indicates that the removal of all the vegetation in a lush watershed in the Northeast raised the water yields the first year from 4 to 12 inches. In various partial cuttings, extra yields were only an inch or two.

Failure to undertake logging operations on forested watersheds may restrict water yields substantially.

On the other hand, watersheds may produce both an income from timber sales and additional water if their forests are harvested carefully under a system of even-aged management.

What occurs in forest cutting to increase the water yields is a harvesting of plant forms to favorably change the rates of transpiration and evaporation.

Some of the things taken into consideration are: The lighter colored foliage of grasses versus the darker leaves of trees decreasing the absorption of sunlight; the variation in the period of active growth among different trees and lower growing herbaceous and grassy plants; the depth from which certain plants extract water from the ground, shallow-rooted species versus the taprooted trees; and that plants differ in ability to diffuse water through leaf pores.

Water Hijackers

The watershed management specialists have learned to identify some of the plant forms which use water most extravagantly. Water can be conserved by removing or replacing the species that consume the largest amounts. Occasionally, slow-growing and defective forest trees are removed and then replaced with grass that yields more water. When this is done, however, logging operations and subsequent grazing activities must be controlled carefully to prevent soil and site deterioration.

In arid regions, streambank vegetation—called phreatophytes—uses water that otherwise might be diverted for municipal use. It is estimated that in Arizona alone, phreatophytes, principally saltcedar, consume as much water as is needed to support the city of Phoenix. Removal and replacement of certain phreatophytes with a less thirsty species of plant is a practice that can be employed to increase water harvests.

185

235-917 O - 67 - 15

The supplies of water available for municipal use as ground water also are affected to the extent that water tables are raised by soil and water conserving practices on the outlying farms. In places where the most important use of water is farm crop and timber production, the farmers take steps to retain as much precipitation as possible on the land where it falls. Conservation practices like terracing, contour farming, stripcropping, and grassed waterways increase water storage in the soil.

Complex Process

Modification of the water yield from a watershed by planned manipulation is a complex process with a potentially great impact on municipal water supplies. The requisite skill is both scientific and artistic—the best practitioners are both highly trained and experienced. Because of the costs of producing high quality water, and because economic development and a rapidly expanding population will spur the extensions of resource developments into the upper reaches of all watersheds, the approach taken toward the development and use of watershed lands must be both positive and objective. Development programs must be based on the capabilities of the land itself. Federal and State agencies and private enterprise should be supported in their programs for good watershed management to restore the quality of water in all areas.

Where watershed management practices are prudently employed, we can procure more clean water without short-changing other interests. Added benefits of a well-managed watershed include those that accrue from increased opportunities for recreation and land development, soil stability, grazing, and improved wildlife habitat as well as better forest products.

Most watersheds are more than mere water-producing areas. Except for the extremely rugged, rocky escarpments of major mountain ranges, watershed lands also provide socioeconomic opportunities. Millions of people are attracted to watershed lands every year to enjoy the scenery and facilities they offer for recreation. Watersheds may also provide shelter and sustenance for wildlife and waterfowl, and these lands are a source of summer forage for many thousands of our sheep and cattle.

The ideal watershed lands—like water itself—are in a limited supply and are not distributed evenly throughout the Nation. Of the 1.9 billion acres of land in the continental United States, many millions of acres have been transformed into cities and towns, farms, airfields, and paved highways.

Millions of other acres are desert or so nearly desert they cannot be classified as water-producing land.

Water Rights Involved

Land management and watershed planning are demanding tasks and often involve the resolution of very complicated patterns of landownership. In most cases, and particularly in the Western United States, the question of water rights plays an important or in some cases a dominant role.

The next time you draw a glass of water from the tap, consider the wonders of this resource and the effort that has been expended to allow you to use it so easily. Enjoy your glass of water, but remember the importance of protecting your water supply. How long could you survive without water?

For further reading:
Leopold, L. B., and Langbein, W. B., *A Primer on Water*. U.S. Department of the Interior, Geological Survey, Washington, D.C. 20240, 1960.
Lull, Howard W., and Reinhart, Kenneth G., *Increasing Water Yield in the Northeast by Management of Forested Watersheds*. U.S. Department of Agriculture, Northeastern Forest Experiment Station, University Park, Pa. (In press.)
Piper, A. M., *Has the United States Enough Water?*, Geological Survey Water-Supply Paper 1797, U.S. Government Printing Office, Washington, D.C. 20402, 1965.
United Nations, Food and Agriculture Organization, *Forest Influences*. S. P. A. Tipografica Castaldi, Rome, 1962.
U.S. Congress, Senate Select Committee on National Water Resources, *Future Water Requirements for Municipal Use*. Committee Print No. 7, Washington, D.C., 1960.

Fish Farming—Business and Pleasure *Do* Go Together

ROY A. GRIZZELL, JR., and JOHN GAMMON, JR.

A "NEW" TYPE of farming is gaining in popularity. It combines the best aspects of sound land use and economic opportunities with production of a delicious foodstuff. And it also affords fine recreational and sporting experiences for cityfolk.

This type of farming is called fish farming. It is "new" only in the sense that many farmers and other persons are just beginning to get into the business. Actually, fish farming dates back to the dawn of history, with people "managing" ponds to insure their supply of finny food. However, it is a relatively new enterprise in the United States, with the most rapid development occurring since World War II.

While commercial fresh water fisheries in lakes and rivers have been declining during recent years, well-managed fishponds have been increasing. The State of Arkansas has been the national leader in this enterprise, particularly where several varieties of catfish are concerned. Other States with a significant amount of fish farming include Missouri, Kansas, Texas, Oklahoma, Mississippi, Alabama, Georgia, and the Carolinas.

Two major factors are helping to expand fish farming. The first factor is associated with the quality of fish produced, which tempts the palate of rural and urban people alike. Secondly, the cash returns from fish farming appeal to the farmer in his continuing quest for economic betterment. He finds that fish farming is a real moneymaker.

Fish production, like other aspects of modern farming, must be run on a businesslike basis. The old "Huckleberry Finn" days, when you just tossed a baited line into a stagnant old pond or backwater and hoped you might catch something, do not fit in the picture of modern day fish farming.

Yet there is still a place for hook and line fishing. Some fish farmers make part of their money through charges for the privilege of fishing in their well-stocked ponds. And it's still a thrill to pull a sizable fish from the water.

Recreational fish farms are an especially good place to take the wife and family. Many kids have had their first real taste of fishing—whetting their appetites for enjoyable hours as they grow older. Some places have facilities for cleaning the fish, some will cook them to order, and others provide picnic tables and grills for cooking.

Fish farming is a scientific operation—for best results—the same as successful broiler production or any other successful livestock operation.

Modern methods include improved

Roy A. Grizzell, Jr., is a *Biologist* with the Soil Conservation Service at Little Rock, Ark., giving technical assistance to landowners and operators in fish farming, fishpond management, wildlife, and recreation.

John Gammon, Jr., is a *fish farmer* in Crittenden County, Ark. He also grows cotton, soybeans, wheat, alfalfa, and watermelons on his farm and serves on the Arkansas State ASC Committee.

187

construction techniques, better erosion control, more attention to selection of pond and reservoir sites, elimination or control of trash fish, control of waterweeds, mechanical seines (nets), automatic feeders, pelleted feed and vitamin supplements, mechanized loaders, and control of disease and parasites.

In fact, mechanization is essential to keep costs down. Feeding and harvesting require relatively large expenditures of labor. Processing of fish for the food markets is adaptable to assembly line techniques similar to those used in the production of automobiles where every worker is given a definite task.

One-Man Operation

Fish farming is practicable on fairly small farms, in comparison with those devoted to producing crops like wheat, corn, or pasture. Land poorly suited for other uses can quite often be developed into profitable fish production. At least 20 acres is generally needed for a truly profitable operation. This size operation can be handled by just one man until harvesttime comes, when temporary help will have to be employed.

The initial investment is not small. A typical 20-acre enterprise costs approximately $12,000. Since streams and other natural flowing waters are undesirable because of diseases and parasites carried, the pond should be equipped with a well, pump, and motor where possible. This costs about another $4,500.

Annual costs, from amortization of equipment to feed, labor, fuel, fingerlings supply, and other items, average around $5,800 for a 20-acre operation.

The "profit factor" becomes evident, however, when it is known that this operation will normally yield around 31,000 pounds of catfish. At a conservative price of 35 cents a pound, this means an annual gross income of $10,850 which is almost twice as much as the cost. (Lately 50 cents a pound has been the prevailing price, instead of 35 cents.)

So real opportunities exist for profitable fish farming operations.

Most persons who get into the fish farming business find it is fascinating, which is another factor that contributes to its gain in popularity.

An untypical example is Edgar Farmer of near Dumas, Ark. Like other fish farmers, he thoroughly enjoys his new business—which he started less than 10 years ago. Like the others, he is using modern, scientific methods—mechanization, feed, pumped well water, and carefully engineered ponds.

In fact, the only reason Mr. Farmer is not a typical catfish enthusiast is that he is probably the biggest in the business. He has 40 or more ponds covering some 300 acres of land. The ponds range in size from a half acre up to 50 acres. He continues to build more.

Edgar Farmer is so enthusiastic about fish that he plans to devote his major attention to them in the future. For the present, with his two married sons assisting him, he is producing crops of rice, soybeans, and cotton. He also raises shorthorn cattle and quarterhorses, the latter mostly as a hobby, although he makes money sometimes selling colts.

'No Limit to Demand'

He plans to turn the cattle and field crop operations over to his sons. This will permit him to devote his full time and interest to fish farming and to his other interesting "crop," the blooded quarterhorses that he raises.

"This fish business has grown into a bigger thing than I had anticipated," says Edgar Farmer. "There seems to be no limit to the demands for good food fish—and these catfish are delicious."

Mr. Farmer got into fish farming in a small way with a few buffalo (a large bony fish) which, frankly, proved disappointing. Then in 1958 he began to work with channel catfish, experimenting with feed mixtures and digging new ponds of improved design. In 1960 he made what some people regarded as a mistake—he put a few blue cats in a pond, not knowing that this river fish was not supposed to live in such an environment. However, they thrived—and today are a major factor in the fish farming concept.

Now Edgar Farmer markets channel

188

catfish, albino channel catfish, and blue catfish as fingerlings and as breeding stock. The breeding stock are sold at a weight of about 3 pounds. For food, he sells blue and channel catfish—keeping or selling the rarer albinos for breeding purposes only.

Most of Mr. Farmer's customers come to his big fish shed. They range from families wanting just a small quantity, to restaurants desiring larger amounts, to the fish markets which pick up 1,000 pounds at a time.

Ships to Other States

Edgar Farmer has shipped his fish to most of the areas where catfish are grown. Besides his home State, he has sent large quantities of live breeding stock to Louisiana, Tennessee, Georgia, Mississippi, Oklahoma, Texas, Missouri, and even as far away as North Carolina.

He believes, as do many other Arkansas fish farmers, that marketing of the tasty catfish is in its infancy, with a "mighty long way to go."

A large marketing cooperative, with facilities for processing, freezing, and shipping this new "crop" is seen as the next major step for fish farmers.

Usually, the first step in catfish farming, after development of an adequate plant, is to stock broodfish and spawn enough small fry to stock production ponds the following year. Fish which have shown the fastest growth should be chosen for breeding purposes. They should be free from abnormalities and disease or parasites.

The brood stock should be kept in holding ponds during the winter months and fed pelleted feed that is supplemented with minnows, liver, cut fish, and other protein ingredients.

Brood ponds need to have spawning devices to simulate conditions similar to riverbanks where catfish naturally spawn. Old milk cans or barrels will serve; the most popular device now in use is an elongated square box, almost like a large "rabbit box," built for the purpose.

Spawning usually starts when the water reaches 70° F., with 80° as the optimum temperature. Eggs hatch in 5 to 10 days. Only catfish conditioned to ponds should be used as breeders.

Both the channel and blue catfish are considered as very desirable eating fish. While the flathead catfish is also regarded as tasty, it is a predator and can cut production in a pond. Bullhead catfish have been tried in fish farming, but have not proved very successful.

The cleanest water possible is necessary to produce the best fish. Successful operators in Arkansas use "rice water"—so called because, like the water used to cover rice paddies, it is pure water pumped from deep wells.

Like Edgar Farmer, most fish farmers sell food fish and also stock for other ponds. Besides this, the "sportsman angle" comes into focus, with many of the farmers charging fees for the privilege of fishing. Some even sell tackle and bait.

Besides the fish big enough to eat, one of the most widespread types of fish farming is that which provides live bait. The familiar signs advertising minnows are seen across the country. Most people

While most of the catfish are taken with seines, the sportsman angle still has its undeniable appeal. John Gammon, Jr., the coauthor of this chapter, hauls one in.

189

probably think a minnow is just a minnow. Actually, the list includes six major entries: The golden shiner, fathead minnow, sucker, creek chub, Israeli carp, and goldfish—although he's not exactly the little fellow to be found in the aquarium back home. The aquarium fancier may buy the more colorful goldfish, the remainder going as bait fish.

Minnow ponds range in size from a tenth to a quarter acre for holding purposes. Production ponds range from 2 to 20 acres. Before sale, minnows may be treated to retard fungus and infection, graded and weighed. Only then are they ready to bait the angler's hook.

Live bait minnows are trucked hundreds of miles in aerated tank trucks. Smaller quantities are packed in plastic bags—with a supply of water and of oxygen—and then shipped.

Trout a Favorite

Trout are another favorite food fish everywhere in the Nation. The rainbow trout are the most popular for fish farming. Cold water, and plenty of it, is required for trout production. Springs or cold-water streams must flow a minimum of 300 gallons a minute for successful trout cultivation. Well water and much spring water must be oxygenated.

The marketing of trout is handled in much the same way as for catfish. They are stocked in ponds and lakes on both public and private lands. Fees for fishing often provide a source of income.

Is success assured for anyone entering the fish farming business? Like any other business enterprises, this requires doing a number of "right" things and a minimum of "wrong" things. Back in the 1950's, some farmers in Arkansas got off to a bad start with buffalo fish, often grown in combination with bass, crappie, and catfish.

The buffalo, which grows rapidly on the plankton in fertile ponds, tended to flood the market at certain times of the year, driving prices to a very low level. In addition, competition from such "trash fish" as shad and carp resulted in poor yields. So consequently, many farmers quit producing buffalo fish.

But today, with fewer in the business, the buffalo producers are getting a good income from this fish. However, most farmers prefer to switch to catfish.

Some farmers use fish in a regular rotation with field crops. Rice farmers, particularly, have been converting their ricefields—already a "pond" of sorts—into fish acreages. The practice has been to grow fish for a couple of years, then rice for 1, 2, or even 3 years. Since the pond bottom contains an abundance of available nitrogen after fish, rice yields become substantially higher.

Since most of the fish farmers take this phase of their business so seriously, they usually construct their ponds for permanent fish use, rather than in rotation with other crops. As a result, the ponds are also better suited to harvesting the fish, when the time comes. Most fish farmers harvest catfish when they are a good size for the frying pan, weighing a pound or slightly more.

Who can decide whether or not an individual should go into the fish farming business? Only the individual himself. It does afford an opportunity to make some money from a moderate investment; the market for this foodstuff has hardly been tapped. It also provides an interesting and different land use.

Agencies That Help

Many agencies provide assistance and services to fish farmers. The Soil Conservation Service offers technical assistance in pond and reservoir construction and in fish management. The Farmers Home Administration has a loan program for eligible fish farmers. The Agricultural Stabilization and Conservation Service offers cost-sharing assistance in the construction of reservoirs and ponds that can be adapted to fish farming. The Agricultural Extension Services provide informational and educational materials and services. The State game and fish commissions operate fish hatcheries and can be of help. The Fish and Wildlife Service operates fish hatcheries and a fish farming experiment station where various types of related research are conducted.

190

Beautification

America's Beautification Center—the National Arboretum

JOSEPH M. GARVEY, JR.

THE U.S. National Arboretum is an oasis of 415 acres of nature's beauty that is bounded by the Anacostia River, the Baltimore Parkway, and the business activities of the northeast section of our Nation's Capital. Established by Congress in 1927, its major purpose is to provide information on the landscape, beautification, industrial, and scientific uses of woody plants.

Visitors can enjoy an array of ordered beauty, skillfully arranged in a pleasing setting of woodland and meadow. This beauty, within reach of every citizen, is made up of native trees indigenous to the Northeastern United States, the exotic plants from plant explorations, demonstration plantings, and the nature walks through flowering azaleas, woodland herbs, and grassy meadows.

A stroll through the Gotelli dwarf conifers collection at the Arboretum strikes the visitor with deep impressions of solitude. Here the conifers of normal growth contrast pleasingly with their dwarf counterparts, in an arrangement of rocks and stone-mulched beds, set among velvet-green grass walkways.

The President has called on all of us to look at our surroundings and to determine what can be made beautiful, or more beautiful, or even what should be removed for the sake of beauty. Beauty now comes to have special meaning to us. How can such a plea be translated into reality? How can the many communities in our Nation find answers to the implications of such a task?

Destiny has brought an idea and an institution together.

Fulfillment of the ideal of beauty is now made possible by the existence of this great horticultural center, the National Arboretum, which is a mecca for those in search of beauty. It is a meeting place for the teachers, professionals, and laymen with horticultural interests.

The National Arboretum, with its staff of ornamental horticulturists and botanists, endeavors to present to the public—through its exhibition plantings, gardens, and demonstration plots—the essentials of beautification.

Literature on plant subjects illustrating new plants, planting techniques, and landscape schemes is provided through an active publication series. The lecture series and the formalized courses of the National Arboretum provide the student with technical knowledge and open new avenues of thought. Plant explorations are carried on with the New Crops Research Branch of USDA's Agricultural Research Service and with the Longwood Foundation. Such explorations across the world lead to discovery of exotic plants that might be suitable for landscape use in our own Nation.

With its research programs, the National Arboretum is making both inspirational and tangible contributions to the

Joseph M. Garvey, Jr., is *Curator* of Education at the U.S. National Arboretum, Crops Research Division, Agricultural Research Service.

192

A HUG FOR A TREE

Children who visit the National Arboretum add a special touch. One child threw his arms around a stately tulip tree, as if hugging it affectionately. Actually, he was trying to reach around its mighty trunk. Throughout the nature walk in Fern Valley, he and his companion hugged every tree that they could reach. I imagine if those old fellows could, they would have smiled approvingly and chuckled to themselves. For some 120,000 visitors pass through the Arboretum annually, but few ever stop and give the trees a hug.

national beautification program. In plant breeding, the Arboretum strives to develop new plants better adapted for landscape use—and plants of greater esthetic value. For example, improved fruiting of ornamentals, more disease-resistant plants, and flowering shrubs of greater beauty are being investigated.

Extensive efforts in the field of education are bringing these research findings and new techniques in plant usages and plant requirements to every homeowner and plantsman in the Nation.

New plant specimens are planted in tasteful arrangements in the rolling landscape of the Arboretum. Ready identification of these plants is made possible by conspicuous labels.

The Administration Building complements the beautiful natural setting of the Arboretum. This is a light and airy structure of glass, aluminum, and textured concrete. A visit to this building is a delightful experience. In its auditorium, which is surrounded by a reflecting pool, horticultural and botanical lectures are given and flower shows are held. Its herbarium stores a collection of more than 300,000 dried, pressed specimens. This herbarium enables taxonomists to identify plant specimens for homeowners and nurserymen as well as to determine plant relationships. Plant studies are conducted in the laboratories of the Administration Building.

In the nearby greenhouses, plants are grown for use in Arboretum programs. Here, also, new plants are grown for distribution to other arboretums and botanic gardens cooperating in the plant distribution programs. Workshops in plant handling inform amateur plantsmen on new techniques. Demonstrations in plant propagation conducted in the greenhouse are among the most popular of the Arboretum's activities.

Both youth groups and adult organizations meet at the National Arboretum to learn how to handle and to arrange plants in the landscape. During part of their Washington, D.C., meeting, the 500 delegates of the National Youth Conference for Natural Beauty and Conservation assembled at the Arboretum. These delegates represented 12 national youth organizations whose combined membership exceeds 20 million. Their visit provided them with practical information about plant propagation and tree transplanting.

During a "windshield tour" of the Arboretum, they observed areas skillfully landscaped. Emphasis was placed upon the identification and use of community resources for beautification. Teaching the young people to protect natural resources is among the objectives of the Arboretum's attention to youth.

If the Nation is to spend more time and money on beautification, professional

70,000 AZALEAS

The most spectacular product of National Arboretum research covers the slopes of Mount Hamilton. In late April and early May, 70,000 hybrid azaleas produce their colorful blooms beneath a canopy of tulip, oak, and dogwood trees.

In other Arboretum areas, one may see magnolia hybrids that hold promise to escape late spring frosts, firethorns free of fire blight disease, and hybrid deciduous azaleas that may be able to tolerate the summers of our Southern States.

Hybrids from other breeding projects with hollies, hibiscus, viburnums, and crapemyrtle are, or will soon be, in the hands of commercial nurserymen.

Reflecting pool, Administration Building, at the U.S. National Arboretum.

direction is needed. We envision years of service to the public and also to the professional and amateur plantsman.

A larger auditorium and exhibit facilities for special gardening interests are being considered. Local camellia, rose, and orchid society members and the Washington Botanic Society hold meetings and flower shows at the Arboretum. Surely this meeting facility should reach out to more and more national groups.

The National Capital Area Federation of Garden Clubs, Inc., of Metropolitan Washington holds its annual meeting in our auditorium. Its members meet for discussion of the coming year's program. National garden clubs interested in promoting the art and science of gardening can thus gain needed information. The U.S. Department of Agriculture is represented to help place Federal resources wherever they are needed.

The National Arboretum provides for guided tours for visiting groups. This service is ably carried on by volunteer guides of the National Capital Area Federation of Garden Clubs, Inc.

Individuals are permitted to tour the grounds on their own with the assistance of our brochures.

The National Arboretum reports on its activities to the public by broadcasts on USDA radio and television programs and through Department news releases. By means of these media, the public can become acquainted with the Arboretum activities and take advantage of educational opportunities. Tree selection and care is only one of the many topics.

Because so many plants are available for use in the home landscape, professional guidance is very desirable. The National Arboretum provides services to homeowners through plant identification and publication of recommended lists of plants for landscaping. The question of how to plant and to care for plants is essential to both rural and urban beautification efforts. Through its field trials and experimentation, the National Arboretum adapts the best methods—after making comparisons, and all of these reports are available in the USDA series of popular publications.

In research, the Arboretum will soon initiate a program in shade tree breeding and selection. Specific clones selected for their outstanding qualities will be emphasized. Selection and use of trees in the landscape are critical factors.

The Arboretum is surveying the national interest in horticulture. Student gardener courses that can be tailored to the apprentice-type gardener may be conducted. Courses for the ornamental horticulture extension specialists to update and exchange ideas would be beneficial. Our staff and area specialists would also benefit from personal contacts with such national specialists.

The program of national beautification as it involves the Arboretum suggests many other possibilities. Rehabilitation of the mentally disturbed, for instance, and courses and tours for the blind and handicapped. The utilization of specialized plants such as native plants in the home landscape would benefit the beautification program.

Blending Your Home
Into the Landscape

EDWARD H. STONE

O URS is a land of a unique and a priceless beauty. We are a people who enjoy the home with its multitude of modern conveniences. With the advent of today's prosperity, many are searching for a new or second home— a "different" place, where recreation and relaxation are major objectives; a place where the family can regain a familiarity with forest and pond, mountain and meadow; where the pace is slower, and there is time for contemplation.

Living in harmony with the natural environment can uplift the spirits and refresh the mind. With understanding and good planning, many delightful characteristics of the ocean beach, the rocky crag, and the whispering forest can be utilized or transplanted, in some degree, to the new or second home.

While you shop for the "ideal lot," you may observe desirable features like the large shade trees, fascinating rock outcrops, a gurgling brook, or a breath-catching view or vista. When the final selection is made, prepare a list of all the features that attracted you to this particular location. They might be placed under headings like "Conserve at all costs," "Conserve if possible," and "Nice, but not essential."

The list can then be used as a guide in discussions with the building contractor, the architect, and the professional landscape architect. Designing services by professionals are sometimes omitted because of cost (often only a small percent-

age of the development cost). This is usually a false economy. Their fees are offset by increased resale value, lower maintenance costs, and owner satisfaction with a professionally designed and unique residence.

So often a family obtains the ideal lot with all its desirable features, only to place the house in their midst, destroying them one by one. The trees are cut to make room for construction equipment, the rock is blasted for utility lines, and the brook is placed in a metal pipe so that it cannot stray into a basement. Instead, we might utilize professional talents and methods to locate the dream house where it overlooks the best features

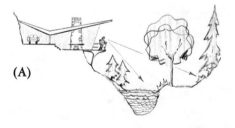

(A)

of the site (A), not where it obliterates the very things we want.

Our structures should be designed to fit these existing and more interesting

Edward H. Stone is *Chief Landscape Architect, Division of Recreation, Forest Service.*

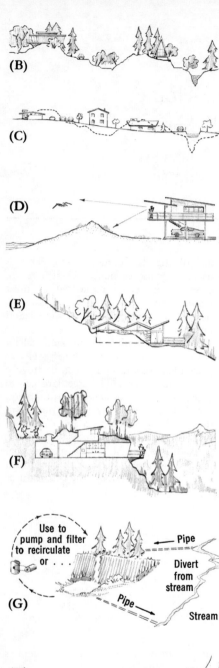

(B)

(C)

(D)

(E)

(F)

Use to pump and filter to recirculate or . . .

Pipe

Divert from stream

Pipe

(G)

Stream

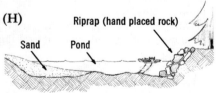

(H)

Riprap (hand placed rock)

Sand   Pond

landforms. We must strive to complement our natural environment (B), not obliterate its features and level the land to accommodate any and all types of "living boxes" (C).

Utilizing modern techniques and materials, we can build above the land (D), into it (E), or even below it (F), thus utilizing and enjoying nature's beauty by harmonizing with her patterns and her forms.

Few items in nature hold more fascination for man than moving water, from the rolling surf of a vast seascape to the wind-rippled waters of a small pond. Where water-oriented points of interest are not naturally available, a partial flow can be diverted from a stream. If water is in short supply, an inexpensive pump can be used to recirculate the water from a small pond to the top of a waterfall. Properly landscaped, such an installation (G) can become a very intriguing focal point for a natural garden or a yard. When it's adequately designed and constructed, this can even be done indoors.

Small ponds can be established in a similar way. The shorelines should slope gradually or be reinforced, either by planting hardy shrubs or by the use of masonry, riprap, or a decay-resistant wood (H).

Edges of such ponds should normally be irregular, offering a variety of plants, materials, and configuration (I). The larger pond can be constructed, and suitable vegetation planted to aid or sustain waterfowl, songbirds, fish, and some species of aquatic animals. The Soil Conservation Service and State fish and game departments can furnish helpful information on construction, financing, location, and types of vegetation to plant.

(I)

(J)

(K)

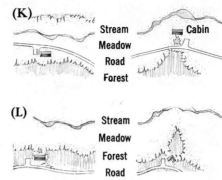

Stream
Meadow
Road
Forest

Cabin

(L)

Stream
Meadow
Forest
Road

The most interesting areas in nature are her "edges," the zones of change between the sand and sea, dark forest and sunlit meadow, or timberline and rocky peak (J). Views of great beauty, variety, and constant fascination are always available here, if they are conserved and properly framed. Man can successfully build and live in these edge areas, if he does so with care and a sense ₚof visual propriety. The structure should not be situated as the dominant point in the landscape (K). It and its utilities are much more attractive if they retreat into the forest or the zone of greatest density (L).

(M)

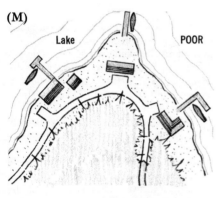

Lake

POOR

This principle is of an even greater importance if several structures are to be built in the same locality (M, N, and O). Practices that were acceptable when the neighbors were few and far between can become chaotic and displeasing with today's growing populations.

An even better esthetic solution is the "cluster" concept (O). Here structures are combined or grouped on a relatively small portion of the available land, leaving a large area in a common-use natural

(N)

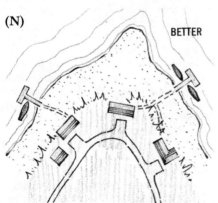

BETTER

(O)

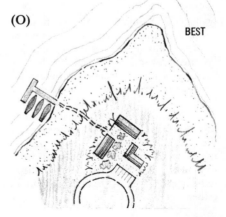

BEST

condition. Clusters can be of the inter-connected "townhouse" variety (P) or

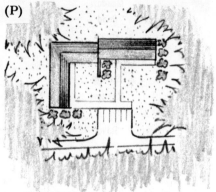

(P)

(R)

(S)

(T)

closely spaced structures separated, for privacy, by architectural and landscaping devices—such as masonry walls, fences, planter beds or boxes, small storage buildings, or varying levels of decks and

(U)

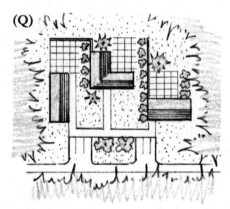

(Q)

walks (Q). Substantial savings are often realized in their construction because of shorter utility lines, common sanitation systems, and fewer roads and walks.

Many of the most desirable homes are constructed near bodies of water where boating, swimming, and fishing are major forms of recreation. In these areas, the appearance of the shore area from the water is as visually important as the view of the lake or the river from the beach. The first family to build is seldom concerned with this problem in esthetics (R).

After a few others arrive, the situation becomes apparent, but has probably progressed to the point where correction is difficult (S), and utter chaos eventually develops (T). At this time, none can see or enjoy the natural characteristics that originally seemed so attractive.

The long-range solution is usually best. Owners can band together to establish or set aside a shoreline landscape zone—land to be kept in a primarily natural state for use by all (U). This not only improves the appearance of the entire area, it often increases the value of each individual holding.

Won't this proposed retreat from the "edge" obstruct the view that we value so highly? Not necessarily. Most pictures need a frame—scenic views are no exception. In fact, most natural views can be improved by framing the desirable (V), blocking out unwanted scenes (W), or by partial screening with a lacy pattern of branches and foliage (X).

Everyone must share in the responsibility, both to our American landscape and to our fellow citizens, to produce the kind of natural surroundings that

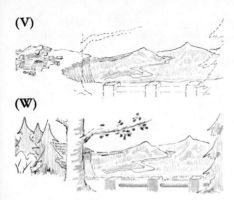

(V)

(W)

(X)

have moved from them and neglected to take examples with us.

Our population is expanding at a great rate. Our land area is not expanding at all. New methods of occupying the land must be adopted. Professional help and guidance is available. It needs to be accepted and put to use by communities, by groups, and by individuals.

we wish to enjoy and pass on to future generations. In most instances, our offspring do not know the sights, sounds, and smells that we experienced as children. They are no longer there, or we

Building Beauty
With Common Materials

EDWARD H. STONE

FOR A COMPLETE and satisfying life, man depends upon a balance between the constructed works that provide for his needs and comforts and the soil, trees, rocks, wildlife, and water of his natural environment. Seldom is he fully content in one without some representation of the other—such as pets and plants in the home, or camping trailers and sleeping bags in the forest.

The tasteful use of natural and certain manufactured building materials can help "bridge the gap" between the two worlds—can bring a touch of natural beauty to the places where we live, work, and play. They can be used to

blend or fit our manmade structures into the landscape itself.

Some of these materials are byproducts or have outlived their first use. Some have been put to only one use, but are capable of much more. They often are inexpensive and can be obtained from wrecking companies, salvage lots, mills and shops, railroads, and other sources.

Only imagination and the "labor of love" are required to transform what are otherwise ordinary objects into useful works of art or interest.

  ✿ ✿ ✿

Edward H. Stone is *Chief Landscape Architect, Division of Recreation, Forest Service.*

For an example, consider the dome-shaped metal disks which manufacturers produce when they fabricate the ends of storage and pressure tanks for water, petroleum products, and for other liquids or gases. With a few added materials and some thought, these can be made into attractive charcoal barbecue grills (A) or be used as a base for an indoor contemporary fireplace (B). And with a plate-glass top, the metal disk becomes a coffee table (C) which can display a collection of colored rocks, ore samples, beach gravel, or—with suitable ventilation holes—a miniature moss and lichen garden. It might also display flower blossoms floated upon water.

Suspended upside down, it becomes a play apparatus for children (D). Standing on edge, it can serve as a neutral background for garden sculpture (E). Fountain bases and miniature waterfall receptacles are another adaptation (F and G). These provide falling, gurgling water—a fascination for people of all ages in many different environments.

(A)

Weld

Steel pipe

Concrete

(B)

Suspended hood

Steel ring base

(C)

Decorative wood base

(D)

(E)

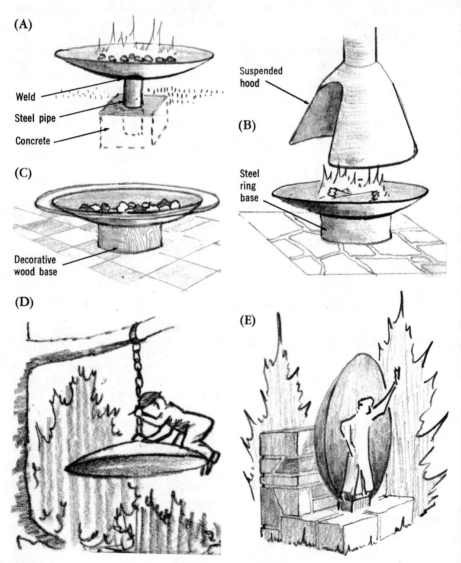

(F)

(G)

Used materials often have more "character," appear more rustic, and are most appropriate for some home or garden projects. This is not altogether unknown; in some areas, for example, weathered planks from old barns and other aged buildings are becoming scarce. In such cases, a little imagination and effort can often be used to make "old ones out of new ones." A coarse, circular wire brush in an electric drill will tear away the softer fibers on the surfaces of planks, leaving a rough, weathered appearance. Properly stained or painted, these make interesting interior paneling (H) or exterior fences (I).

Many materials have manifold uses. Among these materials are discarded telephone or power poles, railroad ties, concrete or metal pipe, bridge timbers, and broken concrete pavement or curbing.

Narrow strip of dark brown hardboard

1" x 2" furring strips—nail to wall

16"

1" x 4" paint flat black and nail to wall

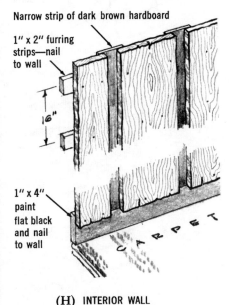

(H) INTERIOR WALL

(I) EXTERIOR FENCE

Retaining Walls

(J)

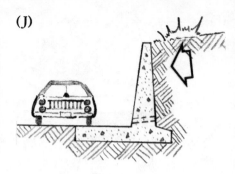

Most interesting land has changes in slope and elevation that offer an opportunity or need for a retaining wall. If the wall is to be high and abrupt (J), the services of an engineer will be needed to design a structure that can safely resist the earth pressures which tend to push or tip it. A small wall, however, can be a challenging and artistic project (K) for the average amateur.

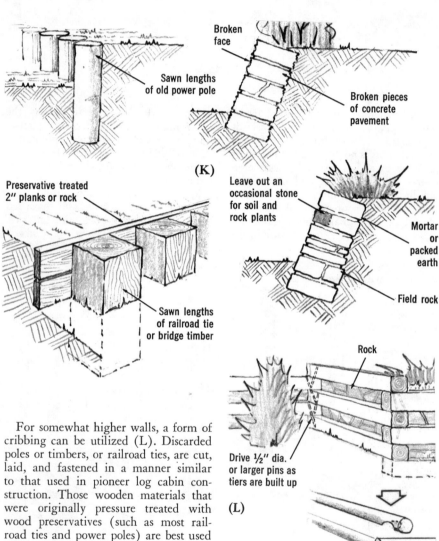

Sawn lengths of old power pole

Broken face

Broken pieces of concrete pavement

(K)

Preservative treated 2" planks or rock

Leave out an occasional stone for soil and rock plants

Mortar or packed earth

Sawn lengths of railroad tie or bridge timber

Field rock

Rock

For somewhat higher walls, a form of cribbing can be utilized (L). Discarded poles or timbers, or railroad ties, are cut, laid, and fastened in a manner similar to that used in pioneer log cabin construction. Those wooden materials that were originally pressure treated with wood preservatives (such as most railroad ties and power poles) are best used when direct contact with the earth is found to be necessary.

Drive ½" dia. or larger pins as tiers are built up

(L)

Walls of this nature are usually best assembled in an irregular or zigzag fashion (M) for variety, interest, and strength. The resulting irregularities or bays provide excellent spots for flowers, blooming shrubs, or garden sculpture.

The same construction techniques can be used to build lawn edgers, planter boxes, or planting areas (N). Broken, cracked, or discarded short lengths of concrete pipe, clay chimney tile, and other construction products can be made into attractive "planters" for both indoor and outdoor use (O).

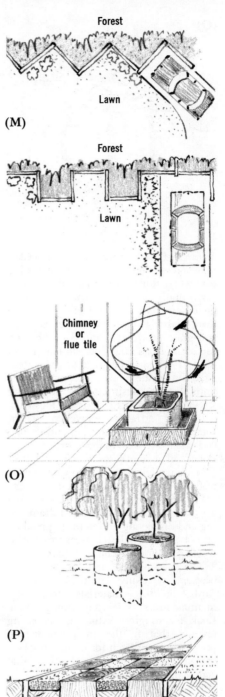

Forest

Lawn

(M)

Forest

Lawn

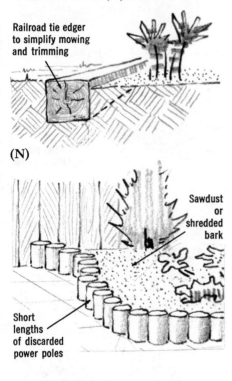

Railroad tie edger to simplify mowing and trimming

(N)

Sawdust or shredded bark

Short lengths of discarded power poles

Chimney or flue tile

(O)

Walks and Planting Beds

Durable and distinctive materials are always in demand here. They are especially welcome if they "belong"—if they fit the natural characteristics of the garden or yard. Ideas? Try sections of railroad ties laid on end and alternated with colorful gravel to make a checkerboard walk (P). Sections of power pole

(P)

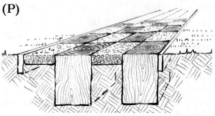

203

(Q)

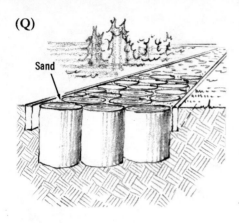

Sand

(R)

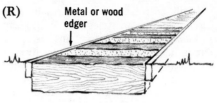

Metal or wood edger

(S)

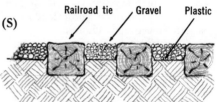

Railroad tie   Gravel   Plastic

or decay-resistant logs such as cedar, redwood, or locust make an interesting path (Q). Railroad ties can also be laid horizontally to form treads. Alternate these with beds of gravel underlaid with sheet plastic to prevent unwanted weed and grass growth (R and S). The ever-useful railroad tie (or similar heavy timber) can also be used to form steps (T). On gentle slopes, "stepping stone" stairs can be constructed by imbedding sections of large decay-resistant logs (U).

Beds of attractive gravel or water-rounded rock are interesting and decorative when artistic "islands" or "stepping stones" of a weathered wood are added (V). A potted plant or two can provide just the proper "dash" of color.

Gravel, stone, or raked-sand beds (W) are often an excellent means of dramatizing and displaying an interesting boulder or last summer's beach treasures (driftwood, glass or cork fishing floats, etc.).

The possibilities are endless. Visit beaches, wrecking companies, salvage yards, building materials stores and manufacturers. Use your imagination. Look for rough, weathered, interesting textures that fit the environment you plan to create. Watch for natural colors—browns, grays, greens, and others that complement the forms and shades of our natural surroundings. The brighter accent colors can normally be best supplied by flowering plants or relatively small objects. Natural beauty can be all around us—if we look for it.

(T)

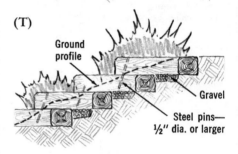

Ground profile

Gravel

Steel pins—½" dia. or larger

(U)

(V)

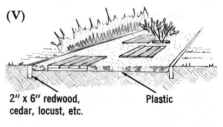

2" x 6" redwood, cedar, locust, etc.

Plastic

(W)

Youth's Spark Makes Living Areas Glow

RUSSELL W. SMITH

A LAD'S cowpoke hat blew off when he stooped to pick up a bottle from a roadside ditch. It skipped on across a naked cherry orchard, into an open field, and sailed into a fence row packed tight with tumbleweed. Freeing his hat from the tangle, the boy whacked it across his leg and walked back to the roadside.

This is the way an Extension worker described one of the over a thousand Yakima County, Wash., 4–H members who turned out to help make the youth for natural beauty program more than mere words. The 4–H'ers fanned out on the secondary highways to gather 200 truckloads of roadside trash. They exemplify the concern of a great many young people about their surroundings.

In every State in this great country, 4–H and other youth have accepted the challenge to become stewards of America the beautiful. They are working individually, in local clubs, and in joint efforts on worthwhile natural beauty and conservation projects.

The major organizations of youth, through planned activities, are heeding the challenges of President and Mrs. Johnson to correct blighted conditions. Under the guidance of volunteer and professional adults, young people are applying a systematic approach to improvements in their communities. Group interest and effort are making it possible to complete vitally needed projects to retain or restore the great out of doors.

4–H and other youth are learning how to survey the beautification needs of their neighborhoods and home communities. In cooperation with adults, they are taking inventory of their time, ability, and resources as a basis for determining the priority of jobs to be done. Boys and girls have adultlike experiences as they draw up work schedules, organize committees, and promote cooperative action among youth in their communities.

Completed beautification projects serve as tangible evidence of citizenship in action. A feeling of pride develops when the community notices and gives credit for improvements and accomplishments. Young people gain a real sense of personal worth when the results of their efforts receive commendation from public officials and citizens of the community.

A big roadside cleanup campaign in Hampshire County, Mass., drew enthusiastic public attention. Almost 100 youth volunteers joined together for a 1-day campaign. 4–H'ers, Boy Scouts, junior high fellowship members, and auxiliary firefighters cooperated with the town's highway department to pick up roadside trash and debris.

The boys and girls were transported to different areas in private cars. They worked in assigned areas until noon, and then the group congregated at a wayside park to have lunch. A special adult committee prepared this lunch with food given by individuals, service clubs, and

Russell W. Smith is *Northeast Regional 4–H Program Leader,* 4–H and Youth Development, Federal Extension Service.

by some other community organizations.

These volunteers hope that the results of their efforts will cause people to consider the effort and cost involved in such a project. They are also confident that their demonstration will lead people to think twice before discarding more trash along the county's roadsides.

During 1963, the mayor of Ronceverte, W. Va., had flowerbeds planted in the business district. The project was then turned over to the Women's Club. After assuming responsibility for the flowers for a time, the Women's Club enlisted the cooperation of the Serendipity Workers Senior 4-H'ers. The girls in the club voted to care for the largest bed, which is 88½ by 5½ feet.

Members of the Women's Club helped the 4-H girls get started by furnishing plants and bulbs. The 4-H members gained valuable experience in keeping the litter cleared away, setting out bulbs and plants, controlling weeds, and cleaning the beds in the fall. The flowerbeds brightened up the community and have made the citizens more cheerful when shopping. Many of the local people have complimented these efforts to beautify Ronceverte.

In Woodbury County, Iowa, 4-H'ers have transformed a 5-acre thicket into an attractive public roadside park. Sparked by the initiative of the county "4-H Builder's Club" (an older youth group), 45 local 4-H clubs became involved in this community service project.

An agreement with the Iowa Highway Commission and the county extension service paved the way for coopera-

Secretary of Agriculture Orville L. Freeman and Mrs. Freeman eat box lunches at the U.S. National Arboretum with delegates from the National Youth Conference on Natural Beauty and Conservation. The delegates toured the Arboretum and participated in demonstrations of plant propagation and tree planting techniques.

tive development of a safety rest area.

The roadside park has now become a popular haven for the local residents and weary travelers. Through the efforts of 4–H members and adult sponsors, the facilities now include picnic tables, fireplace grills, a deep well, and outdoor restrooms. Club members have worked together to prune trees, gather brush, rake the grounds, and plant trees and shrubs. An average of 35 travelers visited the park each day during 1965.

Development of the park has added appreciation and awareness of the natural beauty of the western region of Iowa.

Main Street Cleanup

Farmington, Utah, is a more pleasant community since the Gardening Gays 4–H Club rejuvenated Main Street. Six 4–H girls worked to clean a 72-foot curb side that was covered with weeds, rocks, and debris. Each member volunteered to clean up and to spade and plant five flats of Comanche petunias. They also took turns in watering, weeding, and maintaining the plot.

Participation in this project helped the girls develop a new appreciation for the appearance of their own homes. They have learned how to work with tools and have improved their work habits. One mother indicated that before her daughter was involved in this project she would not even pull a weed. The experience on Main Street stimulated self-improvement and encouraged members to take pride in their home grounds and in the total community.

A violent storm stimulated a group of young people to act in Yamhill County, Oreg. The Baker Creek 4–H Club of McMinnville pledged its support to help restore the beauty of Edward Grenfell Park. This county park became a community improvement project with adults and young people teaming up to reclaim the recreational facility.

County officials are cooperating with the 4–H members in planting trees and shrubs, constructing cooking facilities, picnic tables, swings, and comfort stations. 4–H'ers planted hemlock and western redcedar trees as seedlings and

nurtured them during the early stages of growth. The total park restoration will require several additional plantings in successive years. Members of the Baker Creek 4–H Club have agreed to follow this project through to completion, because they receive satisfaction from the results of constructive work.

Each planting experience provides opportunities for these young people to achieve personal worth.

Teamwork was focused on a beautification project in Indiantown, Fla. The two 4–H Clubs and the Kiwanis Club in this small, unincorporated community initiated a program to develop a central recreational facility. The need for a facility was recognized by the leading industrial firm in the community. The firm made available a large block of land in the center of town for a community park and recreational area.

Under direction of the county commissioner, the 4–H members planted a portion of the park, and the Kiwanis Club provided a palm-thatched picnic shelter and large picnic tables. The shelters are models of a Seminole Indian abode called a "chickee" which is native to these tribes in Florida.

Project Spreads

The project is a growing one and has spread from the park to the school and the shopping center. Palms, flowers, and shrubbery have all been planted in the shopping center. Citizens of the community say this effort has eliminated a "real eyesore" in the town.

North Wildwood Boulevard in Cape May, N.J., has a new look. Boy Scouts and 4–H'ers focused attention upon a beautification-conservation project. Several days of hard work were involved in cleaning trash and debris in preparation for planting. Japanese black pines were planted to improve the appearance of the roadsides and control erosion.

Small markers known as C.B. (County Beautification) signs are fastened to a short piece of pipe to prevent road mowing crews from cutting the trees. The boys who cooperated in this project point with pride to their contribution

Thousands of urban youngsters brighten up their homes with flowers nowadays. This Trenton, N.J., young lady gets advice from the Mercer County Extension Agent.

toward the conservation of the county.

This activity provided an opportunity for these young people to learn that man is part of the natural world. American youth in other States, too, are becoming increasingly conscious of the urgency to preserve the fiber of our civilization.

Tangible and realistic projects in conservation are helping these "adults of tomorrow" appreciate the need to preserve our soil, water, forests, grasslands, and our wildlife.

Interest in pheasant raising and tree planting aroused action in conservation in Minnesota. The Waldorf Peppy Peppers 4–H Club of Waseca County raised 500 pheasant chicks for the State conservation, game, and fish commission. These birds were added to 2½ acres of wildlife area donated to the club.

Members picked up field corn to feed the chicks and transplanted 1,250 trees including black walnut, white-cedar, white spruce, Norway pine, and Colorado blue spruce. Future plans include straightening out the creek and making a wildlife pit for game birds.

Nevada County, Calif., has underway a demonstration area of all of the true firs of the world. 4–H'ers, Future Farm-

ers of America members, and adults accepted the challenge to develop a 65-acre tract of land which was donated for conservation use. In cooperation with the Grass Valley City Council, the California Division of Forestry, and several nurseries, the youth launched a major planting program.

4–H members dug planting holes and carried stakes to the planting sites. The Future Farmers of Grass Valley High School prepared attractive scribed markers for each species group and a large sign to designate the total area. Various 4–H Clubs and the FFA chapters volunteered to cultivate around the trees and water them at 2-week intervals. The halfway point has been reached in the arboretum plantings—with 20 of the world's 40 species now growing. This project has achieved much local interest, and the young people hope that it will be possible to secure the remaining 20 fir species in the next decade.

Cooperation is the key to success in the Kalamazoo County, Mich., 4–H conservation program. The Soil Conservation Service, the Agricultural Stabilization and Conservation Service, and State conservation agencies make it possible for 4–H members to learn about basic conservation practices and how to contribute to beautifying the landscape.

A countywide field day is designed to complement activities in local clubs and communities. Special events are conducted to help young people understand the total conservation plan for a land-owning SCS cooperator. The field days have provided a variety of experiences including tree planting and wildlife cover, assisting in the layout of contour strips, building terraces, selecting and pruning timber, working on the design and construction of farm ponds, and preparing grassed waterways.

The Bit 'n Spur Horse Club in Oneida County, Wis., felt a need for a "campout" area for horsemen. So a site was selected in the heart of the Oneida County Forest, after consultation with county and State foresters and the town of Enterprise. Developing the campout area became a combined community service and conservation project.

Adult leaders and youths worked together to clear debris, dead trees, and underbrush. Areas were cleared for the picket line for horses, for the campers to spread out their bed rolls, and for a campfire site.

The campsite is being developed over a 3-year period. When completed, it will be available to anyone genuinely interested in camping in a quiet, uncongested, and peaceful spot close to nature.

A local florist in Sullivan County, N.Y., touched off a chain reaction. He donated two station-wagon loads of potted plants to 4–H Camp Pines. This gesture sparked an interest among campers and staff to beautify the camp.

Camp counselors and staff members made window boxes and campers transplanted all the flowers. The boxes were placed under the windows of the dining hall and recreation building.

A row of marigolds was set out along the foundation of the recreation hall, while a bed of salvia was planted around the camp flagpole.

Participation in all these beautification activities created a new awareness for the beauty of nature and the opportunities to improve surroundings. The campers also learned about the cultural practices involved in plant propagation.

America's young people are interested in preserving our great out of doors. The kind of landscape they will inherit depends greatly upon the efforts that they expend to conserve it.

Youth will continue to accept the challenge to make our country more beautiful and more enjoyable.

Color It Green With Trees

MARGUARETTE M. HEDGE

W HEN Mark Weyl moved into his new home in suburbia, he found himself a member of a civic association ready to go with a communitywide beautification plan. That fall, members were offered the opportunity to buy pink or white flowering dogwood or flowering cherry trees.

The association took orders from the members and purchased trees in two sizes from a reliable nursery giving a special price for group orders. Members were notified a few days in advance of delivery so they could be ready to plant the trees promptly.

Today, Mark's dogwood trees are still living. But he has seen some of his neighbors replace their plantings, and others simply remove trees that did not survive.

What was the secret of Mark's success, and why did some of his neighbors fail?

Mark and the association officers recognized this fact . . . Successful tree planting for home or community rests on these basic principles: (1) Selecting the right tree, (2) planting it properly, and (3) providing proper maintenance.

Mark's community had been "cut out" of a woods that originally had abounded with native dogwood, so flowering dogwood was a natural choice for street and lawn trees. It was right because the trees were adapted to the climate and soil, and they were at home with the trees which

Marguarette M. Hedge is a *Public Information Officer*, Information Division, Agricultural Research Service.

A communitywide planting of Bradford pear in University Park, Md., in 1954 now yields a bountiful display of lacy white blossoms in the spring and a lavish show of brilliant burnished red foliage in the fall.

plant the tree. City fumes and smoke thwart some trees, like sugar maples, but apparently have no effect upon others, like the London planetree.

2. Select a form that best meets your intended use for the tree—background, screening, shade, or shape. A broad-spreading, low-hanging tree, ideal for a big yard or park, would be unsuited along a driveway. A slim, upright tree, like the Italian cypress, would be good for screening a driveway, but not for boys to climb.

Develop familiarity with the mature shapes of trees so that you will be more knowledgeable when you talk with your nurseryman. (*Trees,* the 1949 Yearbook of Agriculture, has 2 pages, 94 and 95, of tree silhouettes, drawn to scale with a two-story house.)

Community groups wanting to improve their parks, neighborhood streets, or to screen out undesirable sights (junkyards or city dumps) and lacking funds or available professional advice may find the following list useful. You will want to check with your local arboretum, botanical garden, or county agricultural agent to see if the trees you want are reliably hardy to your climate.

were still growing in the community.

Mark won't say why others lost their trees, but his recipe for success is that he planted his trees with care and has given them the essentials of good maintenance ever since.

In general, you will benefit from following these basic guidelines in making your own choices:

1. Start with hardiness. Consider only species of trees that are proved hardy for the climate. Think about extremes of summer heat as well as winter cold. Trees grown in the North have no trouble with southern winters, but may succumb to southern summers. Trees planted north of their adapted range may be killed by the first severe season.

Take soil and atmospheric conditions into account. City soils tend to be compacted and poorly drained and may need to be replaced or improved when you

FOR SCREENING

Deciduous (drop leaves in the fall)

Columnar English oak	Sugar maple
	Red oak
Gray birch	Green ash
Hornbeam	Willow oak
Red maple	Little leaf linden

Evergreen

Red pine	Virginia scrub pine
White pine	Norway spruce
Hemlock (slow growing)	Ponderosa pine
	Chinese juniper

FOR PARKS

Canadian hemlock	Norway maple
American hornbeam	Amur corktree
Colorado blue spruce	Common hackberry
American mountain-ash	Northern red oak
	Red maple
Horsechestnut	Sugar maple
European beech	Tuliptree
European linden	

FLOWERING

Dogwood	Redbud
Flowering cherry	Crapemyrtle
Golden-rain-tree	Goldenchain tree

210

3. Consider the size of the mature tree, its rate of growth, and length of life. Will it "smother" rather than ornament your house? Will it take too many years to provide needed shade? If the tree grows slowly, it may serve your intended use for many years before it gets too big for your lot. It takes a tuliptree a hundred years to reach its mature size, but it might be just right for you during its first 40 years. In today's fast changing communities—from suburbs to satellite cities—perhaps a tree with a shorter lifespan is more practical. It's your choice.

4. Consider undesirable characteristics. Some trees—like the female gingko and white mulberry—drop messy fruit that is unpleasant, especially where foot traffic occurs. (The staminate form of gingko does not produce fruit.) The poplar and the mimosa shed seeds which scatter and sprout all over the lawn.

Trees vulnerable to diseases and pests invite trouble. The American elm is susceptible to Dutch elm disease. Avoid it if you live where the elm bark beetle occurs and spreads the disease. The mimosa attracts webworm, which infests other species, including thornless honeylocust. Pests and diseases require periodic spraying and the pruning of affected branches. Trees may be lost if the pest or disease gets out of hand. Removal of a mature tree usually calls for professional help with adequate equipment to assure safety to people and property when the tree comes down.

Trees which are undesirable in one situation may be acceptable in another. Maples, with roots that tend to raise and crack sidewalks when planted close to them, would be fine in parks or other open places. Red and silver maples, willow, and poplar send their roots in search of water and so are notorious sewer cloggers; they are to be avoided on most home lots. In a park or along a stream, they would add interest without damage.

Once you have selected the right tree, you will want to get the most from your investment of money, labor, and time. Time means not only the hours devoted to planting the tree, but also the growing

time lost if it dies. So the right start is particularly vital if you are a homeowner who buys large trees to provide an "instant" landscape.

To give a tree the right start:
• Dig the hole large enough for the roots and plenty of good soil. For bareroot plants, allow room for the roots to spread out naturally. For balled-in-burlap trees, holes should be 2 feet wider than the root ball and deep enough for trees to set at the same level at which they grew in the nursery.

If soil is poor, dig holes as large as reasonable. Replace poor soil with topsoil or improved soil. You can improve soil from the hole by mixing it with sand and peat moss—one-third of each.

In soil with poor drainage (as in tight clay), plant the tree on the "high side" or provide a drainage zone. To plant on the high side, set the tree in a shallow depression and use good soil to build up a wide area around the root ball. Form a saucerlike bed in the good soil with a ridge at the outer edge to hold mulch and moisture. To provide a

Dig hole for tree large enough for the roots and plenty of good soil.

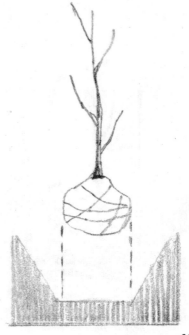

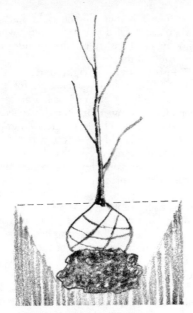

Partly fill hole with good soil so top of root ball will be even with soil surface.

• Stake and guy the tree before filling soil around the root ball. For a small tree (trunk diameter less than 3 inches), use one or two 6-foot poles for staking. Set poles next to the root ball and fasten the trunk of the tree to the poles with a loop of wire enclosed in a section of old garden hose to protect the bark.

For a tree larger than 3 inches in diameter, use three guy wires for support. Loop the hose-covered wires about

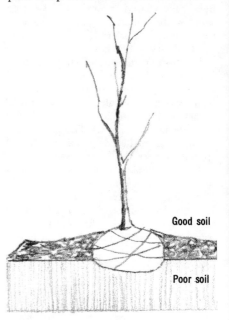

Good soil

Poor soil

Where drainage is poor, plant trees on the "high side" by building up the area around the root ball with good soil.

drainage zone, dig a second hole deeper than the one that the tree is to set in and fill it up with gravel.

Lay pipe or tile from the tree roots to the second hole to carry off excess water.

halfway up the main stem. Stake one guy in the direction the prevailing wind comes from with the other two staked to form an equilateral triangle.

• Fill about root ball with good soil.

• Water thoroughly to settle the soil around the roots.

• Wrap the trunk (burlap or creped kraft paper) to protect the tree from sunscald. Wrap downward. Tie with a stout cord, knotting it approximately every 18 inches.

Trees, like babies, need tender, loving care in their formative first years to get off to the right start.

City trees often suffer from lack of water because sidewalks, driveways, and

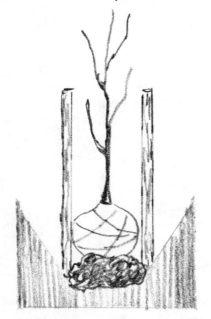

Drive supporting stakes firmly into the soil next to the root ball.

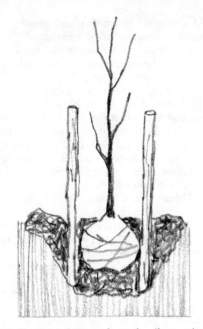

Finish filling hole with good soil, tamping it firmly. Ridge the soil so it forms saucer-like basin.

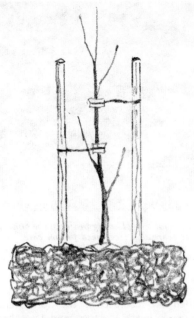

Tie tree to the supporting stakes with hose-covered wire. Water well to settle soil.

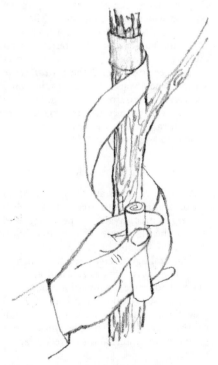

Wrap trunk downward with burlap strip, tieing wrap every 18 inches with stout cord.

For older trees, punch holes for fertilizer with a crowbar—15 inches deep, 18 to 24 inches apart—under the tree drip line. For new trees, scatter fertilizer around the tree at the tree's drip line.

213

In school tree planting projects, the children also learn that trees need proper care. This youngster is spreading fertilizer under tree on school grounds, Marlow Heights, Md.

paved streets carry off rainfall. City soils often are compacted, the water table often is lower in cities, and trees have to compete for water with lawns, flowers, and shrubs. Eventually, trees can become adjusted to a minimum water supply, but must be kept alive until they do.

Water young trees the first two seasons, especially. A good soaking once a week is better than sprinkling every day. For watering curb side trees, a "needle" which attaches to garden hose and is designed for injecting water-soluble fertilizer into the root zone is useful.

Exception: If the soil is tight clay and the drainage is poor, avoid overwatering. Too much water will kill some trees faster than too little.

A mulch—peat moss, pine bark, tanbark, ground corncobs, or peanut hulls—helps hold moisture in the soil around the roots. In the winter, it protects from the sudden temperature fluctuations that cause intermittent freezing and thawing of the root soil.

Let the tree itself be your guide for fertilizing. When leaves are paler and the growth slower than normal, add nutrients to the soil. Use about 2 pounds of commercial fertilizer for each inch of trunk diameter (measured about 3 feet above the ground). A 5–10–5 (mixture

of nitrogen, phosphorus, and potash) or similar formulation is satisfactory.

For young trees, scatter the fertilizer around the tree under outer ends of the branches—the drip line. For older trees, punch holes with a crowbar about 15 inches deep, 18 to 24 inches apart, around the tree at the drip line. Distribute fertilizer among the holes; fill the holes with good soil or a mixture of soil, sand, and peat moss. This provides aeration and water access and puts the fertilizer closer to the roots.

Other planned maintenance through the years would include:

• Pruning—for appearance and for safeguarding the tree's health. Cut off dead or weak wood to eliminate entry points for pests and for diseases. Small pruning cuts heal quickly. Treat large cuts (more than an inch in diameter) with antiseptic tree dressing to seal the wound. Early pruning is usually simple. But if you have to climb in the tree for extensive pruning, call a professional tree surgeon.

• Protecting the tree from injury by pests, diseases, and machines. Most insects and diseases can be controlled by spraying. You can do this yourself when the trees are small. The problem grows as the tree grows, and there may come a time when you will need professional sprayers and equipment. Stakes or low fencing can protect the tree bark from mechanical injury by lawnmowers, bicycles, and foot traffic.

For More Help

All that is necessary if you want to "color it green with trees" is to select the right tree, plant it properly, and give it the right care. If you need additional and specific help, try your county agricultural agent, city park superintendent or arborist, State horticulturist or State shade tree commission, State experiment station horticulturist, the local power company or cooperative, or local nurseryman. These people know your growing conditions and the trees adapted to them.

Protecting Watercourses
With Colorful Plantings

ROBERT B. THORNTON and JOHN L. CREECH

THE COLORFUL HERBS, trees, and shrubs with which nature clothed our natural stream borders have purpose as well as beauty. They protect the banks from the erosive force of flowing water.

Today, with the landscape materially altered by the endeavors of man, many of our watercourses—from tiny rivulet to major river system—lack this protective plant cover. They run thick with mud every time that it rains, laden with material washed from adjoining lands and their own banks.

An artificial watercourse, like a ditch or a constructed waterway, in most cases requires the same plant protection as a natural watercourse. So to protect the watercourse from erosion, the speed of waterflow has to be reduced; and nothing is more effective than a thick green blanket of sod, with its stems and leaves providing thousands of barriers to the direct flow of runoff.

Shrubs are next best. They send up stems from the ground line, splitting the mainstream many times, bending with the surge, and returning upright after the water recedes.

Trees are poor, individually, and are not suitable in a flowing stream or on the bank proper. But back on the land close to and above the main watercourse, a group of trees forms a canopy; the leaves break the velocity of the falling raindrops, and their litter slows the flow and aids in increasing the amount of moisture going into the soil. Also, the roots fill the earth, binding it together.

Each type of plant has its most effective place, and this appropriateness depends not only upon stream size, but on other values as well, such as the use to which the streambank is to be put. Consideration should always be given to the esthetic values of the plants used. Several plants may be equally effective from an erosion control standpoint, but where beauty is desired, the horticultural character of the plants would determine the choice to be made.

For those whose backyards border a stream or through which a stream flows, something a little different may be in order, such as substituting ribbongrass—with its strikingly variegated foliage—for reed canarygrass, and planting the upper bank to daylily or lilyturf.

Among the shrubs, the conservationist might choose coralberry for areas seldom seen. On the other hand, where the planting is in constant view of the public, weeping forsythia with its golden yellow bells in the spring would be better.

Another illustration of this concept would be selection of the red-osier dogwood—with its vivid red bark and conspicuous white fruits—over the silky dogwood, since in this case beauty is one of the major considerations.

For the effective control of runoff from

Robert B. Thornton is the *Manager* of the National Plant Materials Center, Soil Conservation Service.

John L. Creech is *Chief* of the New Crops Research Branch, Agricultural Research Service.

farm or ranch land, we will want a sod-forming grass. Grass waterways, well managed and fertilized, will put water runoff into the nearest stream with the least burden of silt, protecting the croplands as well. In most cases, a grass waterway also can be used for limited grazing or hay production.

As climates, soils, and latitudes change, so do the species employed. In Maine or Oregon it may be the bentgrasses, which require cool climates and uniform moisture. Where streams are large enough not to become clogged, reed canarygrass is highly effective. But you would not use this grass on a slow-moving drainage ditch which has only intermittent flow.

Types of Species

In the South, bahiagrass, sericea lespedeza, or bermudagrass would be used.

In the New England and Corn Belt regions, smooth bromegrass and tall fescue are widely employed.

In the Great Plains, where rainfall is limited, increased dependence is placed on switchgrass, big bluestem, intermediate wheatgrass, and western wheatgrass. The last two have much greater tolerance to alkali and saline soils than most grasses. Fast gaining popularity for the wet sections of waterways is Garrison creeping meadow foxtail.

The landowner will want to make every effort to protect his property that borders on a stream.

Three ways to do this are: (1) Maintain a good sod along and on the banks; (2) protect the banks by fencing where damage by livestock would be a problem; and (3) remove occasional debris which may clog the channel or divert the flow to one side where it would undercut the streambank.

Where the sod is thin, it should be fertilized and reseeded when necessary. If banks have been undercut, they should be sloped and planted. Vegetation, either grass or shrubs, should first be established on the toe of the slope. Where vegetation alone will not do the job, the lower slope should be riprapped with stone or some other support used.

Along most streams concerted action by all of the landowners is necessary to bring about success.

Bush willows are very widely used to stabilize streambanks. Two willows used effectively are the sandbar willow and purple-osier willow. Sandbar willow is a native plant forming extensive colonies. Many of the branches run along the ground, sending out roots where they touch the soil surface. It is found most abundantly in Canada and the Northern United States, although it occurs as far south as Arkansas and Oklahoma.

Sandbar willow works well in areas of heavy spring ice flow, since the block ice will ride over without uprooting it. If some of the branches are sheared off or buried, it sends up numerous new sprouts which may even thicken the original stand. Tree species of willow should not be used.

Purple-osier willow is more upright, with multiple reddish-purple stems, 10 to 18 feet tall. Originally introduced from Europe for basketmaking, this colorful willow has been planted extensively for erosion control along watercourses, since it too can bend with the flow without being dislodged.

Effective Dogwoods

One of the dogwoods found to be effective is silky cornel—although not as colorful, it has gained preference over red-osier dogwood because it has a wider range of site adaptability, both wet and dry. Both silky cornel and red-osier dogwood are American natives. Red-osier has more brilliant winter stem color. Both spread through rooting where the branches remain in contact with the ground. A less vigorous spreader, but with coral red winter stems, is Siberian dogwood. It also has the same height.

Another dogwood which has only limited application is cornelian-cherry. In its homeland in Europe, this is often found along streams and damp areas as a small tree or a large shrub. Two attributes are the large showy early spring flowers and the bright-red, edible fruit.

Not to be overlooked where beauty is also a concern are wichura rose and the trailing forsythias, including the rela-

216

tively new "Arnold Dwarf." Wichura rose is a later flowering rose, distinct in its trailing, semievergreen habit. The dense, far-reaching trailers which root at the nodes make it especially good as a soil-binding plant. Effective plantings of wichura rose have been made on drainage ditchbanks by planting at the top of the slope and letting the runners trail down the bank to the water's edge.

Sometimes we can rely upon native plants which will establish themselves along the watercourse. Willows, poplars, alders, and many others will volunteer. Weak or inadequately covered areas need to be strengthened through plantings of some suitable species.

If the stretch is to be set aside for recreation, swimming, or boat launching, grass species tolerant to heavy foot traffic are selected instead of woody plants. For example, in the Northeast and Northwest creeping red fescue and Durar hard fescue are used for this purpose in areas of heavy shade, and a combination of creeping red fescue and tall fescue in light shade.

Where traffic is not a problem, the species of lilyturfs, either *Liriope* or *Ophiopogon,* can be used. They are

Trees, Shrubs, and Other Plants Used Along Watercourses

Common name	Scientific name
Alder	*Alnus* spp.
American beachgrass	*Ammophila breviligulata* Fern.
Amur honeysuckle	*Lonicera maacki* Maxim.
Autumn olive	*Elaeagnus umbellata* Thunb.
Bahiagrass	*Paspalum notatum* Flugge
Bayberry	*Myrica pensylvanica* Lois.
Beachplum	*Prunus maritima* Marsh.
Bentgrasses	*Agrostis* spp.
Bermudagrass	*Cynodon dactylon* (L.) Pers.
Big bluestem	*Andropogon gerardii* Vitman
Boxelder	*Acer negundo* L.
Coralberry	*Symphoricarpos orbicularis* Michx.
Cornelian-cherry	*Cornus mas* L.
Creeping meadow foxtail	*Alopecurus arundinaceus* Poir.
Creeping red fescue	*Festuca rubra* L.
Daylily	*Hemerocallis fulva* L.
European beachgrass	*Ammophila arenaria* (L.) Link
Inkberry	*Ilex glabra* (L.) Gray
Intermediate wheatgrass	*Agropyron intermedium* (Host) Beauv.
Lilyturf	*Liriope spicata* Lour., and *Ophiopogon japonicus* Ker-Gawl.
Orchardgrass	*Dactylis glomerata* L.
Poplar	*Populus* spp.
Purple-osier willow	*Salix purpurea* L.
Red-osier dogwood	*Cornus stolonifera* Michx.
Reed canarygrass	*Phalaris arundinacea* L.
Ribbongrass	*Phalaris arundinacea* v. *picta* L.
Rugosa rose	*Rosa rugosa* Thunb.
Saltmeadow cordgrass	*Spartina patens* (Ait.) Wood
Sand lovegrass	*Eragrostis trichodes* (Nutt.) Wood
Sandbar willow	*Salix interior* Rowlee
Sericea lespedeza	*Lespedeza cuneata* (Dumont) G. Don.
Shrub lespedezas	*Lespedeza bicolor* Turcz., and *Lespedeza japonica* Bailey
Siberian dogwood	*Cornus alba sibirica* Loud.
Silky dogwood	*Cornus amomum* Mill.
Smooth bromegrass	*Bromus inermis* Leyss.
Switchgrass	*Panicum virgatum* L.
Tall fescue	*Festuca arundinacea* Schreb.
Weeping forsythia	*Forsythia* spp.
Western sand cherry	*Prunus besseyii* Bailey
Western wheatgrass	*Agropyron smithii* Rydb.
Wichura rose	*Rosa wichuraiana* Crép.
Willows	*Salix* spp.

235-917 O - 67 - 17

oriental in origin and are best suited to the southern coastal plain. Since these plants are grasslike in habit they are particularly suitable as ground covers for both shady and sunny areas and can be mowed like grasses without harm. Occasional mowing is beneficial. They are particularly valuable on slopes to prevent washing and will tolerate a considerable amount of dryness, often thriving in sandy soil where grass cannot be grown.

Of the species in cultivation, the best are *Ophiopogon japonicus* Ker-Gawl. and *Liriope spicata* Lour.

Daylilies Useful

The daylilies are native to temperate Asia, with a large share of them found in Japan. They flourish in almost any type of soil. With their brilliant flowers and the ease with which they naturalize along abandoned roadbeds and cutover areas, daylilies are a most useful conservation plant. They will tolerate acid boggy conditions, yet they are at home in poor sandy soil.

Slightly saline waters might dictate bermudagrass or even saltmeadow cordgrass. Sandy soils subject to periods of drought or movement by wind will require such grasses as sand lovegrass and American or European beachgrass. Western sand cherry, beachplum, bayberry, rugosa rose, and inkberry are some of the shrubs which tolerate such sites.

The western sand cherry finds its home on sandy hills, rocky slopes, and shores from Wyoming to Minnesota, south to Kansas. Under good conditions it produces an abundance of tasty and attractive fruit.

In the Northeast, similar sites are occupied by beachplum, which provided the early settlers with many quarts of jelly, and still does for today's residents.

Bayberry, the source of bayberry candles, is mostly confined to the coastal areas and sandy acid soils. It likes both wet and dry sites. Conspicuous during late fall are the light gray clusters of wax-laden fruits.

Salt spray does not seem to deter rugosa rose. In fact, it finds itself at home on New England cliffs and sand dunes. This rose, spreading by numerous underground stems, will take a wide range of sites, persisting with little care. The large red fruits (hips) add food for the wildlife.

Moving on south, our native inkberry comes into the picture. It is common over wide areas, especially in wet situations or those bank areas closest to the streams. Like most hollies, it will tolerate poor soil and variable conditions of moisture. With its evergreen foliage and willowy growth it makes a good plant for conservation use.

In their area of adaptation, the shrub lespedezas make an effective bank cover and wildlife habitat. They not only bind the soil together, but also produce an abundance of dry fruits in the fall, thereby providing winter food for game and songbirds. Two favorites are *Lespedeza bicolor* Turcz. and *Lespedeza japonica* Bailey. Another shrub which will do well on the higher, drier portions of the bank is the Amur honeysuckle which attains a height of 15 feet, maturing its persistent fruits in September or October.

Indian Currant

Coralberry, or Indian currant, would probably not be recommended for planting in the Midwest; there it spreads so extensively it is a pest in many places. In the Northeast, however, the coralberry suckers do not spread so rapidly, and results have been more favorable. Coralberry will tolerate a wide range of soils or climates, forming a dense thicket.

The red berries ripening in the fall provide an emergency food for wildlife, from pheasant and ruffed grouse to deer.

Among the small tree species, autumn olive is adapted to the widest range of soil types. It also provides an abundance of silvery-red tart berries. Some strains mature in mid-August, others not until October. A new strain, 'Cardinal,' released by the Soil Conservation Service, is an abundant fruiter and is hardy to southern New England.

Planting of this species should be confined to the regions which are east of the Mississippi River.

It is vital to observe good planting

218

practices in vegetating watercourses. Fertilizers should be mixed in the bottoms of the planting holes. Planting should be done when there is a good chance of having adequate moisture supplies at the time of planting and afterwards. Soil should be carefully worked in around the roots and firmly tamped. The stock should never be allowed to dry out, particularly the roots.

Where the plantings are accomplished with seedlings, the side-hole method is often employed. In this method, the hole is prepared with one vertical face, the roots of the seedling are placed against this vertical face, and the loose soil then is moved back into the hole and is firmly tamped.

This permits the roots to be in contact with undisturbed soil.

In many cases, it will be necessary to replant in certain spots to assure an adequate stand for an effective control of erosion.

As more and more watercourses are conservation treated with an eye out for beauty, they add a bright splash of color to the land while protecting it.

How the Garden Clubs Can Dress Up an Area

FRANCIS DE VOS

THE LITTLE ravine had undoubtedly seen better days. The scarred streambed told of past struggles with flash floods. The forest floor, now inhospitably carpeted in poison-ivy, sent the chance visitor on a different way. The remnants of a finer flora struggled with that naturalized alien from abroad, the Japanese honeysuckle.

Yet somehow the ancient struggle of plant against plant and soil against water is forgivable, even when the end result is not to our liking. It was the hand of man that most defiled this ravine. The trash of his living was everywhere, scattered among the undergrowth—bottles, cans, and all kinds of ugly things resisting decay. This was Fern Valley at the National Arboretum in Washington, D.C., in 1959.

But within 7 years the beauty of this little ravine was restored, largely through the efforts of the National Capital Area Federation of Garden Clubs, Inc. How

this was accomplished should be of interest to any garden club contemplating a beautification project, for most of the experiences common to projects of this kind were met and successfully resolved.

Leadership, one essential element for success, came from an unanticipated quarter. In a class that I was teaching at the Arboretum, on woody plants, there was a lady in her early eighties, Mrs. Edith Bittinger. When I mentioned that we were interested in developing a certain little ravine, she insisted on seeing the site immediately. From that moment we had the leadership we were looking for. The Fern Valley Committee of the National Capital Area Federation of Garden Clubs, Inc., was soon organized with representatives from the federation

Francis de Vos is *Director* of the Chicago Botanic Garden. He is a former Assistant Director, U.S. National Arboretum, Crops Research Division, Agricultural Research Service.

219

and the American Fern Society and the Arboretum itself.

Mrs. Bittinger provided inspirational leadership. Her chief lieutenant, Mrs. Margaret Donnald, whose name was to become synonymous with Fern Valley, provided the drive and the persistence to bring plans into reality.

Early committee meetings clearly defined the limits of the 3½-acre site and established guidelines for its development. The natural vegetation of this valley would be preserved (except for poison-ivy) and enhanced with fern and wild flower species of eastern North America. Western and exotic species were to be excluded. The work priorities agreed on clearly recognized the need first to rid the valley of honeysuckle, poison-ivy, and trash. They also determined how much working strength could be enlisted for the undertaking.

Facts on the Line

When Arboretum representatives indicated they could provide little help aside from building trails, a small dam, and a lime rock retaining wall for lime-loving ferns, the garden clubs were fairly warned that acquisition of plants, planting, and maintenance would be their responsibilities. The initial need for funds was satisfied when federation members of the committee outlined the proposed project before federation and individual garden club meetings.

The events that followed the organizational meeting clearly indicated that the formula which led to the eventual success of the Fern Valley project was leadership, simple objectives, and a hard core of devoted workers. The effective leadership of Mrs. Bittinger and Mrs. Donnald brought the project through the critical first stages. It has maintained a high level of interest and has attracted financial support totaling more than $3,600 in little more than 7 years.

Having very simple objectives was extremely important, particularly in early phases of the project. The temptation to acquire and grow the unusual and difficult-to-raise native ferns and wild flowers was in great part resisted. Large

220

patches of the easy-to-raise New York and Christmas ferns were soon established, and their most luxuriant growth spelled success and was the tangible evidence needed for increased support.

The solidly established project then moved forward on many fronts. A self-guiding nature trail was established. A combination toolhouse and orientation shelter was erected. Plantings were elaborated and refined to demonstrate the major forest associations of the east coast.

The work went forward and continues to advance because leadership and planning assured the initial successes and because it attracted a hard core of dedicated workers who made themselves available when there was work to be done. There were times when they were summoned on short notice to rescue such choice items as regal ferns (*Osmunda regalis*), the pitcher plant (*Sarracenia purpurea*), and the swamp azalea (*Rhododendron viscosum*) from the path of the bulldozer. At other times they were asked to be part of a planting, weeding, or watering crew. Their tender loving care brought planting plans to fruition and inspired others to emulate their efforts.

The little ravine, now known as Fern Valley, is an enchanting place to visit at any time of the year. The towering oaks, beeches, and tulip trees appear to approve of the changes that have taken place about their roots. In season, hepaticas, Virginia bluebells, lady slippers, cardinal flowers, azaleas, rhododendron, and mountain laurel decorate the forest floor. Ferns in many species hang from rocky crevices, carpet gravelly banks, and keep company with pitcher plants, swamp magnolias, and cypress trees in the wetter places.

The valley has been described by a nostalgic visitor as being like "the woods back home." To the hundreds of school-children who annually travel the self-guiding nature walk, all this presents an intimate and hopefully educational experience with nature.

What are some of the possibilities for beautifying an area? One club selected a several-block-long unsightly weed strip between the highway and railroad. The area was cleaned up and landscaped. The project became known as the "Line of Beauty" and resulted in the city installing a sprinkler system and paying for half of the maintenance costs.

Another club filled baskets with seasonal flowers and installed them upon parking meter posts when the meters were removed. A third club raised nearly $4,000, through tours, to purchase trees at wholesale prices, resold the trees to homeowners at cost, and donated 700 more trees to the local parks.

Ravines or gullies are often bypassed as building sites because they are too expensive to fill. They become no man's land and the receptacle for the trash and pollutants of our times. Frequently, they separate one housing project from another. Others may be found on lands adjacent to schools or municipal, State, or Federal road systems, or building complexes. Many are ugly. Here is a challenge for a garden club or group of clubs wishing to beautify an area.

Easing the Burden

The maintenance burden which has resulted from Federal, State, and municipal plantings under beautification programs is truly staggering. Ways must be found to ease this burden. Garden clubs could take the responsibility for weeding, and in some cases watering, these numerous islands of beauty that have sprung up within our cities and along our highways.

The first job for a committee is to determine ownership of the land selected for beautification. Land not in current use may be scheduled for future development. One garden club found out too late that the site it beautified would soon be used for highway purposes.

If permission is granted to use the land, the committee should set up some definite objectives. With any untried group, it is essential that the objectives be simple. Each step, as it is performed, can well represent a completed project. Clearing of trash and weeds and the selective thinning of shrubs and trees can transform a neglected woodland into a place of beauty. Partially denuded

ravines or gullies may need plantings of indigenous ground covers, shrubs, and trees to stabilize the soil. Work of this kind can be assigned to local Boy Scout troops wanting conservation and community service projects.

After the initial cleanup phases, the project should be reappraised. Is there enough interest and support in sight to begin planting? If not, it is much better to accept the fact that a good cleanup job is a contribution to beauty, and that the stage has been set and awaits the awakening of dormant interests.

If the climate is right for going ahead, the committee should refine its thinking on the type of plantings desired. Plantings of species native to the area are most likely to succeed and are of special value to school groups and others interested in their indigenous flora, but mixed plantings of native and foreign species usually have broader appeal. Whatever the decision, it is extremely important to limit the initial plantings to species that are easy to grow and maintain.

The committee's chairman needs to develop a resistance to the well meant contributions of tidbits from garden club members, especially if they do not fit the plans and are hard to grow. Nearby botanical gardens, arboretums, departments of horticulture at State universities, and local plant specialists can be of assistance in selecting species. The advice of a landscape architect is also desirable for producing plantings of maximum esthetic effect. Easy-to-grow species like narcissus and daylilies can give an immediate touch of success to plantings, and generally require little maintenance.

The Achilles heel of most beautification projects is maintenance. Many well planned and well executed projects have been lost in the weeds, or ravaged by insects and diseases, or they have wilted under the summer sun. Even with the easy-to-grow plants some maintenance is required. Watering and weeding during the first 2 years can mean life or death for newly transplanted plants. It is only through continual care, however, that we can hope to produce a spot of beauty to pass along to future generations.

Roads That Fit
Our Environment

MYLES R. HOWLETT

WITH the advent of the automobile age back in the early 1920's, roads became a major landscape feature. The demand for roads has grown at a phenomenal rate, and highway agencies have responded. In the United States there are over 3 million miles of roads and streets, and despite many deficiencies these roads are the best and safest in the entire world.

As a highway engineer, I cannot help but be proud of that accomplishment, yet I also hope that all of us with a clear look at the past can see a far better future for our highway system. We must retain and improve the concept that all highways will be functional and safe. In addition, we should now exert every effort to make our highways and streets an integral part of their environment.

Above all, the driver and passengers should feel safe and secure. The relationship of the road and its appurtenances to the terrain and the blending of the roadside with adjacent features are important elements in achieving this sense of serenity which is so necessary for safe—and enjoyable—driving.

These are not simple objectives. They cannot be attained without a feeling for the man who drives the road and unless the structural elements of the road are recognized as part of the total landscape. This sense of total appropriateness cannot be obtained by superficial planting, covering of blemishes, and facing structures with stone. These all are essential elements of a beautification program, but if highway engineers accept this as the only requirement for beautiful highways they will create monuments to poor taste and booby traps for motorists.

There can be no formula to be blindly followed in achieving a sense of appropriateness for a highway. In areas where man has shaped his environment, as in cities and other developed areas, structural design that conforms is appropriate; in a commercial area the result is a neat tailored look with a minimum of formalized landscaping. But in a residential area where homes are extensively landscaped, our highways should be, too. In the slums, we should not build down to the neighborhood. Experience has indicated that good highway design can be a tremendous stimulus in getting people to raise their own maintenance standards.

Abstract philosophies, such as we have just indulged in, are helpful as a basis for the understanding of objectives, but the hard facts of life must be faced before the bulldozer takes the first bite below the cut stake. For there are some less ephemeral approaches to the design of our highways which can be used as guides. I want to repeat again before

❧ ❧ ❧

Myles R. Howlett is a *Staff Engineer,* Division of Engineering, Forest Service. He previously was in charge of transportation planning and design for the Division, and he has served as member of the President's Council on Recreation and Natural Beauty task group to develop a report on scenic highways and parkways.

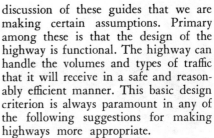

(A)

discussion of these guides that we are making certain assumptions. Primary among these is that the design of the highway is functional. The highway can handle the volumes and types of traffic that it will receive in a safe and reasonably efficient manner. This basic design criterion is always paramount in any of the following suggestions for making highways more appropriate.

The designer must consider basic relations between road design and the terrain. Long straight tangents and short-radius curves (A) should be avoided. In any terrain condition they appear foreign to the environment. The designer must break with the traditional concept of straight lines between location controls connected by circular curves.

(B)

Using flowing curves with short tangents or spirals, we can fit the road into the landscape (B).

Timber, concrete, or metal crib walls can be used to avoid major cuts and an unsightly overcast in solid rock (C). These walls can help retain the natural vegetation and eliminate many potential maintenance problems.

Bridges which the public will pass underneath or see in profile should be designed as light-appearing objects of functional beauty which do not obscure the landscape or create a tunnel effect (D). Bridges in scenic areas should normally have the major or heavier structural elements below the road surface (E). Structures like guardrails and railings above the pavement should be designed to minimize blocking of the motorists' view of the scenery.

(C)

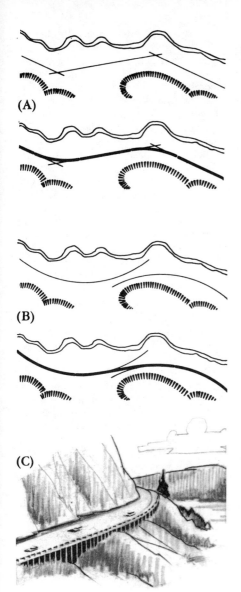

(E)

(D)

(F)

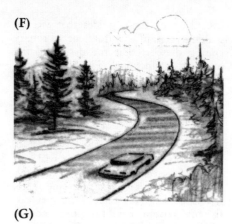

(G)

(H)

(I)

(J)

Perhaps the most important element in both highway location and landscaping is variety. The ever-changing scene—suddenly opened, well-framed vistas; blooming trees and shrubs, the interplay of light and shadow, fall colors, and snow on the conifers—all contribute to enjoyable and memorable travel (F). The monotony of a seemingly endless tunnel of trees can be relieved by carefully selected cuttings.

A divided highway can add to safe and relaxed driving, economy, and the beauty of the landscape (G). Each lane should seek its own best location, set apart from its twin by a variable-width median of natural terrain. The driver feels secure and can enjoy his pleasant surroundings without major distractions of oncoming headlights or traffic.

A discontinuous alinement, such as broken-back curves or hidden dips, tends to disrupt the road user's attention and spoil a pleasing relationship of the road to the terrain (H).

Cuts through ridgetops in a direct line of sight from the roadway should be avoided; they create an unnatural break in the skyline (I). A combination of vertical and horizontal curves will make the road appear fitted to the landscape (J). The driver is safely led into the horizontal curve.

A pleasing relationship of the road and terrain can be achieved by skirting meadows or crossing vantage points from which such openings can be seen.

This is done also by setting maximum sight distances and by using combinations of horizontal and vertical curvatures that restrict long-distance views of road segments (K).

(K)

The previous illustrations are examples of what I consider to be major design considerations. But smaller details can be just as disruptive to the appropriateness of any highway.

For example, take a narrow bridge or a culvert which is too short. On a narrow bridge, the guardrail is inside the shoulder line (L). On a short culvert, there is a headwall. Then there is an approach guardrail so the driver won't hit the headwall, plus clearance markers, reflectors, and a "Narrow Bridge" sign. The construction and maintenance costs to make an inappropriate, unsafe structure usable can exceed by far the cost of an appropriate original structure. The driver feels squeezed, unsafe, and the structure simply doesn't "belong."

Traffic hazards are created by a failure to do adequate right-of-way clearing or by improper landscaping practices. You have all seen that tree too close to the road, with the scarred trunk (M). The driver who has been a victim of that tree can never associate it with beauty. He cannot drive this road again with the feeling of serenity which is essential to enjoyment of the landscape.

We mentioned that planting cannot cure the problem of inappropriate highways, but there are places where planting can be utilized as a screening (N) for temporary disruptions (O) in landscape patterns due to construction, etc.

Watershed protection is a requirement in the location and design of roads. The natural characteristics of streams should not be interrupted adversely. Channel changes in firmly entrenched streams should be minimized, and encroachment on stream channels must be avoided or else adequately protected.

Additional measures should be taken whenever practical, like careful routing to prevent earth movement and the balancing of cut and fill. Systems for the collection and discharge of surface water must be designed with due regard for the protection of embankments and fills and the erosive effect of additional water on minor channels. All disturbed areas subject to erosion must be revegetated or otherwise protected.

(L)

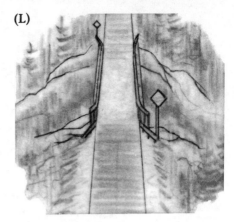

(M)

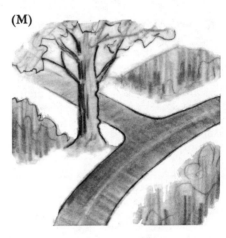

(N)

(O)

225

Conservation Solutions to the Town Dump Mess

LLOYD E. PARTAIN

NOT ALL town dumping grounds are potential beauty spots or recreational sites, but they need not become eyesores and the sources of pollution and health hazards.

On well-selected sites and with proper conservation treatment, the solid waste disposal areas can be made to grow trees, shrubs, and grasses which protect and beautify the landscape.

What's happening to town dumps in the St. John-Aroostook resource conservation and development project in Maine serves as a good example of using conservation techniques in waste disposal.

Sixty towns within this project are planning to use modern land and water science in relocating old waste disposal dumps and in selecting sites for new ones. Basic to the solution of this problem is the location of suitable soils which permit safe disposal and which will respond to conservation treatment. Once potential sites are found, the technical help of an engineer and a plant materials specialist is needed to complete the job. The technical assistance necessary is made available within resource conservation and development projects by the Soil Conservation Service of the Agriculture Department.

Similar help is available in nearly 3,000 soil and water conservation districts throughout the United States.

A dozen towns in Maine have already obtained the necessary onsite technical information to help assure that future dumping will not result in unsightliness and pollution of water supplies. Evidence

that waste disposal areas respond to conservation management are already visible in communities such as Allagash, Eagle Lake, Sinclair, Frenchville, and Van Buren—scenic areas long popular with campers, vacationers, fishermen, and with hunters.

Before adoption of the new techniques, the local practice (as in most areas of the country) was to dump waste into sand and gravel pits and along streambanks and the roadsides. Besides the ugliness created, the porous soils readily released contamination affecting nearby streams, lakes, and ground water. Since many homes in the area use driven wells and springs, human health as well as fishing and scenic beauty was endangered.

The new installations are located on soils suitable for solid waste disposal and in areas where they do not offend the eye. These for the most part are deep, moderately permeable, well-drained soils. Soil particles in these soils filter out most of the obnoxious pollutants as water drains into the earth. By making special interpretations of soil survey data, the soil scientists have designated alternative areas for suitable waste disposal.

Other conservation techniques applied to the modernized waste disposal areas include the time-tested method, contouring. Trenches to receive the wastes are dug along contour levels laid out by SCS

Lloyd E. Partain is *Assistant* to the Administrator on Recreation, Soil Conservation Service.

technicians. Waste materials placed in these are covered by soil dug from the next contour elevation. The filled contour is planted to adaptable trees, shrubs, or grass. The result is a terraced effect with screening and beautification instead of an ugly surface dump.

Where needed, diversion channels and water-spreading devices are installed to keep the waste disposal area from eroding, flooding, or otherwise threatening community health and safety. Dikes are sometimes built to restrain all water on the dumping site. All the conservation-assisted disposal areas are now planned so that their drainage will not affect other watershed resources.

Residents in northern Maine, like those in many other attractive rural areas, feel the impact of commerce, industry, and highways along with attendant homesite and tourist developments. Waste of all kinds is a growing problem. Costs of disposal go up and up. Modern soil surveys show that well-suited soils are often found on high-priced farmland. Ways must be found to meet these costs. They may be held to a minimum through the cooperation of local, State, and Federal agency planning and cost sharing with landowners and operators.

As a Van Buren, Maine, civic leader described the situation, "We can face the costs; but we couldn't go on facing the puzzle of not knowing what to do next. We're many steps ahead of the game now. With our dumpsites inventoried, we can plan 25—maybe 50—years ahead. That's a lot better than shopping around for a new dump just about every time a town meeting rolled around."

Many communities everywhere across the country are applying conservation techniques to convert open dumps to more pleasing sites. Others with waste disposal problems should investigate the possibilities. Those who do will make for themselves and those who come to enjoy the countryside a more healthful and beautiful place to live, work, and play.

'Yankee Doodle Darlings'
Bring Beauty to the Land

EMMA KURETICH

IT HAPPENED in 1966 on the Teton National Forest. Twenty-five of us, self-proclaimed as "Yankee Doodle Darlings," had dared to dream the impossible—and the dream came true.

This is the story, essentially as it was told to me by Susan, one of the teenage girls who participated in carrying out the "dream" project.

The dream developed out of the first National Young Women's Christian Association Conference on Outdoor Recreation and Conservation, in 1964, at Jackson Hole, Wyo. There was need, someone said at that conference, for a foot trail out across the base of the great Gros Ventre landslide, one of the largest mass earth movements in the United States, located in the Teton National Forest in Wyoming. One day in June 1925, the entire side of a mountain broke loose. The earth and its debris,

ॐ   ॐ   ॐ

Emma Kuretich is *Information Specialist* in charge of Women's Activities, Forest Service.

"There—that's just right!"   *A sign tops off the Y-Teen project.*

like a wave of water, cascaded from an altitude of 9,000 feet, crossed a valley, and dashed 300 feet up the opposite slope. The opportunity to discover this fascinating geological feature should be available to everyone.

And some of the teenagers who were a part of the conference could scarcely wait to voice their ardent agreement. They, too, believed it was important for the individual to be able to touch and smell and see at close range the wonders of the slide area—so important that they wanted to help the Forest Service provide the opportunity for this particular recreation experience. Unabashed, they promptly imagined a pathway directly into 50 million cubic yards of wildly displaced rock, earth, and trees—a pathway they would help build.

The next time that Susan saw the Gros Ventre Slide it was 1966, and she was part of a national Y-Teen pilot work camp group. Organized to give substance to their dream, 25 girls had rendez-voused at the specially classified Gros Ventre Geological Area of the Teton National Forest to blaze the trail.

Teenage girlpower—14 to 18 years of age—they had come from big places and from little places; from the North, the South, the East, and the West. They represented 17 different States across the face of our Nation.

Many had wanted to help, but the number was limited to 25. Consequently, those who were selected to do this service for their country pledged to do so in the highest traditions of the spirit of '76. Modern day patriots, they wanted a better life for all people. And they were willing to labor hard to help achieve it—even labor hard on the rockpiles of the Gros Ventre Slide. For they recognized the importance of helping to develop in their own countrymen an appreciation of natural beauty.

For 2 weeks, home away from home

was a wilderness-type camp, sheltered in a red-cliffed canyon. The swift Gros Ventre River was their constant companion—as were two YWCA national board camp executives, two counselors, and a wonderful cook.

The cook's prebreakfast specialty on icy crisp mornings was finger warmers (hot hard-boiled eggs to have and to hold). But by the time the girls finished camp chores and traveled to work, Old Sol was operating efficiently. And at noontime, temperatures exceeded 90°.

Males Lead Way

The program could be described best as a plan-work-evaluate process. In the work phase, building the trail, Forest Service male counterparts led the way. The total operation was carried on by Ranger Alden Schuldt of the Gros Ventre District under the direction of Supervisor Robert Safran of the Teton National Forest. Forest Engineer Thomas Grant supervised the construction. Five well-trained university students helped and served as unit work leaders. They taught the girls in groups of five what to do and how to do it safely, and then they worked right along with them.

The girls became well acquainted with rakes, crowbars, shovels, wheelbarrows, and the pulaski or forester ax, a combination of a grub hoe and ax. These were the tools—plus a dream. Work gloves, sun hats, and water canteens were standard operating equipment.

Each morning the girls cleared and leveled and filled and surfaced. They removed derelict trees that blocked the way (after they had been sawed into girl-size pieces, of course). By the handful and by the half wheelbarrow full, they relocated earth and rock—moving and smoothing to open up a trail into the slide area.

At midday the girls would recess from trail building. But their enthusiasm continued on. It was significant that daily departures were never marked by goodby's. Calls of "See you in the morning" always echoed round the bend as the girls' bus moved campward.

Afternoons were spent both in and out of camp. On occasion the girls visited other areas of special interest in the vicinity. Some afternoons were devoted to hobbies, like painting and photography. When the waterfront director declared the river "open," water frolics and freshening-up activities began.

Often the girls organized nature walks when the ranger was on hand to lead them. With his help they compared the responses of plants to growing conditions in the camp area with the plantlife in the slide area. They also improved their knowledge of what a national forest is.

"Even our quiet moments held excitement," Susan told me. "When relaxing, we savored the comfort of resting our work-weary bodies. Although tired, we were exhilarated. And we would ask ourselves: Is this feeling part of the reward of being totally involved? All our energies are committed to a purpose in which we believe. Our heads, our hearts, and our hands are working together."

Evening was the time for planned appraisals and around a central campfire was often the place. The girls looked forward to those sharing periods. They helped bring to full circle the essence of the plan-work-evaluate program. What this work-learn experience meant was expressed in various ways.

Chance To Grow

There was the opportunity to grow as a person. They gave of themselves to develop something that needed developing. Yet, the giving was also receiving. For what greater reward could these girls have than the knowledge that they were contributing to the happiness of others? Because from this time forward, every person—man, woman, or child—who visits the Gros Ventre Geological Area of the Teton National Forest and walks the trail out over the landslide will be a little nearer to understanding some of the deeper meanings of nature.

The 25 young women appreciated being able to help make the trail safe, available, and beautiful. At the same time they learned how to take care of the earth, their heritage.

This is the story of a dream that came

true in Wyoming. Twenty-five Y-Teens made a little bit of America a lot more beautiful. But these girls are not alone. Similar scenes are taking place all across these United States.

In May 1965, the White House Conference on Natural Beauty awakened a nation's spirit to create a more beautiful America. Sparked by the enthusiasm of the First Lady, thousands of women around the country found the climate was most favorable to spearhead their beautification projects.

Community projects became prestige projects as the greatest volunteer force in America embarked on a crusade for beauty. The mystery of beauty began to take many forms as yesterday's dreams unfolded to become today's successes.

Paramus Plantathon

A dream unfolded in a small town in New Jersey, called Paramus. With ingenuity and boundless energy, over 1,000 citizens responded to transform a barren piece of land into an instant park. The Keep Paramus Beautiful Committee launched its idea of a "plantathon." The garden club and chamber of commerce organized Keep Paramus Beautiful to promote civic pride. Civic pride led to self-improvement as townspeople of all ages signed up for the plantathon. In 24 hours over 500 trees, flowering shrubs, and evergreens were planted and their efforts produced the "instant park."

This is typical of what is happening throughout America today. To create a good place for people to live is to focus and coordinate community programs in a meaningful way.

City, suburb, countryside, each is only what its people make it. And when women get themselves and their community together to tackle community problems—make way for progress.

Look what happened in Utah and eastern Nevada: 8,500 determined Girl Scouts put into action their "Trees for Beauty" project, a conservation education project in cooperation with the State forestry departments of Utah and Nevada and the U.S. Forest Service.

The girls energetically surveyed the need for trees in their communities on an individual troop basis. The need was great—and so was their challenge. Local citizens who were qualified consultants helped to select the sites. They recommended schoolyards and public properties. This conservation education project focused attention upon the importance of natural beauty to a quality environment—where people care.

The tree nurseries of the Utah and Nevada State Forestry Departments gave the seedlings. The Forest Service provided technical training in tree planting and in followup care.

Then to observe Arbor Day and to honor Juliette Low, founder of the Girl Scout movement, the girls planted more trees and shrubs throughout Utah and the eastern part of Nevada.

As these girls care for the seedlings, both the seedlings and girls will develop new capacities for growth and service.

Programs sponsored by nonprofit organizations are making vast changes in communities all over the country. For example, the Sears Roebuck Foundation provides women's clubs with the incentive, information, and training needed to spur action for community improvement. The women's organizations take the initiative and join forces in their communities to reach the desired goal. Award-winning scrapbooks record the community improvement success stories. Tangible achievements in thousands of communities make way for progress.

The seeds of progress are taking root throughout the land in the minds of the young and old alike. Fired with the vision of accomplishment, women are making important contributions to both their families and communities. And like the "Yankee Doodle Darlings" of the Gros Ventre Slide project, they are learning that in giving of themselves—heads, hearts, and hands—they are also receiving. Their harvest is a better place to live, a more beautiful America.

Container Gardening

MARILYN H. JOHNSON

CONTAINER gardening, an ancient practice, is coming more and more into favor these days. It now can be seen in various forms and locations and may consist of a variety of materials, plants, and mulches. The age-old problems of esthetics and culture still exist, with age-old solutions as well as contemporary ones.

Plant containers today are used for a variety of purposes. They can direct the pedestrian traffic, provide visual barriers and windbreaks, contribute color, texture, and shade, and even furnish a transition between the interior and the exterior.

Plant containers, if below eye level, are a helpful and subtle method of controlling pedestrian traffic patterns. The pedestrian might become instantly aware that a container garden is contributing color, but if the elements of color and texture are skillfully handled, his attention will usually be captured, and he will be unaware that he is being guided.

Sometimes—especially in these days of the terrace, the patio, and the roof garden—visual barriers are required for privacy, to obstruct a view, or as a windbreak. Container gardening is one way of controlling these problems. A row of tall-growing material of the columnar type, planted in a long planter or in identical individual tubs, is one way to acquire a strong and unified effect (A).

Another solution is the vertical garden which, however, takes time, patience, and many plants. It is portable, attractive, and worth the extra effort. A wooden frame first is covered with chicken wire. Then this is packed with well separated and dampened peat moss or sphagnum to receive annual plants with small root balls covered with soil. These should be placed almost vertically in the peat moss. If plants are applied to both sides, a freestanding wall is achieved. If one side is to be set against the building wall, tar paper or other water-resistant material should be placed between the garden and the building. This will keep the moisture in the garden and out of the building.

There should be a regular watering schedule, and the garden should be dampened thoroughly. There must also be a regular liquid fertilizing schedule, since the plants require nourishment in order to perform well.

I have found the container is a very effective transition between interior and exterior. By repeating, with an indoor planter, some of the plant material which I have used outdoors, a bond is created between the two.

Container gardens are flexible and versatile and can be used in a variety of locations, such as entrances and exits of buildings, as freestanding tubs on streets and terraces, as elements in exciting roof

(A)

Marilyn H. Johnson is the *Landscape Architect* at the National Arboretum, Crops Research Division, Agricultural Research Service. She has designed many container gardens for the Agriculture Department.

231

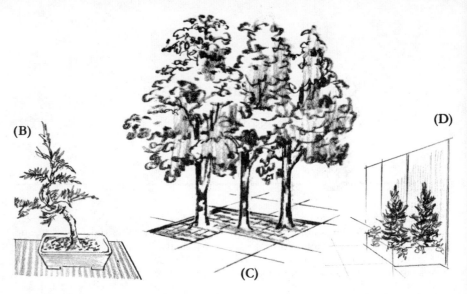

(B)

(D)

(C)

gardens, as vertical garden walls, and as window boxes. They can be used in groups to enliven interiors, and they can be used as single features, such as bonsai (B), inside and outside.

Container gardens, found in a variety of forms and locations, fulfill many purposes. Some can be portable, such as boxes, tubs, pots, and hanging baskets. Some can be made even more mobile with the addition of concealed casters. In fixed open

(E)

areas in the paving (C) and in fixed raised areas (D), the container gardens will, of course, be stationary.

More and more contemporary buildings seem to be surrounded with expanses of concrete which, in the summer, produce a tremendous amount of reflection. Ways to combat this problem include use of free-standing containers (E and F), opening of planting areas in the concrete, or raised planting areas—all to accommodate trees, shrubs, or bedding plants.

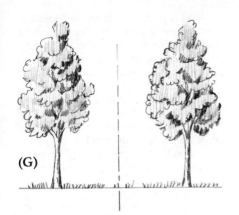

(G)

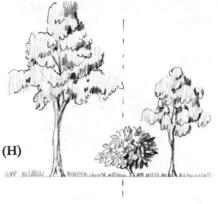

(H)

Perhaps the one element that makes the greatest contribution to any garden regardless of size is the careful thought (or design) devoted to it. Some of the components of design are balance, scale, color, texture, dimensions, and harmony.

(F)

Since the same design principles apply, equally, to the small or portable garden as to the larger, stationary one, the plan is of a primary importance. Within the plan, consider balance first. For a successful planting, it plays an important, but unobtrusive part. Formal balance (G), most frequently used, is probably easier and more suitable than informal balance (H).

One element which seems difficult for the layman to understand is scale. The plants, the container, and the surroundings should be the proper size in relationship to each other (I). An ingredient too small in scale is insignificant, and one too large is overpowering. Center is just right.

(I)

Color can be used as a dramatic contrast to a building if tones of a contrasting color are selected. Complementary colors can be used to accent your building. If a pleasing combination is used, it can do much to make a planting attractive. Since too many colors weaken the effect, fewer colors should strengthen it. I recommend using no more than three complementary colors and one contrasting color in any container composition.

233

Even the smallest planting should have contrasting textures (J) for variety and

(J)

interest. I would suggest two for a small garden container and more for a larger planting. As with color, however, do not introduce too many textures, since this tends to weaken rather than to strengthen the composition.

There should be a variety of heights as well as textures and colors in a planter. If the planter is to be seen primarily from the front, I suggest using three heights with the tallest in the back, the intermediate one in the middle, and the low or trailing type in the front so as to achieve a softening effect.

If the container is free standing and can be seen from all sides, I would place the tallest plants in the center, the intermediates around them, and the low or trailing ones near the edge of the planter.

The pleasing relationship of the integral parts—balance, scale, color, texture, and dimension—results in a highly desirable situation which is called harmony.

The choosing of materials for your container garden is limited only by your imagination. In addition to the traditional materials like wood, terra cotta, ceramic, and concrete, others—rope, Transite tubing, plastics, and aggregates—can be both very serviceable and attractive.

But one important question should be asked before building or buying containers. What is your container supposed to achieve? After you have decided its purpose, you can select your materials. But first, study them and be sure they are a suitable choice. Perhaps the materials have to blend with a certain type of architecture. If so, the proper choice will result in a charming composition.

Wood is preferable to metal because it does not retain heat. Good containers of redwood, pine, cedar, outdoor or marine plywood can be made or bought. If you are building your own, allow for drainage and moisture absorption. Use brass bands or brass screws as fasteners to avoid rust. Most woods should have either paint or a preservative coat—nontoxic to plants— inside and out, for durability.

Redwood, rustic in feeling, is really not suitable for urbanized areas or for sophisticated settings.

Attractive garden containers can be made by facing plywood with solid color plastic material—the kind which is used on kitchen counters.

A concrete container, if not massive or heavy in appearance, can have its personality established by the plants that it holds.

Transite tubing, cut and painted, makes an attractive container (K). So do painted

(K)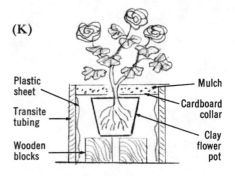

Plastic sheet

Transite tubing

Wooden blocks

Mulch

Cardboard collar

Clay flower pot

chimney flue tiles. Both can be obtained from your local terra cotta tile dealer. Use different heights and diameters for the pleasing compositions that will result.

A mulch helps considerably whether indoors or out and gives a garden a finished appearance. Many mulches contribute organic matter to the planting and most help to retain moisture and protect the plant roots from heat. Since mulches come in a large variety, you must choose for your own particular purpose.

Wood chips are rustic, good for large areas, and coarse in texture. They are suitable for rustic architecture or for an outdoor rural setting.

Peat moss and tanbark are both good, and both are dark in color. Peat moss possesses the finer texture of the two. Its texture and richness of color make it suitable for more delicate architecture and for urban settings, but it also may be used for rustic settings.

River washed stones, or slag, make attractive mulches although they do not contribute organically to the planting. These, I would say, also are more suitable for the refined, sophisticated setting (L).

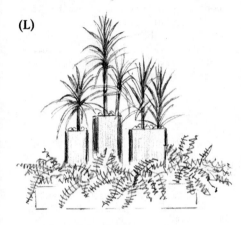

(L)

The choice of plant materials can do much to establish the success of the container garden. It can be made to look delicate, substantial, heavy, gaudy, gay, colorfully pretty, severe, plain, uncluttered, sophisticated, or whatever is desired. I have found (especially with indoor planters) that it is wise to have extra plant material to rotate and freshen the appearance of the container.

There are so many bedding plants which will not only live, but thrive in container gardens that there are almost no limits to the choice. The garden can be planted year after year with almost no repetition of plants. A good book, or garden center, will usually provide the needed information, both for interior and exterior plants. Those interested in bonsai will require special books and information about this subject.

No matter how much attention you pay to the esthetic elements and the plant material, your container garden will not flourish unless you consider the culture of the plants. They, like all other living things, have many requirements. Every plant must have light, food, and water to thrive. A good soil mixture and spraying program and good drainage contribute greatly toward healthy plants.

A regular fertilizing program will do much to make planting succeed. I would recommend, in addition to fertilizer in the original soil mixture, that a liquid fertilizer be applied at regular intervals. Since requirements vary according to the soil mixture, geographical location, and type of plants, it would be wise to consult your local garden center. Here, too, a spraying program and precise proportions for soil mixtures can be obtained.

The two most common complaints of portable container gardens, too much or too little water, can be solved in many ways. The container should be slightly raised above the ground to provide airspace. There should also be drainage holes in the bottom of the container, and they should be covered with large pieces of broken crockery. In the window box, a 1-inch layer of broken crockery should then be placed over the entire bottom surface. In a larger container, the entire bottom surface should be covered with gravel 1 inch in diameter to a depth of about 3 inches (M). For all types of containers, I place a double thickness of porous fiber glass over the material. This

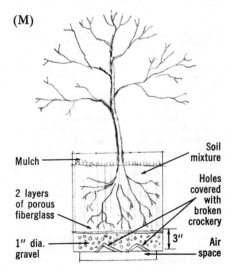

(M)

Mulch

2 layers
of porous
fiberglass

1″ dia.
gravel

Soil
mixture

Holes
covered
with
broken
crockery

3″

Air
space

helps to keep soil from washing out and discoloring the surrounding sill or terrace. Raised beds have a built-in drainage system, of course.

The best soil mixture, usually a light one, is placed directly on top of the fiber glass. Although the components will be determined by the plants you intend to use, almost all mixtures contain some combination of loam, sand, peat moss or leaf mold, bonemeal, and well-rotted manure or dried cow manure.

Culture for plants in container gardens is the same as for plants growing under more normal conditions—with added problems. Most vigorously growing bedding plants benefit from cutting or pinching back and from the removal of dead flowers or seed pods which will extend the bloom of many plants. Since they react quickly to heat, wind, and reflection, the trees and shrubs must obtain proper moisture. Watering should be stopped in freezing weather, but can be resumed on the mild winter days.

Although container gardening has been practiced since the time of the ancient Egyptians and has flourished over much of the world, those of us in the cooler climates of this country are still in the pioneering stage. With the trend toward modern architecture and the growing popularity of beautification, the interdependence of building and landscape effects is giving us more and more experience with container gardening.

⚱ ⚱ ⚱

For more information:
• *Consumers All,* the 1965 Yearbook of Agriculture. "Basic Points of Landscaping," pp. 279–282, Marilyn H. Johnson.
• Agricultural county extension agent and department of horticulture at your State university.
• Various horticultural handbooks of plants and gardens, Brooklyn Botanic Garden, Brooklyn, N.Y. 11225.
• Various Sunset Gardening books by Lane Books, Menlo Park, Calif.
• Bonsai information from Bonsai Society, c/o New York Botanical Garden, New York, N.Y. 10458.

Suggested trees for containers: Cornelian-cherry (*Cornus mas*), Washington Hawthorn (*Crataegus phaenopyrum*), honeylocust (*Gleditsia triacanthos* varieties), crabapples (*Malus* species and varieties), sweetgum (*Liquidambar styraciflua*), and Japanese pagodatree (*Sophora japonica*).

Suggested shrubs for planters: Glossy Abelia (*Abelia grandiflora*), camellias, Japanese holly (*Ilex crenata* varieties), crapemyrtle (*Lagerstroemia indica*), drooping Leucothoe (*Leucothoe catesbaei*), Oregon hollygrape (*Mahonia aquifolium*), Japanese Pieris (*Pieris japonica*), Japanese Pittosporum (*Pittosporum tobira*), Portugal-laurel (*Prunus lusitanica*), azaleas, and rhododendrons.

Suggested annuals for containers: Floss flower (*Ageratum* (dwarf)), sweet alyssum, asparagus fern (trailing) (*Asparagus sprengeri*), ornamental basil, amethyst (*Browallia*), calliopsis (dwarf), dusty-miller (*Centaurea gymnocarpa*), California poppy (*Eschscholtzia*), gazania (*Gazania splendens*), transvaal daisy (*Gerbera*), satin flower (*Godetia*), heliotrope, candytuft (Iberis), sultan's balsam (Impatiens (dwarf)), lantana, lobelia (trailing), double French marigold (dwarf), nasturtium, nicotiana (dwarf), blue cup flower (*Nierembergia*), petunia (trailing), phlox (dwarf) (*Phlox drummondi nana compacta*), rose moss (*Portulaca*), wishbone flower (*Torenia Fournieri*), verbena (dwarf), periwinkle (*Vinca*), pansy (*Viola cornuta*), and zinnia (dwarf).

Suggested colorful plants for containers: Begonia, begonia (tuberous rooted), chrysanthemum, geranium, and geranium (ivy-leaf).

Suggested textured plants for containers: Stonecrop (*Sedum*) and hens and chickens (*Sempervivum*).

Suggested foliage plants for interiors: Small plants—*Aglaonema* varieties, grape ivy (*Cissus (Vitis) rhombifolia*), Dracaena varieties, jade plant (*Crassula argentea (arborescens)*), Boston fern (*Nephrolepis exaltata bostoniensis*), heart-leaf philodendron (*Philodendron oxycardium (cordatum)*), and English ivy (*Hedera helix*).

Large plants—Madagascar dragon tree (*Dracaena marginata*), figs (*Ficus* varieties), split leaf philodendron (*Philodendron pertusum*), large leaved Mexican breadfruit (*Monstera deliciosa*), African pine (*Podocarpus macrophylla*), mock orange (*Pittosporum tobira*), and spineless Joshua tree (*Yucca elephantipes*).

Suggested plants for bonsai—many can be used, but the most popular are species of: Maples (*Acer*), hinoki cypress (*Chamaecyparis obtusa*), gardenia (*Gardenia jasminoides*), ginkgo (*Ginkgo biloba*), hollies (*Ilex*), junipers (*Juniperus*), oaks (*Quercus*), pines (*Pinus*), cherries (*Prunus*), dwarf pomegranate (*Punica granatum nana*), and zelkova.

236

Let's Keep Our
Backroads Beautiful

EUELL C. RICHARDSON

THE TERM "backroad" has taken on a new concept with the coming of our interstate highway system. This has now come to mean the place where the people are, the backroad-homesite complex. These are the roads more and more motorists are choosing, where the travel is slower paced, and a passerby may note the things which give an area its own particular individuality.

In many instances, however, the backroads expose the wayfarer to mile after mile of rilled and eroded sections of the landscape. These are tiring to a traveler and will soon come to be shunned by man as they are by the wildlife. Even the lowly earthworm avoids such areas and seeks out a more desirable place to live.

Nor is the unsightliness of an unprotected roadside area its only liability: The sediment output from it is often destructive, costly, and even dangerous.

In August of 1962, my family and I traveled from Georgia to a meeting at Cornell University in upstate New York. From there we journeyed on north to Ottawa, Canada, then turned westward through Canada to Detroit, Mich., and then south through the Midwest.

In general, we followed the backroads, seeking out historical sites, scenic drives, and other places of interest along the route. This backroad-homesite complex interested us for we were learning something of the areas' past; the older houses looked different from those of our section of the United States.

The new homes, the outmoded man-sions, the trees, flowering plants, and shrubs all showed us something of present and past practices and conditions.

As we motored along, we noted the erosion from backslopes of roadside areas. It was plain to see how much the erosion increased as the steepness of the road-bank increased. Ice crystals, called spew-frost, no doubt had sparkled beautifully in the early sun on a clear and frosty morning that followed a rain, but they had also lifted sheets of soil. Rocks had been pried from stony faces. Stones filled the road ditches in many places—some probably rolled onto the paved road surface, creating hazardous conditions.

Certain soil types had eroded much more than others had.

When the winter ended and the heavy rains of spring arrived, most of this loosened material was washed out of the ditches to culverts, stream channels, and reservoirs, causing great damage. Many prized family fishponds were muddied and partially filled with sediment. Where rocks and sediment remained in ditches, highway workers had to remove them.

These ugly—and wasteful—areas can and are being successfully treated and beautified. Grading banks to a slope low enough to accommodate the preparation of soil, planting, and cultural treatment

Euell C. Richardson is an *Agronomist* with the Agricultural Research Service, stationed at the Southeastern Tidewater Experiment Station, in Fleming, Ga.

237

Helicopter seeds grass on banks of road to Lacrosse, Wash.

is helpful for growth of vegetation. The creation of low slopes is not possible in all the cases. But where feasible, gentle slopes—which are accessible to machinery—can be more economically treated and maintained. Fertilizer and lime can be spread mechanically and incorporated into the root zone of the soil. Seeding, planting, mowing, and other maintenance can be done by machinery.

Though a good vegetative cover is the ultimate solution for the erosion and the beautification problem on roadside areas, the basic concept of what constitutes a good and desirable cover varies with the individual's viewpoint. To the agronomist and highway engineer, acceptable cover is a good protective growth of grasses, legumes, vines, or a mixture of species, adapted to the local climate, site, and exposure, that can be economically established and maintained.

The horticulturist and the garden club member would most probably desire more ornamentals and flowering species. Biologists and hunters would favor the shrubs and seed-bearing plants which provide nesting sites, shelter, and food for birds and other wildlife. The homeowner by a railroad track would most likely prefer

a screen planting which would cut the view and muffle the noise of the passing freight trains.

These viewpoints are logical and good, and plantings of all these types can be observed and enjoyed. Basically for roadside stabilization, the initial cover should be of the sod type with the others fitted into the desired pattern.

An outstanding example of plantings that stabilize and beautify is found on the scenic drive leading from Prescott to the capital at Ottawa, Canada, which will forever be a living and refreshing memory to me.

Here, the old canal of other years and a simple but modern highway paralleled each other. A well-maintained sod of green grass blanketed the landscape, with maples casting their shadows in the cool sun. Massive petunia beds, in full bloom, beautified the incline above the road the length of the drive.

In November 1965, I was on a trip in southeastern Georgia. At the outskirts of Statesboro, Ga., I observed a median area at the junction of two roads. Daylilies (*Hemerocallis*) had been planted in the median strip the year before, and appeared to be doing well.

While I was making photographs of these plantings, three city employees drove up in a truck. Two laborers got out of the truck and began to pick up beer cans and bits of scrap paper and other rubbish from the planting. When I finished photographing, I engaged the foreman in conversation. He gave the following account.

"The ladies of Statesboro dug up lily beds in their yards or home gardens and pooled the plants for the project. Choice varieties were included. A nearby dairyman gave needed manure to fertilize the area. He also supplied trucks and labor to haul and spread the manure. Highway people applied fertilizer and lime. They sent labor and equipment for soil preparation. City officials of Statesboro furnished supervision and labor for planting, mulching, and maintenance."

This was a community effort. Through full cooperation the people of Statesboro created a thing of beauty and a place to enjoy and remember.

This median type planting can and is being extended to include the roadside areas. Individuals and groups provide much of the beauty adjacent to these backroads. Well-developed lawns, properly fertilized, watered, and mowed, are attractive.

Trees, flowering shrubs, vines, and beds of flowering plantings all enhance the beauty of the area.

There are other great opportunities for group action and group enjoyment. For example, church groups could sponsor projects for improving areas adjacent to churches and cemeteries. Scouts, schools, Future Farmers of America, 4–H, garden clubs, civic clubs, and other groups could lend a helping hand to beautify sections.

Agency Assistance

Highway people could, and generally do, assist in developing suitable slopes where feasible. Agricultural agencies like the Extension Service, State agricultural experiment stations, the Soil Conservation Service, and Agricultural Research Service all supply information on species, fertilizers, and cultural treatments. The Agricultural Conservation Program can assist the landowner with beautification work off the right-of-way by cost sharing.

The total effort will lift the spirit of all who participate. Through planning and working with our hands, and giving of ourselves, we come to appreciate the thing that is created. Thus we do more than create an attractive landscape or create a thing of beauty—we develop the habit of searching for the beautiful.

In early September of 1964, my family and I spent a vacation in the Appalachian Mountains. On a Sunday, we drove up the parkway enjoying the scenery and stopping occasionally to photograph interesting scenes.

In late afternoon, we took an exit road from the summit. The exit road was paved. However, grading was such that it did not destroy the surrounding vegetation. Native shrubs, which bloomed in season, bordered the road. Overhead, limbs hung in lattices.

The drive was little more than a tunnel through a refreshingly cool forest.

A small mountain stream with an occasional waterfall paralleled the drive, which was approximately 7 miles in length.

Some eight to twelve hundred migrant urbanites were in the area. Some came just for the day, while others with tents came for the weekend or longer. Small children played in the family camping areas. Larger children played in the stream. Some panned for gold. Adults read, slept, and relaxed.

Retreat roads are a basic part of the backroad system. They are used mainly for getting away from the heat, stress, and strain of city living. They make it possible for us to get close to nature, renew our spirits and strength, and enjoy spring flowers and fall colors.

Nothing can be more pleasing to a tired, road-weary vacationer than a roadside park, beside a mountain stream or on a scenic overlook, where a picnic lunch can be enjoyed. Here the picnicker or traveler can rest, take a little needed exercise, or study nature.

Land Usually Rented

Land for roadside park areas is usually rented by the State from an adjacent landowner. In some cases, the generous highway neighbor may provide the land gratis. On occasion the land is purchased by the State or is donated to the State for these rest areas.

Rest areas vary in size, but regardless of size they are all equipped with tables and litter barrels. Some of the larger rest areas have running water, cooking facilities, and restrooms.

Many rest areas are landscaped with flowering shrubs or shrubs with colorful foliage to enhance their beauty.

Our Nation was settled along the backroads.

Then, the roads were little more than muddy trails in winter and dusty paths in summer. Now, the muddy and dusty trails have been replaced by paved roads. The people still live there.

If you want to see America in all its rustic beauty, travel the backroads, but let's keep them clean and beautiful for all of us to enjoy!

Spotlighting Natural Beauty

HUGH A. JOHNSON and JUDITH M. HUFF

THE LINE straightened, the pole bent, and the boy reeled frantically. His whole body tensed as he watched wet line rise from the water. Anticipation mounted. Then, from the murky depths, a rusty can bobbled into sight.

What might have been a squirming, splashing prize became obviously only the discarded trash from a careless consumer.

In our onrushing pursuit of economic growth, we have extracted a fearful price from the quality of our environment. Producing quantity is no problem, given our economic structure. But the pursuit of quality has never proceeded with equal vigor. Sewage, suds, and smog pollute our soil, water, and air. Residues from our planned obsolescence pollute the countryside with junkyards and rubbish.

Numerous programs, both government and private, have been designed to improve the quality of our total environment. This improvement may take many forms—restoration, preservation, and conservation. It will be difficult and expensive. American initiative and creative ability are being challenged. Meeting this challenge involves each of us, both individually and collectively.

No one professional group provides all the skills required to achieve the goals of improved esthetics in our environment. Engineers, miners, highway designers, architects, urban planners, agriculturists, landscapers, conservationists, builders, and others must play their part. Science and technology must handle the more technical aspects of quality management.

All of us are affected by our environment. We are part of it. We constantly interact with it, shape and mold it. And we are molded by it. Our environment reflects our attitudes, interests, goals, and culture. Its quality is, primarily, determined by the manner in which we relate man, nature, and man's technology. Our attitudes toward the environment are crucial to our present and future welfare. And they are changing. We are no longer willing to tolerate or accept environmental "misfits." We now see the need to strike a balance between man's manipulation of his environment and the physical resource base. Growing public support for beautification projects and pollution control demonstrates the concern of millions of citizens about the present imbalance.

This recognition of the relationships between man and nature comes at a time when our ability to change our environment has never been greater. Tempering this ability with realistic attitudes toward the use of resources can improve the quality of our environment. Converting these attitudes into positive tangible results requires assimilating esthetic criteria into planning and design.

One sticky problem with this general statement is, however, that we lack standards for acceptable esthetic levels.

Hugh A. Johnson is in charge of research on the economics of outdoor recreation and natural beauty for the Economic Research Service. A *land economist*, he has written extensively about problems of resource management and adjustment to changing economic situations.

Judith M. Huff is an *Economist* studying the economics of natural beauty for the Economic Research Service.

When is something beautiful? When is something unacceptable? And when is something adequate?

Sometimes one plant, standing alone, can provide breathtaking beauty—whether contained in a household planter or scattered over a barren landscape like the saguaro or the Joshua trees of our deserts. Blooms of the dandelion in city lawns or the thistles of farm fields are intricate examples of beauty in nature.

Puffs of pink and white from scattered red bud, cherry, and dogwood blooming in forests still winter-gray are both pleasing and inspiring.

We do not stop to analyze the beauty of a clear blue pond nestling in a wooded valley, a tree-framed vista along a country road, or the rich colors of fall reflected in a millpond pool. Instinct tells us that these are perfect combinations. They give us esthetic pleasure.

Who of us, especially the men, has failed to strain his ears and scan the skies to trace the flight of honking geese—and not sighed when they are gone?

Some environments tantalize the imagination. People travel long distances to Yellowstone Park to witness the eruptions of Old Faithful, observe the streams and pools of boiling water, and the seething springs of bubbling mud. The esthetic values of this geyser valley, largely a barren wasteland, lie in the unique environment which it provides.

Different environmental features evoke different impressions. One's perception of the city fountain, usually with carefully landscaped greenery, is quite different from one's perception of Old Faithful, surrounded by acres of salty flats.

Both types of water jets have special properties of beauty. Each observer visits them for a different purpose; his mental attitude toward each is different; and the benefit he receives from each experience is different.

The regional differences in our environment may attract some people, but repel others. Residents of flatlands and prairies frequently feel confined and hemmed in by mountains. People accustomed to hilly and wooded country are sometimes overwhelmed with the windswept vastness of the plains. Yet just as frequently, greenery

appeals to desert dwellers, and the harsh desert atmospheres appeal to persons from lush environments.

Ideas of what is acceptable and attractive in one's environment gain depth and breadth as one acquires widened experiences. People pick up ideas from other places. The small Japanese garden, for example, can be used effectively in certain restricted environments. The architectural styles indigenous to other countries have been adapted to fit some of our environments. And, of course, the Department of Agriculture sends scientists to odd corners of the world for new plant varieties.

An esthetic environment and a polluted atmosphere are mutually exclusive. Pollution abatement and control practices will increase our stock of usable resources. The intangible benefits such as improved esthetics will be reflected in a healthier, functioning environment.

Once our tendency for expanding any way we choose is moderated by planning and design practices, the quality of our environment can be improved. Freedom of expression will be augmented when man learns how to capitalize on the vast differences in geology, vegetation, and climate found in our landscapes. As Dr.

241

Contrasts in natural beauty. Old growth redwood (opposite page) in California. Sand, flora, and animal tracks in New Mexico (above).

243

Dasmann of the Conservation Foundation observed, ". . . There is as yet only a small effort to build our manmade townscapes and cityscapes to emphasize the diversity of natural landscapes . . ."

Basic esthetic criteria are also liberating keys. Form, harmony, texture, order, unity, focus, contrast, and continuity are components of beauty. They are not inflexible, unyielding, or rigid.

Blending together these principles and landscape patterns and regional distinctions can produce pleasing and, in some cases, beautiful surroundings.

The anarchy of honky-tonk businesses lining many of our secondary roads provides diversity and contrast in the environment. But principles of order and continuity are seriously violated. Diversity without order creates chaos.

Simple orderly patterns, repeated in a variety of landscape settings, create monotony and visual boredom. Designs native to New England spread to Florida. Those designed for California spread to New York. Little attempt is made to integrate site or region into building styles.

The short grass country, the ranges and the deserts, the mountains and the western slopes, each have their peculiar beauty.

Tidewater Virginia, the Carolina piedmont, the bayous of Louisiana, the vast plains of Texas and the Southwest, all have a basic beauty from which man can build his environment.

Frank Lloyd Wright, a noted architect, paid especial attention to site, purpose, function, and materials. His own homes, one built in the rolling hills of southwestern Wisconsin, the other built in the arid desert of Arizona, are very different. The character of the surrounding terrain determined the features and design of both homes. They are integral parts of their different environments. They are in harmony with their sites so that the site and structure seem to be one, interacting and intensifying the characteristics of each.

A ranch-type bungalow facing a New England village common, a widow's walk on an Ohio home, or a Dairy Belt gambrel barn in Florida jar one's sense of the appropriate. But an A-frame house in the ski country or a ranch-style home upon the

The flight of honking geese moves us all.

A mailbox becomes a thing of beauty.

Plains seem to fit their surroundings; they are a part of the environment—graceful, not disgraceful.

The Church of the Resurrection is surrounded by tenements in the heart of Harlem, New York City. The triangular shape of the sanctuary jutting forth from two rectangular structures provides diversity and interest in an otherwise dismal environment. This church is a source of inspiration to all who see it.

In agriculture, rectangular boundaries, clean, straight furrows, and checkerboard squares appeal to one's sense of order and balance. They are good farming practices in certain areas. But, if these same orderly patterns are applied to rugged terrain, erosion results. Sweeping curves and furrows following the contours of the rugged terrain control erosion. They were determined by the nature of the terrain and by man's need to work with the natural formations.

The clean, straight lines of cornfields sweeping across the Plains add contrast and diversity. Yet, great expanses of these, emphasized by the sameness of the environment, can also create visual boredom. Sweeping, curving lines found in more rugged terrain are less apt to become boring. The variety of landscape which frames them maintains one's interest.

The esthetic sensitivity that we retain, restore, and integrate into our environment is one measure of our social and cultural maturity.

Conflicts among goals for esthetics, economy, and efficiency should be expected. Yet, these tensions will subside as we are able to demonstrate how the goals complement one another.

The task of blending goals for beauty with existing situations lies before us all. We have the resources. We have the talent. We have the opportunity.

Will we meet the challenge?

245

Our Land's Golden Splendor: Beauty and Bounty Together

GLADWIN E. YOUNG

CONTOUR farming has long become a hallmark of soil conservation, a symbol of good husbandry, a creator of natural beauty, and a protector of the earth's great bounty.

Terraces and stripcropping on the contour are now an accepted technique for managing water that runs off farms and fields. It is a way of intercepting surface water which, uncontrolled, would erode away hillsides and send fertile soil down streams and rivers in times of floods.

Alternate strips of grain and grass following the contours of the landscape are subjects for the artist's canvas and at the same time protectors of the Nation's basic resource—protectors against soil erosion that robs land of its productivity, pollutes our streams with mud, and shortens the useful life of our reservoirs.

Rarely Out of Sight

When you fly from one end of this country to the other, you are seldom out of sight of soil conservation measures. In the more abundant rainfall areas, terraces are in evidence upon the hills. In the Great Plains, golden strips of wheat and fallow land conserve the moisture and help to prevent wind erosion.

When you drive through the countryside, you see some of the 2 million farm ponds which make water available at the right time and in the right place.

When you seek a day in the country for recreation, you see firsthand the trees and shrubs that have been planted as shelter-belts and windbreaks to prevent wind erosion, conserve moisture, and to create nesting places and feed for wildlife. As an added bonus all these conservation measures add to the beauty of the landscape.

America is beautiful because of what man has done to assure the continuation of nature's abundance. Nature itself without man's stewardship has rarely been productive enough to meet man's needs.

Giant Quiltwork

This country of ours could not be beautiful to 195 million people if it were still untouched, unspoiled wilderness.

The beauty of America and its bounty go hand in hand. Man's stewardship that protects the one enhances the other.

A countryside of well-kept farms and villages, grass-covered rolling fields, a quiltwork of orchards and cropland, tree-covered hillsides and streambanks—all this we have come to know as "America the Beautiful."

This is indeed the splendor of America because it reflects man's ability to work along with nature.

This is the landscape that produces our clear streams and steady water supply. This is the land that produces so abundantly our food, our clothing and shelter, and that makes beauty a meaningful human experience.

꽃 꽃 꽃

Gladwin E. Young was *Associate Administrator* of the Soil Conservation Service from November 1953 to April 1967.

Contour strip cropping near Poy Sippi in Wisconsin.

But just as beauty and bounty go hand in hand, so do ugliness and poverty.

Duststorms arise from land made barren of its vegetation. Floods begin with water racing down the slopes of gullied and wornout fields to join the torrents from denuded forests and to spread ruin across the fertile valleys.

Poverty begets ugliness, and ugliness begets poverty.

The Nation's efforts to assure successful farms and healthy rural communities are integral parts of the war on poverty and a crusade for a beautiful America.

For those who are able to make longer journeys across the country, there are opportunities to enjoy the diversity of scenery of the great desert areas, the majestic mountain scenery, the national forests and parks. And for a relatively few people the wilderness areas offer a particular kind of beauty.

These also are part of the beauty of America that must be preserved.

Most of the land in the United States—around three-fourths of it—is privately owned or operated. Private ownership has created a heritage of pride in the appearance of properties. But a big job still remains to further enhance beauty through erosion control and pollution control, fire control on forests and woodlands, flood control, reforestation, adequate rural development, beautification of roads and highways, and the correction of other blemishes upon the landscape.

Daffodils grown on the contour, nursery at Multnomah City, Oreg. Mt. Hood is in the background.

Landowner Decisions

Decisions about the use and management of most of the Nation's landscape are made by millions of landowners and operators—not by public agencies. This means that the public can express its interest in how the landscape is used only as it finds ways to cooperate with these millions of owners.

Fortunately, much experience has already been gained about effective ways to do this. For more than a generation a nationwide soil and water conservation program has been gaining momentum under the leadership of local soil conservation districts, with help from the U.S. Department of Agriculture.

A nationwide crusade for developing a deeper appreciation of America's natural beauty would be relatively meaningless if it did not place first and foremost emphasis on the splendor and beauty that already exist, and that can be further enhanced through soil conservation measures on the productive farmlands, woodlands, and grazing lands across the Nation. The beauty of the deserts, the mountains, the wilderness, and swamps and marshes are part of the total beauty of the country only because they contrast with the bountiful lands on which life itself depends.

We need not give up one for the other. We have both. We need to keep them in proper perspective as we seek to find ways to enhance these great values.

248

Good Manners in the Outdoors

CHARLES H. STODDARD

WE GOT UP early and checked out of our motel. My wife Pat, the boys Mac and Jeff, and I were on the last leg of our drive from Washington, D.C., to Wolf Springs Forest, our summer home at Minong, Wis.

As we ate our breakfasts, we noticed a waitress delivering a neatly wrapped picnic lunch. The idea hit Pat and me about the same time: "Let's have the waitress fix a picnic lunch for us. Then we can save time on the road and reach Wolf Springs Forest that much sooner."

Soon we were rolling along; minutes and miles were ticking. By noontime the picnic lunch became the prime topic of conversation. It wasn't long before we saw a road sign, "Picnic area 2 miles ahead."

The boys were first to spot the turnoff sign, and we headed toward a wooded area which, from our distance, seemed cool, clean, and inviting. But that was before we got up close and surveyed the grounds. You never saw such a mess in your life—picnic tables standing in a sea of beer cans, garbage, empty cartons, and old newspapers. We couldn't stand the place. Even the boys lost their appetites.

It made us wonder, as we drove on looking for a clean picnic spot, just how many other Americans had experienced this sort of thing, and why good manners aren't always practiced in the woods the same as at home. We wondered, too, just how the people who had made the mess, and left it, would feel if they had found it in that condition when they arrived for a picnic of their own.

When you multiply this experience of one American family by thousands, even millions, you have a major problem—that of bad manners in the outdoors.

I should add that it wasn't very many miles—and about as many minutes—when the boys spotted another wooded area off to the right of the highway. We pulled in to give it a look. It was delightful—spotless, attractive, inviting, and charming. Previous users had picked up every piece of litter, every tin can and bottle, and placed them carefully in the trash cans provided for that purpose. Even the picnic tables and benches had been wiped clean. This was the place. We ate our sandwiches, cleaned up our litter, and rolled out for Minong.

Of course, the Stoddards have not been waging a major antilitter campaign, but we have become very alert to the responsibility of all individuals to exercise good manners in the outdoors. If the minority sees a good example from the majority, then the majority will get bigger and gradually phase out the minority or reduce its ranks to a minimum. Good manners are contagious.

Bad manners, of course, sometimes take the form of criminal acts, such as desecrating private property. I recall that on one occasion we returned for a visit to Wolf Springs Forest and found our whole clearing littered with trash and beer cans. The culprits had even cleaned out the trout from our spring ponds. Because of this, I have had to display a sign at our

❦　　❦　　❦

Charles H. Stoddard is *Executive Director,* Citizens' Advisory Committee on Recreation and Natural Beauty.

235-917 O - 67 - 19

A spotless campground in the Sierra National Forest, Calif.

gate which reads, "Access by Permission Only. See Caretaker." I hope it works.

There is a better deterrent to bad manners than signs and gates—the Golden Rule. This we too often forget.

Our outdoors is growing smaller because more people are using the outdoor facilities. We find ourselves elbowing each other on the highways, in the parks, picnic areas, mountain retreats, and resorts.

Bad manners outdoors are expensive. It costs no less than $1.5 million a year to pick up litter in the national parks alone. Add dollars expended by other agencies of government—Federal, State, and local— and you can see that hooliganism, or bad manners, means that taxes go up—your taxes. One national organization has estimated collecting litter adds $1.5 billion to Federal, State, and local tax bills.

Teaching Youngsters

We all need to instill good manners in our children, not so much to please us, but to teach them the immense satisfaction of having proper consideration for the other fellow. One simple way to do it is to show your youngsters how to clean up litter and put out the campfire when you leave your campground for the next fellow. Teaching by setting the example yourself is easily the best method.

There are many ways to show good manners in the outdoors, and sometimes we need to be reminded of some of the things that we should and should not do. Maybe these tips will be helpful:

Always be careful with a fire in the woods or on the range. The thoughtful citizen will do everything he can to prevent wildfire. Fire destroys timber and grass, kills wildlife, and leaves the soil open to erosion, which results in muddy streams that kill fish. Make sure your campfire is dead out when you leave.

Extreme care and good manners are vital to the safe use of guns. Bad manners with a gun can cost someone his life, even yours. Shooting up signs, gates, locks, insulators, rural mailboxes, and other property is a wanton disregard for the rights and property of others.

As you leave your camp, why not leave a supply of firewood for the next camper?

Litterbugging at its worst is seen (top) in a roadside collection of tin cans and refuse. (Below) Boy Scouts prepared the sign and its surroundings to spur people to practice good manners while enjoying the outdoors.

Lassie, enlisted in the war on litter, drops trash in a receptacle on the Mall in front of the U.S. Capitol.

Litterbugging is extremely bad manners, on the road or off. There are laws against it. When you travel—anywhere—take a litterbag in your car. Scatter no debris along the highways or from your boat on waterways; put it in your litterbag and carry it home for disposal.

Today we have sound pollution, as well as air and water pollution. Unless you keep your radio and TV volumes low, people who seek peace and quiet in the outdoors may not find it.

Acts of friendliness on the open road, in the parks, and elsewhere all add up to more good manners, more courtesy for the other fellow. The man in trouble needs a friend. He may be out of gas or have a flat tire or a dead battery. Or he may be just plain lonesome.

Always there's need for good manners in water sports, such as boating, fishing, swimming. Boatmen who race their outboards up and down a lake, disturbing fishermen and others, are showing bad manners—lack of consideration for the other fellow. Human relationships are strained to the breaking point by this kind of conduct.

The result is strong conflicts between boating enthusiasts and the fishermen that could easily have been avoided by thoughtful outdoor manners.

If good manners are born of habits we acquire through self-discipline and by training, and bad manners spring from ignorance and thoughtlessness, then we need a national program to educate our urban citizenry in outdoor manners. Couldn't this be done in the same way that Smokey Bear has brought public awareness of forest fire danger? I think it could. Some of the antilitter campaigns we now have are helping to accomplish this in part. But the time has come to unite all civic-minded groups into a national campaign against litter before we drown our civilization in our own waste. The Citizens' Advisory Committee on Recreation and Natural Beauty stands ready to give substantial impetus to such an effort.

This little act of courtesy will be good for your soul; it will make the next camper happy, too. Above all, see that your campsite is left clean—all refuse burned or buried, cans and bottles removed.

A littered campsite is a campsite which is eliminated from further use—at least until it has been cleaned up. Or to put it in another way, try to leave your camp in the same condition in which you would like to find it.

Then there's the matter of using private lands and some public lands without permission. Good manners require that you first obtain permission from the landowner before going on private land. And, once the permission is granted, good manners dictate that you close gates, prevent litter, use care with fire, and practice rules of safety with firearms. Good manners mean privileges for the next fellow, while bad manners will keep gates shut tight.

252

Signs to Complement Natural Beauty

VIRGIL R. "BUS" CARRELL

FOR A QUICK look at the signs of our day, let's locate our credit cards, jump into the family car, and take off to see America first. On our way, allow me to point out some things about signs you might like to know.

The signs we will see are just about as varied in purpose and tone as they are in design. They welcome, plead, command, guide, remind, warn, identify, interpret, inform. Whether regulating traffic, identifying places or plants, calling attention to a bump in the road or a garbage pit in a campground, inviting the motorist to a nearby motel or restaurant, they are the numerous silent voices that help bring some order and safety to our cities, highways, and other places where the public gathers or travels.

To do these things well, good signs are designed, made, and erected with skill and according to plans. A sign is good when its function is achieved without calling attention to itself.

Notice the traffic signs, for instance. These are designed to be read at high speed. The letters must be 10 inches in height, and some are 18 inches. At 60 miles per hour, we are forced to quickly "absorb" the traffic sign message without consciously reading it. See how the use of letters, shapes, colors, and text format help us quickly comprehend. Helping, too, is the uniformity of certain signs.

To enjoy the great American outdoors, we need good traffic signs to direct us to a destination, warn of dangers along the way, and regulate the flow of traffic.

A major national effort is being made to get standard, uniform traffic control signs into use. The U.S. Department of Commerce has published a manual called *Uniform Traffic Control Devices for Streets and Highways,* which describes them and their use.

Signs other than those used for traffic control can no longer be placed along a high-speed road without special consideration of traffic control signs already there and coordination with them. In addition to the commonsense need for safety considerations on all our roads, the Highway Beautification Act of 1965 further limits the placement of signs on interstate and primary highway systems constructed with Federal aid. The purposes of the act are to protect the public investment in these highways, promote safety and the recreational value of public travel, and preserve natural beauty.

A second group of signs called identification—or sometimes information—signs identify things for us and add pleasure to a trip. At least I always like to find signs announcing a familiar name or place. A name of a river on a map can

🌼 🌼 🌼

Virgil R. "Bus" Carrell is a *Staff Assistant* in the Forest Service. He was assigned to a special project in October 1961 to review and modernize the Forest Service's sign program. Following a study of signs made and used all over the United States, he began the task of designing signs that were effective, yet in keeping with the environment in which most would be placed. His work is the basis for the new standard Forest Service signs.

Old Oregon Trail Route sign features art, clear lettering, simple design, and use of native materials.

increase anticipation, but it cannot compare with the excitement that comes with seeing the sign that says "MISSISSIPPI RIVER, mightiest of all American rivers." Anticipation is then at its peak and is (or should be) second in intensity only to the actual scene.

An identified landmark can have a special significance to the viewer. For example, a sign that identifies boundaries of the 154 national forests is welcomed by the sportsman who knows that here he can hunt, fish, or just tramp around in the forest and glades.

I once saw 35 vehicles parked near a boundary sign that identified an entrance to a national forest. It was the first day of hunting season. The hunters' tracks upon the light snow were all inside the national forest behind the sign. The sign assured them. They knew just where they were, and that they could engage here in an exhilarating hunt for deer.

Many persons have said it is also reassuring to come upon signs that identify public or semipublic authorities like those of an automobile club, State police, or the forest ranger's headquarters. We can stop at the latter to find out where

Achieving two objectives with one sign is rarely successful, but Virginia does it. This sign at the Tennessee line catches your eye with art identifying the Virginia State bird and flower and welcomes you with its clear, easily read script on a simple sign.

the fishing is good (and hope for a clue to a little known, good fishing hole!).

If the sign has an understandable purpose, is properly designed, made, and appealing to sight and emotion, it adds to the security, understanding, and pleasure of the tourist. Imagine the pleasure of entering strange country and finding an information sign that tells you what's ahead, where the tourist accommodations may be located, and rules and laws you should observe. Such a sign should be designed and located where it is safe to stop and to park off the road while reading it. Roads to and from it should be designed to let you leave and reenter the streams of traffic safely. The scenic view from the main highway should be screened with trees or shrubs to avoid risking damage to the natural lines and native beauty of the landscape.

Information signs that tell us the rules can be the most important of all signs. Fire prevention signs are a case in point. Without effective wildfire prevention on rural America's forest and range lands, the initial noticeable result when fire destroys is loss of natural beauty. Land managers know that in addition to ugly fire scars, the aftermath is also loss of payrolls, recreation pleasures, fish and game, and loss of the soil, which in turn

makes scouring, muddy, low quality waters. Clubs like 4–H, Boy and Girl Scouts, Future Farmers of America, and the fraternal or civic organizations often sponsor erection of a major fire prevention sign, supporting competent stewardship of our priceless natural resources.

Interpretive signs also appeal to sight and to the emotions. A good interpretive sign may stimulate the mind, help us to understand what we see, or help us to imagine for a minute that we are part of an important past or present event. This enriches our personal experience and makes a visit to strange lands more enjoyable. The historical sign that creates the feeling that "but for the years, I was there" has appealed to the emotions and succeeded in its interpretive mission.

The interpretive sign is the most difficult to make and requires a skilled designer. He first studies the site, then the message or the purpose. He employs many techniques. He knows that the effectiveness and attractiveness of interpretive signs are improved through good headlines, a wise choice of lettering, skillful use of artwork, and professional arrangement of shape and colors. He knows, too, that the design of the sign support and the use of these techniques should complement but never overwhelm the sign's message. The sign, its support, and its placing on the site should be designed in view of these requirements.

Such things as conservation practices, identification of breeds of stock or crops, are being interestingly indicated with

A boundary of public land is pleasingly marked, at the foot of Mt. Dana in California. The sign's shape, colors of cream on brown, trademark lettering for national forest, and arrangements of symbols and identification are standard.

HORSETHIEF PARK

Here in an earlier day,
when justice was swift, two gents
were hanged for possession of
horses without a bill of sale.

*Sketch for an interpretive sign whose dead-
pan humor is now brightening the day of
visitors to the High Rockies.*

signs. Tourists like to learn the names of crops which are unfamiliar. A well-planned sign gives Dad a good chance to tell his son, in a knowledgeable way, that that crop he's looking at is peanuts or cotton or seed grass.

The text is the most important design feature of all signs, but far more so for interpretive signs. If you think about it a minute, the text is the reason for the sign's existence. All the other features are designed to exhibit the message in its most effective and pleasing form. So the text must be readable, brief, and above all, accurate. You don't like to be misled by error or otherwise, and neither do I. The text should develop no more than one topic and have a warm tone.

The sign I saw at Horsethief Park in the High Rockies illustrates the brevity, clarity, and effectiveness that are sought in an interpretive sign.

Good headlines attract attention. For example, a sign which interprets a conservation practice, like the place of a pond in a successful farm plan, might be titled "Harvesting Raindrops" rather than "Erosion Control Project." I remember the sign that stood on a dry spot in a marshy area with the message "Swamp Regeneration." This meant a great deal to those who were reclaiming

the land for forest and wildlife habitat, but certainly not to me.

No matter what the sign's job may be, it is wise to use the best materials available at a reasonable cost. To keep costs low, signs should be uniformly standard and simple. A sign does not have to be the gaudiest, the biggest, and the most colorful to be the best one.

Signs and their supports need to be proportionate, well balanced, and constructed with materials which can stand the test of time. There are many good materials for signs and supports.

Wood has proved its worth for many years. It blends naturally with the rural environment. It is attractive, and this must be a component of all signs. It is available, easy to shape, fit, preserve, paint, color, and maintain. Wood is also inexpensive. But it must be used right.

500-Page Handbook

The *Wood Handbook,* Agriculture Handbook No. 72, is available from the Superintendent of Documents, Washington, D.C. 20402, for $2.25. Its nearly 500 pages tell the proper ways to use wood, paints, glues, and wood preservatives, among other key tips. Whatever material is used, signs must be maintained to retain their intended usefulness. Rangers have told me that a good sign, kept in good condition, will not be vandalized as readily as one that is poorly maintained.

Signs can be made to serve people in a variety of useful ways, yet complement the beauty of our environment, if there is forethought in planning, skill in execution, and if people really care. Improvements are being made in signmaking to help you to travel safely at the pace you like to go, to find the basic facilities that you need, and to learn more about our wonderful land.

I suppose the test is that if you have arrived at your destination without any difficulty and you have enjoyed the trip, the chances are that the route was well signed—not too much, nor too little, but just right.

Project Green Thumb

HAL JENKINS

WILLIE JOHN TAYLOR at long last felt that he was doing something of value for the Arkansas county where he was born and had lived for some 65 years.

As a worker-trainee in Project Green Thumb, created to combat rural poverty and rural ugliness, he is one of a corps of rural senior citizens recruited in a pilot program launched in 1966.

Taylor spoke for the 426 other Green Thumb workers when he said: "Planting to beautify our roads makes me feel that I am doing something worth while. What we do will be seen and appreciated for many years by the people who drive along our highways."

Doris Gray, Green Thumb office secretary at Trenton, N.J., developed a warm feeling for the project when the first job applicants reported. "This group of elder citizens had read about the project in the newspapers, and they crowded into the office," she said. "We didn't have enough chairs so they just stood around, waiting patiently to be interviewed.

"What impressed me most was their eagerness to be useful, to do something worth while—and actually to be needed. These men have been active and independent all their lives, and it must mean an awful lot to them to think they can still work and earn a little money."

The low-income farmers and farmer-retirees felt the same way in Minnesota. More than 218 of them applied for jobs even though only 77 could be hired.

In Oregon, two applicants—one 69 and the other 76—proved that having a green thumb wasn't necessary. In fact,

it wasn't necessary to have a thumb at all. Both had lost a thumb in accidents, but they still passed their physicals and joined the crews of roadside beautifiers.

"Perhaps our major problem," said Jim Johnson, State director of the project in Arkansas, "is keeping them slowed down enough so it will not injure their health. We insist our foremen give them more than adequate rest breaks."

"Operation Green Thumb" was conceived by Dr. Blue Carstenson, formerly the executive director of the National Council of Senior Citizens. Dr. Robert McCan, then director of Older Persons Programs for the Office of Economic Opportunity and a former teacher in Boston University's School of Education, helped develop the idea.

Drs. Carstenson and McCan are now the national director and the associate director, respectively, of Green Thumb, Inc., a subsidiary of the National Farmers Union. And Henry E. Wilcox is the national State director.

The program is guided by a National Advisory Committee of 11 headed by U.S. Senators Gaylord Nelson of Wisconsin and Harrison A. Williams, Jr., of New Jersey. Ex officio members include five representatives of the Department of Agriculture.

The project was approved late in 1965, and Federal funds were provided in February of 1966. The U.S. Office of

ٷ   ٷ   ٷ

Hal Jenkins is *Chief* of the Information Services Branch, Information Division of the Soil Conservation Service.

Campfire festivities along the Crow Wing Trail, Huntersville, Minn. Green Thumb work crews helped to clear and beautify this trail.

Economic Opportunity allocated $768,000 to carry out pilot demonstration projects in some selected counties of New Jersey, Arkansas, Minnesota, and Oregon. Indiana was added as the fifth State. The Federal allocation is nearly matched by $680,000 in contributions from the State highway departments and other governmental agencies, the Farmers Union, and other groups cooperating in the program.

In Minnesota, for example, about 43 agencies, organizations, and officials are cooperating.

Dr. Carstenson says Green Thumb's basic objectives are:

1. To provide employment to men in poverty. (The average family income per year of Green Thumb workers is $980.)

2. To provide employment for older men, on a part-time basis, and demonstrate that these men can work, want to work, need to work, and ought to have the opportunity to work.

3. To beautify the roadways and parks,

as part of the national emphasis inspired in large part by Mrs. Lyndon B. Johnson.

4. To help public agencies, such as highway departments, to see the wisdom of changing employment policies so that older men can work on a part-time or a seasonal basis.

In its first year, Green Thumb operated in 22 counties having concentrations of older farmers in the below $1,700 individual income bracket, which is the limit for qualification.

Most participants are 65 or older, although some younger than 65 are still accepted. Each applicant must pass a physical examination. The men work 3 to 4 days a week and can earn up to a maximum of $1,500 a year. They receive several days training before going out on the job—in proper planting methods, operating equipment, pruning, safety practices, and the like. Worker-trainees receive $1.25 to $1.50 an hour. A foreman receives $1.50 to $1.75 per

258

hour and operates a car pool to transport his crew to and from work.

In Arkansas, the first State to get into operation, Green Thumbers planted trees every 20 feet along the right-of-way of a 40-mile stretch of road. In all, they planted 150,000 trees.

In Minnesota, Green Thumb crews planted 105,000 trees, cut several miles of brush that obscured views of two lakes, and cleared and cleaned up along the 40-mile Crow Wing Saddle and Canoe Trail.

In New Jersey, the crews concentrated upon planting and caring for shrubbery in medial strips of highways to reduce headlight glare for safer night driving.

Those are just a few of the tangible accomplishments reported in the third quarter of the first year.

What about the future of Project Green Thumb?

"Naturally, we hope to continue and to expand the work," Carstenson said.

"More than 1 million older and retired farmers over 65 badly need additional income. We have proved they can and want to work; that they can carry out projects of value to the public."

Director Carstenson said an important byproduct of the project is developing new skills among the oldsters so that, once the age-prejudice barrier is overcome, they can obtain useful part-time employment as gardeners, nurserymen, landscapers, and similar work. Another is rural opportunity loans to help them set up nurseries to grow plants for future beautification work.

It can safely be said of Project Green Thumb that it is helping to alleviate poverty among our rural senior citizens, stimulating the self-pride and economy of small towns, beautifying the highways, retraining oldsters to a useful trade, and providing motorists with travel pleasure.

Healing Strip Mining Scars

MAURICE K. GODDARD

ALTHOUGH the extraction of minerals is important to our material well-being, it is the duty of government, industry, and the people to protect the land from surface mining damage in order to maintain a livable and pleasant environment.

This case study illustrates how planning procedures, developed and carried forward to fruition by government, industry, and local communities, can erase the scars of strip mining operations and restore a pleasing appearance to a thoroughly blighted area.

In the beginning, the anthracite region of northeastern Pennsylvania was a rich, mountainous land. It was spectacularly beautiful with deep forests and countless clear, sparkling streams.

Deep underground mining was conducted in this region for over 100 years. Great masses of debris, consisting of the material removed in driving passages to reach coal seams and refuse from the breakers, accumulated around the collieries. This material encroached upon the surrounding communities.

After the transition to the open pit mining of coal deposits which began in the early 1930's, the appearance of the

ໜ   ໜ   ໜ

Maurice K. Goddard is *Secretary of Forests and Waters*, Commonwealth of Pennsylvania.

landscape began to change very rapidly.

A vast amount of the surface material which was stripped away to expose and extract the underlying coal was spread over wide areas. Today a visitor to the region sees that large portions of this once bounteous and beautiful land have been severely damaged by years of mining operations which have despoiled about 24 percent of the total land area. Open pit mining has accounted for 76 percent of the 112,928 acres of the land surface which have been affected by coal mining activities.

Although landscape beauty and prosperity should go hand in hand, visitors and industry encouraged to locate in the anthracite region were repelled by the scarred landscape, eroded spoil banks, waste dumps, burning culm piles, and polluted streams. The detrimental effects of surface mining offset the many favorable factors which could bring about an industrial development and economic growth and thus contribute to the prosperity of the region and the happiness of those working and living there.

Since steps have been taken to deal effectively with the scars of mining operations, the economic growth of the region has been stimulated. Industry and people have been attracted to the area in ever increasing numbers. A total of 750 new industries have located here since 1946. Job opportunities have been created for 56,326 people with a payroll of over $214 million.

Trees have always been the objective in the reclamation and improvement of surface mined areas. Their propagation still stands as one of the best methods of attaining an improved economic benefit by restoring the natural beauty of an area which has been very extensively disturbed by strip mining.

A need to enhance and restore the esthetic beauty of the anthracite region, in order to further its economy and to provide an attractive, wholesome, and satisfactory environment, was recognized early in 1961 by the Pennsylvania Power & Light Co. Financed by funds provided by the company, "Operation Trees" was developed in cooperation with the Northeastern Forest Experiment Station.

The Forest Service technical personnel started a three-phase research study of the problem. They located, classified, and mapped all areas disturbed by surface mining in the anthracite region extending from Carbondale, near the northeast corner of Lackawanna County, to Lykens in Dauphin County. Disturbed areas were classified and shown on 41 detailed maps as strip mine bank or spoil piles from deep mining operations. Towns of over 5,000 population formed the basic unit where possible. County and regional maps were also prepared. The areas were further classified on the basis of the

Strip mined area near Trevorton, Pa.

amount of natural vegetation present, as well as their suitability for screening. Roadside plantings would not only beautify the highways, but would also screen bleak spoil piles from view.

Areas visible from the main highways were outlined on the maps and then were classified as to whether roadside screens would be effective. If not, cover plantings on the spoils were designated.

Revegetation research was undertaken under controlled conditions upon mine spoils to determine growth, survival rate, and suitability for cover and screening.

Results of the three-phase study have provided information and principles for tree planting upon spoil banks in the anthracite region and also have indicated where additional studies are required.

The spoil banks are now classified into four types, according to the characteristics of the material and acidity. A survey which included height measurements, vigor, and survival counts was made of the species established on graded spoils and related to individual coal seams. Investigation of the oldest tree plantation has disclosed that some spoils will produce timber products, and that the tree survival is generally better with spring planting. It also was found that certain species are suited to certain spoil types, as European white birch for extremely acid sites. Species selection is important on good sites to produce commercial timber, and is essential on poor spoils for obtaining the best cover.

These studies have demonstrated that one solution to the problem of recapturing the beauty of the anthracite area is the planting of trees which will shield unattractive spoil areas, giving the impression of great wooded areas. Evergreens, which provide year-round cover, are the most suitable for this purpose.

Screening and the small amounts of cover planting will later have to be followed by extensive cover planting and by a physical reworking of the land—grading and leveling.

Up to September 1966, the Pennsylvania Power & Light Co. has spent about $100,000 on "Operation Trees" and has furnished nearly 625,000 seedlings for this ambitious project.

It is estimated that 100 million seedlings will be needed in the anthracite area to plant all the disturbed areas to recommended standards. The company has supported studies in 41 demonstration areas utilizing 14 tree species which include 10 types of conifers, 3 hardwoods, and hybrid poplar clones to determine the performance of these forest tree species on strip mine spoils.

The Pennsylvania Department of Forests and Waters supplied all the hybrid poplar cuttings which were used in these experiments.

Community Support

Planting of seedlings which began in 1962 has received the cooperation and endorsement of entire communities, as well as government agencies. Participants in plantings include civic, business, and social groups, coal operators, landowners, merchants, unions, and youth groups like school classes, Girl Scouts, Boy Scouts, 4–H Clubs, Future Farmers of America, and Future Homemakers.

After 3 years, enthusiastic interest in the tree planting project has been sustained, and the screening phase of the program is about completed. The project promises to bring about a remarkable improvement in the area's appearance during the early 1970's.

The company is embarking on a research program for the use of a mechanical process that will seed mixtures of grasses, legumes, and trees.

Studies will also be continued on the adaptability of several types of grasses and trees on spoil piles.

The first tree plantings on anthracite spoils were made during 1938 by Stanley Mesavage, a forester, for the Susquehanna Collieries Co. A preliminary survey of the problem was also undertaken in 1940 by C. E. Ostrom of the Allegheny Forest Experiment Station, followed by the experimental greenhouse studies on spoil acidity and fertility conducted by William E. McQuilkin in 1943 at the Northeastern Forest Experiment Station.

These latter studies were concurrent with studies made by Joseph Paddock, forester, with the Wilkes-Barre Chamber of Commerce during the early 1940's.

In 1944, the Pennsylvania Department of Forests and Waters initiated experimental plantings. After the passage of the first Anthracite Strip Mining and Conservation Act for the Commonwealth of Pennsylvania in 1947, the department administered the tree planting required under the law.

A total of 200,000 trees were planted by the department of forests and waters between 1944 and 1950. Results of planting could not always be evaluated due to failures and losses occurred in restripping. Some 25 to 30 percent of the volunteer plantings, during the 1964–65 seasons, have been affected by restripping and the relocation of highways and industrial sites in revegetated areas.

Research Unit Set Up

About 1955, the Pennsylvania Department of Mines and Mineral Industries began to administer the planting of trees on anthracite spoils. During the 1963–66 period, the department supervised the planting of about 3 million trees. Over 1 million were planted in spring of 1966.

In 1957, the Pennsylvania Department of Forests and Waters, in cooperation with the Northeastern Forest Experiment Station and the School of Forest Resources of Pennsylvania State University, formed a research committee to solve the problems of tree planting on coal mine spoils. This committee now includes the Pennsylvania Department of Mines and Mineral Industries, Pennsylvania Game Commission, Pennsylvania Conservation Association, Izaak Walton League, West Virginia Pulp & Paper Co., and Pennsylvania Coal Mining Association.

It has made important contributions concerning the knowledge and methods of strip mine revegetation. Although this committee's research has been primarily directed toward bituminous revegetation programs, the work has been very closely coordinated with the anthracite area's revegetation program and has aided it.

A total of 6,625,000 trees are estimated to have been planted on anthracite spoil piles since 1938 by the U.S. Forest Service, the State department of mines and mineral industries, the State department of forests and waters, by industry, and by community groups.

About 20 percent or 22,400 acres of the disturbed areas in the anthracite region of Pennsylvania has been revegetated by natural processes. Screen plantings of 1,000 trees per acre have reclaimed another 600 acres in other areas.

I feel that our knowledge and progress in the reclamation and revegetation of mined areas has greatly improved. However, much research in these fields needs to be done before the problem of revegetating mine spoils is solved.

We need a greater knowledge of the physical and chemical characteristics of spoil materials. Our knowledge of the species of trees, shrubs, herbs, grasses, and methods for their establishment on highly acid spoils must be enlarged. Active research in this direction is being continued by personnel of the Northeastern Forest Experiment Station at Kingston, Pa., assisted by industry, State agencies, and private groups.

For further reading:

Czapowskyj, Miroslaw M., and McQuilkin, William E., *Survival and Early Growth of Planted Forest Trees on Strip Mine Spoils in the Anthracite Region.* Forest Service Research Paper NE–46, 1966.

Davis, Grant, Ward, W. W., and McDermott, R. E., *Coal Mine Spoil Reclamation Symposium, Scientific Planning For Regional Beauty and Prosperity.* The Pennsylvania State University, University Park, Pa. 16802, 1965.

Frank, Robert M., *Screen and Cover Planting of Trees On Anthracite Mine Spoil Areas.* Forest Service Research Paper NE–22, 1964.

Heddleson, Milford R., Farrand, Edward P., and Ruble, Ralph W., *Strip Mine Spoil Reclamation.* The Pennsylvania State University, University Park, Pa. 16802, 1964.

Limstrom, G. A., and Merz, R. W., *Bibliography of Strip Mine Reclamation.* U.S. Department of Agriculture, Washington, D.C., 1963.

Research Committee on Coal Mine Spoil Revegetation In Pennsylvania, *A Guide For Revegetating Bituminous Strip Mine Spoils in Pennsylvania.* Northeastern Forest Experiment Station, 6816 Market Street, Upper Darby, Pa. 19082, 1965.

Ward, W. W., *Revegetation of Areas Affected by Mining.* Governor's Conference on Natural Beauty, The Pennsylvania State University, University Park, Pa. 16802, 1966.

The Countryside

Neighbor With a Helping Hand
... for Conservation

HORACE D. GODFREY

NO MATTER how many times I may fly over the foothills of the Blue Ridge Mountains in North Carolina, my mind's eye always shows me the eroded red slopes of overfarmed cotton land I knew as a boy. The contrast with what I see today is a joy to behold.

Today, the whole vista is in shades of green, interspersed with the familiar red soil of tilled fields, but with almost no ugly gullies and hardly any scars left to show that the gullies were ever there.

A prime example is the area of Cleveland, Lincoln, and Rutherford Counties, with good green sod by the square mile, augmented by lush cover crops.

The mule is gone. Beef and dairy herds and hundreds of thousands of laying hens provide high-quality food for the millions of people who live and work in the industrial - commercial - agricultural Piedmont Carolinas.

This changeover did not just happen, of course. People made it happen; people aided by programs and Federal funds.

Prominent among the people were the Agricultural Stabilization and Conservation (ASC) committeemen, men like Charlie Hamrick of Cleveland County, who administer the conservation and land use adjustment programs, with vast effect upon the face of the land.

The story of Charles James Hamrick, chairman of the Cleveland County ASC Committee, is one of dedicated service and effective work toward a better agricultural tomorrow for Cleveland County and is generally representative of over

9,000 county ASC committeemen in America. These committeemen use their time and influence in huge quantities, mostly without recompense except for the satisfaction of seeing their work bear fruit.

Cotton was king for many years in the Carolina Piedmont. But the boll weevil along with the surplus problem called for a lot of changes.

In 1967, these Piedmont counties have only about a fourth as much cotton acreage as in 1948. The transition has cost millions of dollars and untold man-years of work and planning by people like Charlie Hamrick. It had to be done, and the doing augurs well for the future.

Hamrick is a big man. He is losing his hair, and he likes to wear bib overalls and chew plug tobacco. He doesn't look like the executive you picture as board chairman of a million-dollar-a-year business. But that is what he is as chairman of the county ASC committee.

The million dollars goes largely into the job of diverting land from surplus crops to soil-conserving uses, helping to bridge the economic gap caused by giving up income of cash crops, and spending money to establish conserving crops. Some of it is used to cost-share with the farmer expensive soil-saving work like terracing, stripcropping, and the establishing of cover crops and trees.

🌼   🌼   🌼

Horace D. Godfrey is the *Administrator* of the Agricultural Stabilization and Conservation Service.

Hamrick and his fellow county committeemen, Otis Royster of Lawndale, the vice chairman, and Charles Goforth of Kings Mountain, are responsible for expending the funds to meet the objectives stated by law fairly and equitably.

But program cost figures and the direct benefits derived do not take into account the immeasurable good done gladly by Chairman Hamrick on a 7-days-a-week basis (ASC committeemen are paid per diem only for the time while they are in official session).

"Kind of hard, if not impossible, to separate what I do as committee chairman from normal, everyday neighboring with the folks here in Boiling Springs (his hometown) and this end of the county," is his modest description of his day-to-day activities.

Actually, to his neighbors and friends he is the final authority on ASC program interpretations, and to walk down the street with him, ride down the highway, or stop by a favorite hangout for farmers is to witness these calls for assistance. Even at church on Sunday he is still the ASC committeeman, as well as a good citizen and helpful neighbor.

Hamrick was first elected a community

ASC committeeman in 1938 in neighboring Cherokee County, S.C., where he has operated a farm for many years. He has served continuously since that time on an ASC committee, the last 9 years on the Cleveland County committee, about a year as chairman.

His own background in education stands him in good stead, too, as a committeeman and community leader. Graduated from Wake Forest College with a bachelor of science degree, Hamrick taught school for 9 years. He quit in the spring of 1942, devoting his full time to farming during World War II.

But Hamrick couldn't stay away from teaching for long. When World War II veterans began returning to his county, many desired to begin farming, but lacked the know-how, so Hamrick was persuaded to pitch in and help. More than 150 young men came under his guidance during a 7-year period, and one of them, G. Gilbert Greene, told me, "He was just like a daddy to us in the training class. I don't know what I would have done without this training."

Greene milks 54 cows in his one-man grade A dairy operation and has 179 acres in pasture. Hamrick shares Greene's

Strip cropping in Springwater Township, New York State.

265

enthusiasm for the conservation work he accomplishes with Agricultural Conservation Program (ACP) assistance.

"Going from row crops to pasture, trees, or some other conservation practice is an expensive proposition from two directions," Hamrick commented. "In the first place, it costs a lot of money right off to establish permanent pasture—$50 or more an acre, depending upon existing conditions. And during the time this is all taking place, that land isn't bringing in any income.

"So the ACP has to step in and give the farmer a hand."

Fortunately, there are Charlie Hamricks all over America, helping administer this conservation effort. Their effects can be seen wherever you look and can be felt wherever you live.

Reserving Open Space
So Cities May Breathe

ARTHUR A. DAVIS

DURING the next generation America will have to build as many homes as have been built in the previous 10 generations. A large majority of these homes will be built in the urban regions of the country where two out of three Americans now live. By the year 2000, three out of four of us will live in these urban concentrations. We have become an urban nation.

But although our suburbs face tremendous development and our metropolitan areas even now are pushing out at the rate of around 3,000 acres a day, little thought has been given to the land. Haphazard growth has taken its toll. Lands of unique scenic and historic value have been stripped. Prime farmland has been lost at an accelerating rate, even where there is a good supply of other land available for urban development.

Lands and waters for recreation have been lost. Marshes have been filled in for homes and for industry. And forested uplands have given way to accommodate new subdivisions.

Continued, haphazard urban growth poses a basic question for both town and country: How can we provide in our crowded urban areas of the future a place for nature and a place for man? This chapter will tell some of the positive steps which are being taken.

County and city action has expanded dramatically in the past 20 years. In 1942, total local expenditures for park and recreation stood at $128 million. Two decades later in 1963 these expenditures had risen to nearly $1 billion.

In an average year, however, only a third of the local expenditures were for permanent improvements like land and buildings. Maintenance and operations needs overshadowed all other costs, and little was left for new acquisitions. Land was being acquired, but hardly enough to keep up with growing recreation demand, let alone meeting the projected needs of the future. We estimate that we are several million acres short of meeting minimum acreage open space standards for the

Arthur A. Davis is *Acting Director* of the Land and Facilities Development Administration, Department of Housing and Urban Development. Within this organization is the Open Space Land program, which he directed until late 1966.

266

increased urban populations of the 1970's and the 1980's.

The private response to the deterioration of the natural environment has been varied. Some private developers have been guilty of a lack of respect for the land. Monotonous rows of houses are a familiar sight in every metropolitan area.

Happily, all developers don't act that way. Robert Simon and James Rouse are two who had a vision of a better form of human settlement: Planned, privately financed new towns with their own public facilities and open space. This idea was not very easy to sell.

Simon looked to a long list of the major financial institutions in the country for support. They didn't think the American people were ready for such a development. But finally he found support. The result? Reston, a pace-setting new town, 18 miles west of Washington, D.C., on 6,800 acres of rolling woodland and pasture. Reston will be home for 75,000 within a few decades. It is handsomely designed around

several villages and has 14 percent of its land as permanent open space.

Not far away, in Columbia, Md., James Rouse hopes to create a new town for over 125,000 people on 14,000 acres. This will be within easy reach of both Washington and Baltimore. Other examples of new towns include Irvine, on the 93,000-acre Irvine Ranch at the site of the new University of California campus; and Clear Lake City, on ranch land near Houston, Tex., adjoining the NASA installation, with future expansion plans for a population of 200,000.

Cluster developments are generally similar. In common with new towns they vary densities so that buildings are concentrated on part of the property, leaving a maximum of open space for enjoyment of the residents.

Some communities require that new subdivisions dedicate a certain percent of land to parks. Others have zoning laws flexible enough to permit variation in density within a single tract.

Pennypack Park, part of Philadelphia's Fairmount Park system, leaves a narrow strip of open park land amid large areas of urban expansion.

In addition to the farsighted developer, other private organizations and individuals have played a key role in the effort to preserve the natural environment. Organizations like Nature Conservancy have saved hundreds of valuable natural areas through gift or purchase.

Private citizens have also played a critical role in preserving the environment. The Regional Plan Association has estimated that roughly a third of the public open space land in the New York metropolitan region came from private donors.

Scenic Easements

Some citizens have found gifts of scenic easements a desirable form of land philanthropy. Donation of a scenic easement means that current or future owners of the property can make full use of the site as long as they do not impair its scenic beauty. A variation on this is donation of land subject to life estate. Under this provision the land reverts to the public upon the death of the owner.

Donations of land or interest in land is encouraged by our tax laws. They may be included, up to certain limits, in the lists of charitable contributions which can be deducted from the Federal income tax. Also, several States, including New York and Maryland, permit reduction in property tax in return for donation of scenic easements on selected properties. Landowners have taken advantage of this provision in the Maryland area opposite Mount Vernon on the Potomac River.

New York and New Jersey passed large bond issues in the 1960's to purchase State parks and assist communities in buying local open space. These were followed by Pennsylvania's "Project 70" and California's $150 million park bond issue. Washington State, Rhode Island, and other States also have local assistance programs.

The Federal Open Space Land program was created in 1961 and expanded in 1965 to help communities purchase and develop urban open space land. Several years before, the Urban Planning Assistance program was initiated to help cities, counties, and States plan for future urban growth and development. Under this program, State and local open space plans can

be prepared as part of comprehensive plans. Both the open space and the urban planning programs are administered by the Department of Housing and Urban Development.

In 1965, two new programs were created which help communities and States acquire open space within and outside of urban areas. One was the Land and Water Conservation Fund, administered by the Department of the Interior. The Department deals only with State governments, who in turn may assist localities in buying and developing open space land. The second program is the "Greenspan" operation of the Agriculture Department's Cropland Adjustment Program which assists State and local governments in purchasing and developing excess cropland to remain in permanent open space uses.

With this Federal and State help, communities are no longer alone in their efforts to preserve the quality of their natural environment. The extent of this assistance is illustrated by the Open Space Land program, which has made 777 grants totaling $106 million to help acquire over 222,000 acres of open space land in communities in some 40 States.

Model Watershed

"Assunpink" is an Indian name for "Stony Waters." This is the name of a 58,000-acre watershed in the center of the eastern megalopolis—the urbanizing region extending from Massachusetts to Virginia. A few years ago it was subject to erosion, flooding, and was rapidly being urbanized. It was not an asset to neighboring Trenton, N.J., through which its streams emptied.

In 1957, local farmers interested the Soil Conservation Service in undertaking a model watershed program under Public Law 566. Almost a decade later, in 1966, work began on antierosion projects, including 11 small dams to reduce flooding. The total cost will be $7 million. The plan is one of the most diversified in the Nation. It was the joint product of the State, 2 counties, 10 townships, and the Federal Government.

The Assunpink watershed work was supplemented by the Open Space Land

268

program which made a $2 million grant to the county to help acquire 2,346 acres of open space. Grants were also made to two of the local townships to preserve 300 acres for local parks.

Joint Federal, State, and local action should make this watershed a center for recreation and a model of conservation in the center of the most densely developed State in the Union.

Santa Clara County, Calif., is part of the richest farming area in the country. It is also one of the fastest developing: In 13 years, its population nearly tripled. To preserve prized agricultural lands, the county has undertaken a variety of measures. One, which has enjoyed limited success, was to zone 100,000 acres for exclusive agricultural use and create an agricultural greenbelt that would separate and penetrate urban communities. Thousands of acres of this farmland have been urbanized by being annexed by a neighboring city, but much land remains open.

Santa Clara County has also taken other measures to preserve its natural features. With Federal help over a period of years it has extended several park chains.

One of these parks, Coyote Creek Park Chain, will eventually extend about 18 miles between San Jose and a large reservoir. It will combine streamside preserves with small parks.

North of Baltimore lies a plateau surrounded by two beautiful Maryland valleys. Several years ago, the local property owners association became disturbed about the loss of their valleys to haphazard urban growth. They engaged planners to prepare a plan for their area. The result was a bold attempt to reconcile rapid growth with environmental preservation.

Their "Plan for the Valleys" called for concentration of development on the plateaus and preservation of the valley floors and slopes in low density open space uses. It proposes a broad series of steps to accomplish this objective: No sewers would be permitted in the valleys; highways would be keyed with the development pattern; traditional and new zoning techniques would be employed; and land would be purchased.

But the most advanced departure would be the creation of a local real estate syndicate, composed of local property owners.

The syndicate could purchase much of the lands in the valleys. It could finance these purchases by the acquisition, and later sale, of land on the plateau. Sale of this land would result in surplus funds since it would be intensely developed.

In essence, the syndicate would serve as a mechanism for all the owners in the area to share equitably in the costs and benefits of the plan.

I believe several conclusions may be drawn from these examples of private and public action.

First, we have both the wealth and the legal tools to preserve urban environments of grace and beauty. Ugliness is not inevitable. With a mid-1966 national wealth of $730 billion, we can afford to preserve a decent environment. We are also rich in legal tools developed in the diverse State and local laboratories in our Federal system. Some of these need to be sharpened and improved; but we have only begun to use those we already have.

The second relates to the theme of the book: The importance of the individual's relationship to the environment which sustains him. In the age of big institutions, the individual still has a critical role to play in preserving a decent environment. Local apathy will mean defeated bond issues, behind-the-scenes zoning deals, and insensitive planning. But a vocal and informed local demand for a better environment will spur local officials who may have given very little thought to the problem.

To be fully effective, individuals must do more than join a single-shot protest movement—though these have their place. They must develop a continuing concern for the quality of their environment as they have for the quality of their schools. They must inform themselves and take long-term, determined action based on this knowledge. Such organizations as the League of Women Voters have done most useful work in this field. Citizen action, or lack of it, will have a critical bearing on the quality of our environment for generations to come. A decent physical environment, like freedom, is worth fighting for.

It doesn't just happen.

Second Homes

HUGH A. JOHNSON

MANY of my neighbors can hardly wait for Friday night. Warming spring weekends send them scattering like quail—to beaches, mountains, and country sites where they own or rent a second home. These second homes and the recreational satisfactions they provide lure many friends from city and suburbs until school or cold weather drives them back again for the winter.

Other people no longer are satisfied with second homes for only weekend and summer use. They want winter or year-round use as well.

The second-home movement is typical of our times. Its growth has been spurred by our new middle-class affluence, our increased leisure, and our generally improved health. We are far more footloose than the previous generations were. Our growing philosophy for enjoying life currently is emphasizing physical fitness, scenic beauty, and a return to nature. Many second homes are havens from a hectic life. They are relaxing places where people come for emotional renewal and for physical rest. Others are more or less simply refueling stops for activity-oriented people.

Owning a mortgage on only one home was enough for most of us only a few years ago. Now, several million families own second homes. Their numbers grow each year. True, some of these homes have been inherited. Most, however, have been financed by increased earnings and easier credit. Mortgages on second homes sometimes can amount to 90 percent of the cost of land and improvements.

Automobiles and good roads make it easy to get away quickly from most cities. Men I know commute 70 miles to mountain subdivisions where their families spend the summer. And these trips take them only slightly longer, night and morning, than commuting takes me to and from my home in the suburbs.

We used to think of summer homes as places to escape the heat, and of winter homes to escape the cold. Air conditioning, central heating, and modern architecture are changing these patterns. Actually, several historic New England villages now bustle with winter activities. Chic, ultramodern new villages in snow country across the Nation are capitalizing on the demand for snow-season homes.

Numerous seasonal homes are simply the physical extensions of urban living—and often without commonly accepted conveniences, safeguards, and public services. Demand for them varies with individuals, their present situation, and their longer term plans. Second homes can be luxurious or simple, isolated or part of a complex, rustic or modernistic, large or small, built for formal or informal living. A surprising number of young people buying recreation homes also have their sights upon possible future use as year-round and retirement homes.

We no longer need follow historic kinds of construction and of furnishings; for

꙳ ꙳ ꙳

Hugh A. Johnson is a *Land Economist* in charge of research on the economics of outdoor recreation and natural beauty for the Economic Research Service. He has written extensively about problems of resource management and adjustment to changing economic situations.

Modern materials and new designs add variety at moderate cost for vacation homes.

recreation uses, they may be passé. Some of the modern designs, modern fabrics, and new equipment offer whole new fields of vacation pleasure. Technology is providing new gadgets and play tools. Freedom from routine and standardization seem to be the rule. Therefore, look for what you want. Don't take large acreages or sprawling old mansions when what you want is a groovy weekend chalet. Don't buy isolation when you crave action; and don't buy into a fast game when you want peace and solitude.

So very much of your satisfactions with your second home will depend on whether you really knew what you wanted—and whether you wanted what you got.

How will the home be used? Will you want it for only short periods? Will children be using it? Is it designed for easy casual living, to capitalize on scenic strengths of your location, to benefit from climatic quirks, and as a home of which you can be house proud?

Though planned with an eye to present vacation needs, can you anticipate longer term uses and special climatic problems that relate to potential year-round occupancy? Can you protect and enhance the beauties of a stretch of beach, a mountain view, a majestic tree, or other scenic attractions?

Will the home wear well? One mother reported that "when the weather is good, our house is practically deserted. When the weather is bad, everyone is underfoot. You have to plan for play space and overflow guests and a lot of other things you don't think about at home."

Pitfalls most frequently occur because people fail to face up to their real reasons—or the absence of sound reasons—for owning a second home. One trap that catches parents is the idea that married children, grandchildren, and friends will benefit. Unfortunately, they may not want what you want. They may want other kinds of surroundings and activities you cannot provide. They may want action, or they may stay away because some other places are more popular with their groups.

If you are beginning to think about slowing down a bit, you probably won't be very happy in a big, noisy, recreation community. The constant busyness all around may disturb the atmosphere that you are seeking.

On the other hand, I'm told that too much sameness, too much quiet, and too many people with the same incomes and attitudes can make for a very boring existence. We can see this pattern already solidified in the monotonous bedroom subdivisions which girdle our cities. It shows up, too, in many seashore developments established a generation or so ago and still occupied by a preponderance of the original owners. The pattern of a safe play life composed of hobbies, shuffleboard, and release from care has been carried out well in numerous retirement villages and communities.

Rent or Visit

This may be what you want. You may have tried the alternatives. Fine. But, if you are accustomed to the activity and variety of a mixed community, the change may be bitter medicine. Renting for a few weeks or a season, or visiting friends with places like you are considering, may be a bit like dipping your toes into unknown waters. You can test whether to dive in and buy or wait for another day.

Friends and neighbors at home often build or buy their second homes in the same area and continue their satisfactory established relationships. They may take over considerable acreages and each have his rural estate. Or they may settle closer together to benefit from location values and availability of utilities.

Having congenial neighbors is more important than the price one pays for his land. We are happiest when we fit in well with our surroundings and are doing what we like to do. If your tastes are modest, you will not be happy in a community in which the social structure is organized for a different scale of living.

Sooner or later you will face locating on a single tract by yourself or in a more densely developed community. Seasonal communities catering to special needs relating to second, recreation, homes are one alternative.

Why and how do these seasonal communities develop? Someone senses that a demand exists or can be created for them. I know several developers who started as urban building contractors. They moved into developing seasonal communities because they wanted to broaden their operating base, saw opportunities for significant profits, or had ideas for desirable developments which they wanted to put into effect.

The "how" of developments varies with the developer, his objectives, and his opportunities. Suitable land must be available. It must have a key feature for promotion purposes. Idle or abandoned farmlands and holdings with good sites for potential water developments are keenly sought by prospective developers.

The plans may be well done or flimsy, depending on the developer's intentions and local planning and zoning requirements. In some areas, where planning procedures and building codes are well developed, a prospective buyer need have little fear about the quality of design, size of lot, water quality and supply, waste disposal, access, police protection, and similar public services. The roadways, the utilities and services, are designed for ultimate public operation. But in too many other areas—*Caveat emptor*—let the buyer beware. Low prices for quick sales and glowing promises of services to be provided at some future time may be the tipoff to a "sell out and get out" operation.

Some people buy lots in second-home developments for investment. Others may have only vague plans about building sometime in the future. If you buy a home or plan to build, you may want to look into the ownership of nearby vacant lots. Do the owners plan early construction? Is their land use compatible with yours? Does the developer have any control over maintenance of the vacant lots? Vacant unkempt lots frequently detract from the desired appearance in residential areas. Suitable land uses such as timber growth on vacant lots, however, can contribute to the sense of isolation.

As the number of permanent homes grows in relation to summer and weekend ones, use of water goes up, needs for waste disposal increase, and demands for other services multiply. Additional road maintenance, police protection, and snow-plowing (in the North) also are required. Offsetting these potential disadvantages are the obvious advantages of increasing employment stability and business activity in the community.

A surprising number of people buy lots in recreation subdivisions pretty much on the spur of the moment. Replies on a study of rural residential recreation subdivisions I did in parts of western Virginia and nearby West Virginia (Agricultural Economic Report No. 59) showed that some people simply had been driving by, stopped to look over the development, and bought without shopping for alternatives. Only about one in five bothered to check land titles before they bought.

Some Lots Too Small

Six out of seven owners of vacant lots and three out of four householders failed to check for State and county sanitation restrictions, building codes, and zoning regulations. This failure to check brought disillusion to many owners when they were ready to make improvements. Some owners found their lots too small to meet code restrictions, and they couldn't even build cabins, let alone drill wells or sink septic systems.

I must hasten to add, however, that the reputable real estate developers of second homes probably outnumber the sharpsters many times. Most of them are making extensive long-run investments in these properties. They will benefit from having a substantial and satisfactory community of second homes fully as much as will the buyers. One developer whose operations I know quite well plans to drop his other extensive activities and concentrate the rest of his working life on developing and managing the variety of services people want in his recreation community.

Second-home communities often are simply extensions of rectangular urban patterns into a basically rural setting. Lot sizes and street widths often are the same. When this kind of pattern is discovered, it often indicates an absence of imaginative planning and may be a tipoff to potentially serious problems. In one such development which I frequently visit, the roads run up and down steep slopes, rain

273

water and snow slush run down the ruts, cars slip and slide on the mud. And imagine trying to build cabins on steeply sloping lots 50 by 100 feet!

Planning for new communities has captured the imagination of many real estate developers. They can see the need for new concepts and new designs.

Landscaping and site developments, exciting patterns of circulatory systems through the developments, capitalizing on major attractions, and service centers that preserve natural elements of beauty can be used to enhance the intentionally manipulated environment.

Fitting the facilities for leisure living unobtrusively into the natural environment helps sell lots. Sound landscape design pays off in better prices and easier sales. People like what they see. They buy more frequently for use than for speculation. They plan to use what they buy.

Careful planning, a personal feeling of involvement by the developer and his staff, and ability to carry the considerably larger initial financial burden are necessary if the scenic and cultural amenities are to be adequately conserved and utilized under these circumstances.

Multiple Housing

In contrast to the one lot, one house concept for a residential development, crowded conditions and the need to preserve open natural beauties of the areas have encouraged new ideas about ownership and occupancy of space. Although traditional single-family homes still are the most popular, increasing numbers of couples are considering modern multiple housing designed for seasonal living.

A cluster development, for example, allows grouping the houses more closely, yet saves the scenery and reduces the costs for streets, service facilities, and maintenance. Developers can afford to leave half or more of the land in open uses and can make it available by deed or covenant to the residents for their joint uses under some form of community ownership.

High rise apartments with an adequate setback often provide more scenic beauty to more people than traditional subdivision developments ever could. Adequate

design to help the buildings blend with their environment can add immeasurable satisfactions.

Cluster developments and high rise apartments both require community plans based on future development of larger surrounding areas. Open space values must be protected. Plans can be designed to connect open spaces into chains of green. Trails for walking, biking, or riding; wooded glens for meditation or bird watching; valleys for flowing brooks and silvery waterfalls; playfields for noisy activities; waterways and water bodies for sports and scenic values can be worked into these planned uses. Leisure living is provided for a season or for all seasons.

Increasing numbers of families are considering cooperative apartments or condominiums. Both have certain marked advantages over other kinds of ownership. Having major maintenance, security, and special services provided by management, for example, removes much of the worry so often associated with homeownership.

Actually, we should also include in our list of innovations the modern travel trailer parks. They service vagabonding second homes that may linger in one spot for shorter or longer periods. These trailer parks can match the imaginative planning which is available for other second home developments.

In any case, look for imaginative developments where the plans and the layout protect and utilize natural features of the landscape. The recreation activities—the facilities for boating, golfing, beach clubs and other clubs, and the array of enterprises needed to keep people busy and happy—are almost sure to be around if the demand is strong.

Around 200 suggestions for potential buyers were listed in my study of recreation subdivisions. I have combined them into 10 general ideas. These ideas apply equally well wherever you are or whatever the type of second home that you are considering. Here they are:

1. Don't trust anything, anytime, anywhere when you are dealing in real estate.

2. Shop around, check other developments, investigate the situation before you sign the contract. Don't let yourself be rushed into a deal.

274

3. Go slow. Don't buy on impulse. Be sure your family agrees. Know what you want before you buy. Make several trips to places being considered. These trips help you examine ideas for use during the several seasons, difficulties of access, and your attitudes toward the spot and the community.

4. "Unless you are going to use the property—don't buy." This advice came from a lotowner who still had not built on his lot after several years of ownership. One could buy lots as possible investments, although this procedure is frowned upon by most reputable developers, and taxes and special assessments could eat up anticipated profits.

5. Be sure you (and your family) like the types of recreation these developments furnish before buying, and don't buy in a development which has a clubhouse and swimming pool unless you are sure that you will use them.

6. Use sound business tactics; deal with a reputable developer, don't expect Santa Claus—don't expect to get something for nothing. Think, get promises in writing, buy only if the management has a continuing responsibility in the development, and check every step with a lawyer before signing the contract.

7. When buying lots for construction, call in builders and inspectors before you buy, if possible. Make sure the conditions will allow the kind of structures that you want and need.

8. Visit your prospective neighbors. Will they be compatible? Check up with people who have owned property here and sold for a reason.

9. Know the rules, restrictions, dues to be paid, carrying costs, perquisites and prerequisites involved in the community organization—and plan to abide by them if you do buy.

10. And most important—if you like this kind of a recreational development, then go ahead and buy!

Making the Plains Bloom Again

ROBERT E. WILLIAMS

ACROSS the rolling hills the "Wagons Ho" of the wagonmaster rings again. The great wheels turn, their steel rims creasing the waving bluestems and the grama grasses.

From a gathering point in Texas a herd of longhorns follows the long dim trail to Dodge City, Kans.

From New Mexico to North Dakota herds of buffalo, protected now from the ruin that awaited them, graze the green seas of grass where the Blackfoot, the Comanche, and the Sioux once harvested buffalo with flint for food and shelter.

Up and down the vast Plains country has spread a fierce determination to save and honor the meaningful values the pioneers knew, to restore and to conserve the riches and the beauties of the endless expanse the settlers feared, soon respected, and then learned to love.

The return of the cowpokes and cowgals from the towns and cities of America,

꽃   꽃   꽃

Robert E. Williams is *Head Range Conservationist*, Plant Sciences Division, Soil Conservation Service.

275

to ride the wagon trains and follow the cattle trails of long ago, is one of the new recreational benefits of the conservation drive that is laying, carpetlike, a thick and useful matting of grass over lands easy to blister and tear.

Nature had designed cover suited to climate and the diverse soils of the Plains. On the shallow soils and in the drier country were the short buffalograss and blue grama. Midgrasses—little bluestem, wheatgrass, and needlegrass—grew on the loamy uplands; and along the bottoms and on some of the sandier land were the tall grasses—big bluestem, Indiangrass, switchgrass, as tall as a man on horseback at times.

These were the grasses that could ride out the droughts, the heat, and the intense cold. With their bounty in nutrition, they could sustain the vast herds of the buffalo,

Farmer Kenneth Kendrick keeps a careful check on the condition of his young wheat near Stratford, Tex., to avoid overgrazing that would leave the fields subject to wind erosion. Wheat, major cultivated crop in the Southern Plains, supplements native pasture as grazing for livestock during the fall and winter.

DOWN THE TRAIL

The cry of "Wagons Ho" echoes across the western plains of Kansas as covered wagons move out along the old Butterfield Trail.

"Wagons Ho" is a new income-producing recreation project for Frank and Ruth Hefner of Quinter, Kans. Frank is a supervisor of the Gove County Soil and Water Conservation District.

Guests of the Hefners spend several days and nights on the trail, enjoying many varied activities and the quiet beauty of the Kansas prairie.

Potential pioneers usually arrive at a selected campsite the evening before the trip begins. They get to know one another, while the Hefners explain the activities to come. The next morning, it's "Wagons Ho!" And the wagon train starts its journey down the trail.

---

the means of survival for the red men.

Evidence indicates that in 1830, some 40 million buffalo lived on these grasses. The Indians took about 2 million a year.

Slaughter of the buffalo by the white newcomers—for hides, meat, and as a means for bringing the defiant Plains tribes to heel—opened the way for the longhorns, the leathery, tough offspring of the early Spanish cattle.

These longhorns filled an economic vacuum after the War Between the States. Eastern markets begged for beef. Over 10 million head of longhorns went up the trails from their Texas breeding grounds to shipping points during the two decades following the war.

Prospects of quick fortunes in cattle built a ranching industry in the Plains by 1900. Bad management, bad weather, and the overstocking of the grasslands doomed the industry. Only the hardiest and best managed outfits survived.

The homesteader began his inroads even before 1900, bringing his oxen, his horses, and his plows. He filed his claims on choice parcels of land, often around precious water, and built his fences. It was the end of cattle trailing, the end of the vast cattle enterprises, and the beginning

(left) Covered wagons and riders hit the old Butterfield Trail in Gove County, Kans., as part of the Wagons Ho recreation project. (right) Mr. and Mrs. Frank Hefner, operators of Wagons Ho, dance a pioneer number during a night on the prairie.

of a big new era in the development of the Plains.

The longhorn was hard on the land, but the plow of the homesteader brought destruction. The plow turned millions of acres of fine grass for the planting of crops. Much of the land was poorly suited to the purpose. Crop stubble and residues, now known to protect and stabilize cropland, were burned and grazed.

By 1930 the scene was set for calamity. Successive years of drought and the usual high winds of winter and spring fashioned the Dust Bowl.

Dust from the Plains blew into every county of the Nation. Crops shriveled. Livestock herds were disposed of before they starved. Communities, like the parched land itself, just dried up.

Farming and ranching practices to cope with the climate and other Plains conditions already were developing. New Government programs dealing with the problems of the land came into being. One of the agencies formed for direct action upon such problems was the Soil Conservation Service, which grouped specialists in the various land and water technologies at locations where landowners could draw promptly on their skills. Soil conservation districts, formed under State law across the Nation, enabled the Soil Conservation Service to carry on its efforts with the organized cooperation of landowners.

An outgrowth of the drought of the 1950's—longer, more intense, and more widespread than the one of the 1930's, but less damaging because of agricultural progress—was the Great Plains Conservation program (Public Law 1021). This program provided Federal funds to repay the landowner in part for the expense of a thorough job of soil and water conservation, done in a series of scheduled steps with priority help from the technicians of SCS. Special emphasis was on getting the unsuitable cropland back into the kinds of grass that were there in the days of the buffalo.

It was a pilot program—a trial—but in less than 10 years more than 1 million acres of low-grade land had been returned to good grass cover. Stockwater developments, erosion control, fencing for better management of grazing, brush control, tree windbreaks, and various practices for the conservation of available water were among other practices wrapped into the package. It was evident that the principles of the Great Plains Conservation program were effective in hurrying the soil and the water conservation job in the critical Plains area.

Throughout the vast Plains area—once known as the Great American Desert—a new attitude toward the land and its related resources has taken over. Landowners, with profound respect now for the conditions prevailing in the area, are using their resources with understanding and availing themselves of the techniques known to deal best with the relentless hazards of the Plains.

Grass is a part of it, grass even better in many cases than the pioneers knew.

Duststorms are less frequent and much less dense. The hazardous lands, more and more of them, are under the kind of grass cover nature designed. The wounds of the Dust Bowl days have healed for the most part, and across the Plains is the beauty of broad sweeps of grass and the contoured strips of the cultivated lands. The handsome windbreaks of hardy trees adorn the landscape and shelter birds and small animals.

Instead of an agricultural liability, the Great Plains is acknowledged to be a vital source of foodstuffs for a hungry world. The prediction of the Great Plains Committee in its 1936 report is being fulfilled: "The land may bloom again if man once more makes his peace with Nature. Careful planning will give him back the foothill trees; terracing will save lush foothill farms; a wise use of the land will restore grass for controlled grazing; fewer and larger farms on scientifically selected sites may yield under the plough a comfortable living; dams will hold back the waters from rains and melting snow, giving power and controlling the flow of the life-giving streams; springs may be developed, water pumped by windmills to fewer cattle, moisture held in the soil by scientific methods of tillage, by such means the life of man on the land may be made happier, more prosperous, more secure."

A modern-day longhorn drive from San Antonio to Dodge City, Kans., crosses the Red River. When riders outnumber cattle, you know the drive is for fun.

A Cinderella Town Wins
the Recreation Prince

RICHARD H. DRULLINGER

GAYLORD is a "Cinderella town" situated in the heart of northern Michigan's huge water-winter wonderland. Just 60 miles south of the mighty Mackinac Bridge that spans the junction of Lakes Michigan and Huron, this Cinderella is decked out in an eye-catching Alpine motif complete with townsfolk in lederhosen and buildings with Alpine architecture.

That new look is designed to make Gaylord the reigning queen in the booming recreation area that entirely surrounds the town with 7 ski resorts, an elk herd, a dude ranch, 5,000 vacation homes, and dozens of other attractions. In 1966, Gaylord's second Alpine Festival drew 20,000 visitors. Thousands more come to participate in the year-round activities that abound here. And besides its vacation atmosphere, the town has a solid new industrial base for a prosperous economy. Yet just a few short years ago, Gaylord was sitting amid the ashes of a burned-out agriculture and a stone-cold lumber industry—tired, threadbare, and very much down-at-the-heel.

No fairy godmother gets the credit for the change in Gaylord, however. The miracle was wrought by mortals—a handful of untiring, civic-minded local people who combined vision, a hardheaded business sense, and persuasiveness into a big new facelifting plan.

This plan involved:
• Creating a public image with the Alpine motif. (This was chosen because there were at least two establishments in the community with that motif; the area was already known as the Ski Capital of Michigan; and finally, it is a distinctive styling that is generally acceptable.)
• Providing plenty of offstreet parking for the convenience of patrons.
• Having in the stores merchandise of character, in keeping with the theme.
• Staff training to provide good, well-informed people to work in the stores.

Today, just 2 years after the inception of the plan, the first two objectives are well along towards completion, while the third is nicely underway.

The fourth point, staff training, has yet to be accomplished.

A grant for long-range planning, small business loans, and reforestation aid are Government contributions to the changes occurring in the Gaylord community.

If there was a magic wand involved, it is interstate Highway I–75 which brushes the west edge of town. This twin ribbon of concrete binds our Cinderella closely to the millions of recreation seekers in the cities of southern Michigan and those of nearby States.

Other towns might fear that such a luxury route would speed the traveler right on past, but not Gaylord. At least, not today!

The transformation got going in 1959 when a group of businessmen headed by

Richard H. Drullinger is *Conservation Agronomist* for the Soil Conservation Service at East Lansing, Mich.

279

Harold Elgas, president of the Gaylord State Bank, took a good look at the town. They didn't like what they saw. There were 15 vacant stores in the three blocks of Main Street. Chronic unemployment among the 2,500 residents of the town and the 7,000 in the county drove young people to look to the cities for jobs and homes. The 2 industries in the town provided an average of 300 jobs. In the entire county the 18 manufacturing establishments employed only 371 people in 1958, according to a statistical compilation by the U.S. Census of Manufacturers.

Business Seasonal

Business for the retail merchants and motel owners was highly seasonal. In the 3 months of summer, the tourist demands far exceeded the town's ability to supply services. And merchants were financially unable to stock shelves with goods that would be in demand only for this short season. During January and February, the three or four developed ski slopes brought an influx of visitors that overtaxed the town's motels. The overflow had to be sent to Vanderbilt and other nearby communities; yet the demand in other seasons could not support more motels.

After analyzing the facts, the businessmen formed an Industrial Development Corp. Through individual subscription, they were able to raise a total of $100,000 with which to purchase industrial sites and lure manufacturers to their town. The fact they were able to raise this much money is proudly pointed out by the town fathers as proof that they were not a totally depressed community.

The IDC took options on three sites in town that were well suited for industrial development. All had sufficient acreage and suitable soils for large buildings, with easy access to both the railroad and the planned interstate highway.

Before they set about wooing industry, the businessmen first looked at the natural resources surrounding the town to determine what kind of manufacturer they should aim their promotion at. They found that within 30 miles of Gaylord there existed the largest supply of mature aspen for pulpwood of any place in the

United States. That was it! They would try for a wood-using industry.

Months of frantic negotiations ensued. This included some land swapping with a State agency, reengineering the county airport, and also conducting a newspaper survey that resulted in 1,800 replies from people who would be willing to work in a new industry at a given starting wage rate. Finally, U.S. Plywood Corp. agreed to construct a huge wood-using plant on IDC land. Today this plant employs well over 250 people, and besides it has under construction an additional 24,000 square feet of plant space.

This tremendous success showed the town what it could accomplish by sound planning and cooperative effort. The pumpkin coach had arrived!

Five and one-half years ago, Gordon

———————————————❦———————————————

SCHLANGFEST

Just 3 miles south of Gaylord, near one of the lakes with the highest elevation in Michigan, is the first commercial building with Alpine architecture in the community. Six-mile-long Otsego Lake was the major attraction for the Leo Schlang family when, in 1945, the family came here from Detroit on vacation and stayed to run a gasoline service station.

Starting out with a shoestring, two gas pumps, and a "we just like people" attitude, Leo, his wife Minnie, and now two sons, Bob and Jim, have developed a typical Bavarian inn that accommodates 225 diners at one sitting. When planning their own Bavarian Festival weekend in 1965, Leo and Bob talked the Gaylord merchants into having an Alpine Festival at the same time.

The response of the recreation-seeking public was tremendous. So for their 1966 festival, the Schlangs erected a big 60- by 175-foot tent to cater to the overflow crowds which attended.

Leo's voice quivers with emotion as he recalls, "You should have seen it— 3,000 people from all kinds of communities and backgrounds sitting together and singing folksongs with our Bavarian band!"

———————————————❦———————————————

Everett came to Gaylord and established a weekly shoppers' guide advertiser. With shrewd sense he realized that if his business was to grow, his community must grow. What would help it most? As he looked up and down Main Street, he was depressed by the timeworn appearance of the old buildings.

How could businesses attract more of the thousands of uncommitted vacationers that hurried by in their search for atmosphere and enjoyment?

Gordon walked on Main Street for months, talking with fellow merchants, looking for an idea—an eye-catcher—a gimmick.

Finally he dusted off an idea that had been suggested years before by a steel industrialist, the founder of the nearby Otsego Ski Club. Why not turn Gaylord into an Alpine village?

He wheedled various architects into sketching a rough idea for storefronts in the Alpine motif. One such sketch was outstanding. Armed with this, Gordon presented the idea to the Otsego County Chamber of Commerce.

This body, which serves both Gaylord and the county, has Harry Collins as its hard-working secretary-manager. With the active leadership of Gordon, Harry, and the chamber of commerce, a questionnaire was prepared and personally presented to each of the more than 50 business establishments. A summary of answers received showed that 45 believed a communitywide remodeling program would be successful in attracting greater numbers of people to Gaylord, resulting in an increase in business. Thirty-one said they knew that financing for individual remodeling was available through Federal Housing Administration business improvement loans. Twenty-eight said they would be interested in having an architect's drawing made of their block at a cost of $2 per front foot.

In answer to the question "Would you attend a meeting of Gaylord businessmen for the purpose of investigating fully such a community project?" forty-eight said "Yes." The meeting was held January 15, 1964. Enthusiasm was high. Individual pledges to remodel were received, and the four-point plan mentioned earlier was then developed.

In the town's facelifting, the Gaylord State Bank, the only bank in the entire county, had already set the pace. Eight unsightly store buildings—five of which were vacant—were torn down and a new bank building erected there.

Folk tunes by musicians in lederhosen create a festive mood at Schlang's Bavarian Inn.

A striking structure costing about a quarter of a million dollars, it advanced the Alpine architecture through the use of native stone, exposed beam ceilings, and attractive landscaping.

Because Bank President Elgas sincerely believes in the future of his community through the tourist business along with well chosen and complementary industrial expansion, he is willing to back merchants aggressively in securing financing for their remodeling.

As Bob Doumas, coowner of a fine restaurant now undergoing the sixth remodeling since its founding in 1919, said: "One of the prime factors of success in a community project like ours is the availability of money. So we simply must have

---

FOLLOW THE BEAR TRACKS

"Call of the Wild" is a recreational attraction that the Industrial Development Corp. helped get started in Gaylord.

A large grottolike building houses 46 nature scenes consisting of more than 150 mounted animals and birds in natural settings. As the visitor follows the bear tracks through the caverns, he views the individually lighted scenes, reads interesting facts about the animals and vegetation of the northwoods, and listens to recorded sounds of the animals.

The Carl Johnson family developed this indoor nature tour with the backing of a Federal small business loan. Banker Harold Elgas says, "Because the Government offers programs which can finance in a business area where private banking firms would find it difficult, we have 'Call of the Wild.'" In 1966, about 140,000 people were entranced and educated by this attraction. Visitors from all States wrote in the 4- by 8-foot guestbook comments such as, "Excellent—inspiring—educational—and so reasonable for families. We need more such displays."

While keeping the exhibit open all year, the Johnsons busy themselves during the slack periods in winter with rock polishing, jewelrymaking, and assembling souvenirs to be sold in their gift shop at the cave's entrance.

---

a forward-looking bank and lending institution."

Cost of the facelifting operation is borne by the individual merchants. New exteriors range from $700 or $800 for a new front on a barbershop to probably $15,000 for a large, elaborate building front. Of course many of the town's businessmen have completely restyled their building interiors in the chalet style, too.

U.S. Plywood, caught in the middle of building when this project started, had their architect redesign the foyer of their plant in keeping with the theme. Two national chain stores with set prototypes voluntarily adopted the Alpine motif for their new buildings here.

With this project well underway, the townsfolk turned their attention to the need for parking space. The merchants startled the Gaylord City Council by asking for a tax on themselves so they might acquire property for offstreet parking.

They have now purchased and are removing buildings from all the land immediately behind stores for a distance of 2½ blocks along Main Street. They have formed a Parking Authority and are financing paving and lighting of the area through sale of a bond issue. They regret having parking meters, but find it necessary to pay off the bonds and make other planned improvements.

This parking development came about when the supervisors were planning on relocating the courthouse. The courthouse sat grandly, but shabbily in the center of the main square, surrounded by green lawn, flowers, and large old trees. When it was proposed that this site would make a good parking lot, the citizens held a protest meeting. Weren't grass and trees important in a town, too?

The citizens won. A new city-county building will soon replace the courthouse, retaining as many of the large trees as possible in order to complement the new lawn and flowers.

And now that they have their offstreet parking about worked out, these same industrious folks are considering plans for parks and playgrounds. They secured a Federal grant through the Urban Renewal Administration of the Housing and Home Finance Agency and hired a firm

Elk in a misty meadow near Gaylord, Mich. A few of the animals released in 1919 in the Gaylord area have increased to a herd of about 3,000. Controlled hunting has been permitted.

of consultants to develop a countywide comprehensive plan. This plan will be used to guide the growth and development of public improvements in the area for the next 20 to 25 years. Parks and playgrounds are part of the plan.

The main accomplishment to date as a result of this plan has been adoption of a countywide zoning ordinance. While our Cinderella is growing up each day, she can't afford to ignore what is going on around her: The 7 ski resorts; the 2,000 to 3,000 people, mostly from out of State, that come to pick mushrooms; the 3,000-plus elk herd; the cross-country horse trail with 3 or 4 riding stables; the dude ranch; the State park; several State forest campgrounds; golf courses; hunting facilities; and the 3,140 permanent dwelling units, and nearly 5,000 vacation homes out in the county.

Gaylord's first Alpine Festival in 1965 found over 1,000 townsfolk—nearly one-third of the population—dressed up in Alpine costume, and at least 15,000 visitors on hand for the celebration. It

will be repeated each year, right after the Fourth of July weekend.

Visitors approaching the town drive past thousands of acres of planted pine and spruce. Reforestation began in earnest years ago with the help of the local soil conservation district and the cooperation of the Soil Conservation Service.

Through an agreement between the soil conservation district, local landowners, and the county highway department, trees furnished by the district were planted for windbreaks along the highway. These trees, now about 18 years old and 30 or more feet tall, beautify the roads. Additional millions of trees were planted on the sandy, hilly soils that proved unsuitable for the potato and dairy farming that started in this area after the old logging days. These pines, planted for Christmas trees and for potential timber products, are now providing beautiful vistas and building sites for both permanent and vacation homes.

Though the future looks rosy, there are some problems that beset our Cinderella. Several of the leading citizens point out that they need protective ordinances. Someone can upset the unity of their theme by coming in with a completely different architecture. They feel, too, that they now have need for a professional coordinator—one not touched by personal interest or professional jealousies.

All agree that the biggest danger to a town, though, comes from not recognizing change or being willing to plan for it.

That the planning done by Gaylord pays out can be seen in the statement of the town's only bank. In 1958, the total resources of the bank were $6 million. In 1966, they are $14 million.

The bank's figures on cash accumulations by months can be used as a business barometer, showing the relationship of one season to another. The recent figures show cash accumulations of $350,000 in January and February, $1.2 million in June and September, and $2.5 million in July and August. Things in town are now moving throughout the year.

Today Prince Recreation has found his Cinderella. We are sure they will live happily together for many years to come.

Trailer Families on the Go-Go

MERRILL D. ORMES

MORE than a million families are having lots of fun in the country with their recreational vehicles, while enjoying rallies, caravans, and other trips. Most are city families, and many belong to various types of camping clubs.

A recent list of clubs published by the Mobile Homes Manufacturers Association lists 14 different national groups of clubs, with more than 700 local chapters. The largest group, the National Campers & Hikers Association, has more than 30,000 families as its members, with 85 percent of them on wheels and only 15 percent in tents.

Rallies which these groups conduct range from 10 families from a local chapter spending a weekend together at a farmer's recreation area 15 miles away to 4,000 families who attend the annual national rally (called "campvention") of the National Campers & Hikers Association at Bowling Green, Ky.

At the rallies there is something for everyone—physician and mechanic, corporate president and clerk, retirees and families that have several children. Some merely wish to swim and to swap experiences around a campfire. Other groups are highly organized, with something going on every minute.

National rallies usually call for a parade through the nearest town and a speech by the governor.

Many local chapters outdo each other in their costumes, with prizes for the most authentic Indians or cowboys or whatever the imagination lets loose.

Potluck dinners are a standard feature at even the smallest rallies.

Technical talks often are a rally feature—types of hitches and their advantages, special menus, gear ratios for your automobile, and so on. Contests are other standard features, with prizes generally for the oldest couple, those who came the farthest, the family with the most children present, and the oldest and newest unit.

Square and ballroom dancing is another fun event at rallies. Often a wide variety of films are shown. And hobby exhibits are usually featured at rallies—rocks, butterflies, stamps, leaves, coins, and other items. Road-E-Os are an innovation, with drivers testing their skill at weaving between posts without knocking them down, and backing into narrow spaces. Sightseeing events range from trips to a nearby cave, an excursion boat-ride, or touring the White House by bus from nearby Annapolis, Md.

Well-known rally guests have included a daughter of President Johnson, Lynda Bird, whose travel trailer was among the more than 2,000 present at Laramie, Wyo., during her 2-month trip through the West in 1965.

Rallies are good business for the communities that are involved. Chambers of commerce in Bowling Green, Ky., Cadillac, Mich., and Auburn, Wash., estimate that a half million dollars was spent at each of their communities by participants in major rallies. These larger rallies, with more than a hundred units, are for either

Merrill D. Ormes is *Executive Director*, Travel Trailer Division, Mobile Homes Manufacturers Association, Chicago, Ill.

Caravan (above) heads for Alaska. Below, campers in Sawtooth National Forest, Idaho.

a national group or their State division. In picking a site, the organizations work with the local chamber of commerce.

They may rent a farmer's flat field and bring in portable toilets. Or they may camp at the county fairgrounds. A local chapter, with 10 to 50 families, prefers when possible to use an already established campground, travel trailer park, or farmer's recreation area.

It's only natural that participants enjoy themselves at these rallies and caravans, for they are among the most friendly and gregarious folks in the world. Surveys show that prior to their purchase of a travel trailer, 64 percent knew another owner. After the purchase, 30 percent knew nine or more other owners.

For further reading:

Mobile Homes Manufacturers Association, *Code of Ethics For Recreational Vehicle Owners.* 20 North Wacker Drive, Chicago, Ill. 60606.

—— *Recreational Vehicle Park Guide, 1966–67.* 20 North Wacker Drive, Chicago, Ill. 60606. $1

—— *Travel Trailer Park Kit.* 20 North Wacker Drive, Chicago, Ill. 60606. $2.50

—— *Wheeled Recreation.* 20 North Wacker Drive, Chicago, Ill. 60606. 35¢

U.S. Department of Agriculture, *Forest Recreation for Profit.* Agriculture Information Bulletin 265, Washington, D.C. 20250, 1962.

—— *Rural Recreation Enterprises for Profit.* Agriculture Information Bulletin 277, Washington, D.C. 20250, 1963.

U.S. Department of Health, Education, and Welfare, *Manual of Individual Water Supply Systems.* Public Health Service Publication 24, U.S. Government Printing Office, Washington, D.C. 20402. 40¢

Fun in the Range Country

DAN LUTZ

"OH, GIVE ME A HOME, Where the Buffalo Roam, and the Deer and the Antelope Play. . . ."

The buffalo may roam no more on the American prairie, as this well-known opening of the western classic, "Home on the Range," portrays. But the deer and the antelope still play . . . and so do thousands of urban, small town, and rural folk who are finding recreation enjoyment in the range country.

The range country covers millions of acres in the western Great Plains, the Southwest, and the intermountain region of the United States. Within this vast reach of territory, the range can vary from the famed sandhills of Nebraska and the flint hills of Kansas to the arid desertlands of Arizona and New Mexico, the sagebrush flats of Wyoming and the high mountain meadows of Montana and other Western States.

And the outlets for outdoor recreation which this range country offers vary as widely as does the range itself. Natural wonders of the West and the urge of Americans since the pioneer days to move westward—now by camper-trailer rather than Conestoga wagon—have long made the range country a mecca of the tourist and the traveler.

Now, however, more leisuretime, the intensive development of land and water resources under various private and public programs, and the awakening of communities and individuals to the potential of income-producing outdoor enterprises all have combined to underscore fun on the range for everyone.

Without downgrading the importance

🌼   🌼   🌼

Dan Lutz is *Assistant Extension Editor* at the University of Nebraska.

of the great rivers such as the Arkansas, Missouri, and Ohio, the recreational development of perhaps greatest impact on interior States like Nebraska has been the construction of artificial lakes. These range from tiny ponds to provide water for stock and prevent runoff and erosion on farms, through the larger watershed retaining structures and moderate sized dams to large reservoirs constructed by the Bureau of Reclamation and the Army Corps of Engineers for controlling floods, irrigation, power generation, and not the least of all, recreation use.

The impetus given to farm ponds and game cover by the Agricultural Conservation Program of the Agricultural Stabilization and Conservation Service can be seen both in statistics and through driving around rural areas in a Western State.

Selecting only 7 from Nebraska's 93 counties at random, ASCS records show that nearly 87,050 acres of farmland have been established as permanent vegetative cover, classed as excellent for hunting. More than 4,500 acres have been planted to trees and shrubs for forestry purposes

and erosion control, but at the same time providing excellent wildlife habitat.

And more than 2,000 livestock water and erosion control dams have been constructed, which are suitable in varying degree for fishing, hunting, and boating.

These figures can be multiplied many times over in Great Plains and mountain range States.

The Forest Service lends assistance in the establishment of trees of appropriate species and capability for the situation. The Soil Conservation Service lends technical assistance in developing land adjacent to the pond or lake. And the State game and fish commission, perhaps the Izaak Walton League, local sportsman's club, or local civic group may assist in the recreation development of the raw pond by stocking it with fish and by providing picnic tables, fencing, boat ramps, and other facilities as well.

Specialists from the land-grant colleges have given valuable assistance in advising farmers on ways to stabilize ponds to prevent water from soaking away behind new dams, in the construction of auxiliary

Guests of the Bankrupt Ranch near Sargent, Nebr., enjoy a wagon ride. At the reins is Robert Hanson, who operates the ranch with his wife.

facilities like vacation cabins, and in fish and wildlife management techniques.

It is estimated that over 2.5 million persons will pursue leisuretime activities in new recreation areas being developed in Nebraska and 18 other States through watershed projects approved by the U.S. Department of Agriculture during a 20-month period in 1965–66. These watershed projects are sponsored and carried out by local organizations with technical and financial assistance from the SCS. The Federal Government may share costs up to 50 percent of enlarging flood prevention dams for recreational purposes, obtaining land rights and rights-of-way, and constructing minimum basic facilities like boat docks, beaches, and picnic areas.

A typical summer scene in the Upper Salt watershed in Nebraska will find heavy Boy Scout camping activity at many of the 27 floodwater retaining structures in the watershed. Camping, canoeing, and fishing are three of the principal byproducts of the watershed ponds.

An example of group use was the recent Pioneer District Scout Camporee in which 274 Boy Scouts, representing 16 troops, camped near one of the dams. They took in a 2½-hour program conducted by SCS personnel and covering all phases of conservation—forestry, soils, land treatment, biology, and watershed development. At the campsite is a 5-acre permanent pool of water, with a shoreline of heavy vegetation—reed canarygrass and switchgrass—which prevents shoreline erosion.

Campers are sheltered by trees, planted mainly to prevent the wave action caused by strong winds.

Another recreational enterprise is the vacation ranch or farm, with activities like horseback riding, fee hunting, hiking, fishing, and boating.

In June of 1966, the semiweekly *Custer County Chief,* newspaper of Broken Bow, Nebr., at the gateway to the Nebraska Sandhills, reported that "after 3 years of operation the Bankrupt Guest Ranch of Sargent appears to be successful." Development of the Bankrupt Ranch as a guest ranch has been a family project of Mr. and Mrs. Robert Hanson and their daughter, Susan. Actually, the ranch's name is misleading—business has shown a steady

Fun in the range country for many years has included trout fishing. Construction of new artificial lakes, like Merritt Reservoir in Cherry County, Nebr., assures even more good fishing than ever.

pattern of progress. And each year has brought a doubling of customers over the previous year.

In 1963, the very first year, 15 families had visited the 3,000-acre working ranch, northwest of the village of Sargent on the picturesque Middle Loup River. In 1964, some 23 families and 125 hunters trekked to the ranch; and in 1965, over 50 families and 60 hunters.

The Hansons have moved in an abandoned schoolhouse and remodeled it with a basement to boost their capacity to 30 persons, and they continue to add features that will add to the enjoyment of guests. Their latest facility is a swimming pool.

The Hansons have one livestock pond stocked with carp, and another stocked with channel catfish.

The Riverview Vacation Ranch of Phillip Dowse near Comstock, Nebr., is an example of the joining of the old and the new. The ranch, on the Middle Loup River, just above a large diversion dam, is the first homestead in Custer County, Nebr., having been filed on in February 10, 1874. Now, the ranch, with its pioneer heritage, is catering to the modern-day vacationer.

Phillip Dowse and his son, Raymond, and family planned ahead for some time before taking the big step into the farm vacation business. One of the first moves

288

was the excavation of a large recreation pond on their land. The pond was constructed on a cost-share basis.

As in virtually every other type of endeavor, there is specialization in the vacation farm and ranch business. Some cater to youngsters, such as the Lake Mary Ranch Camp, which opened its gates in June 1966, near Central City, Nebr. The 1,100-acre spread, with seven lakes, is designed for boys and girls who are 9 to 15 years of age.

In a promotional piece, it was noted that "parents will be able to corral their youngsters at the ranch and spend a quiet camping holiday of their own at nearby Hord Lake Recreation Area." The ranch camp also features individual tutoring programs for the boys and girls in several school subjects. The schedule of studies and the usual run of golfing, swimming, fishing, water skiing, horseback riding, rifle shooting, etc., sends most youngsters to bed droopy-eyed after a full day running from 7:30 a.m. to 9:30 p.m.

A third successful type of recreational enterprise in the Midlands is fee hunting. The farmers and ranchers in the Custer County area of central Nebraska discovered two highly marketable and profitable commodities—game birds and the great outdoors.

A bigtime, countywide project known as "Custer Gameland," and featured in *Field & Stream* and other national publications, started as a small experiment by the Oconto Grange in 1961.

Twelve farm families offered their land for hunting and provided room and board for a fee. Approximately 75 pheasant and quail hunters were attracted to the Oconto area, and both they and the farmers were delighted with this arrangement. The hunters were responsible and respected farm property which pleased—and even surprised—some farmers, and the hunters were able to locate accommodations on farms where hunting was favorable.

In 1962, the Rural Areas Development Committee took the project and established it on a countywide basis. Thirteen volunteer offices set up around the county listed farms open to hunters for board, room, and hunting. These offices answered mail from interested sportsmen and directed them to the participating farms. Advertising was accomplished through news releases to various sporting magazines and newspapers and through the Nebraska Game Commission. The expenses were minimal, amounting to only $107 spent primarily for printing and postage.

It was estimated that through the 1962–63 season, 3,000 hunters from outside Custer County hunted for varying lengths of time. Facilities of hotels and motels were filled to the limit the first 2 weeks of the season. Cafes, service stations, and hardware stores experienced considerable hunter business. Many farm families earned from $200 to $500 for a few weekends of work.

The 1963–64 season was conducted in largely the same fashion. The number of farm families participating increased from around 100 to about 190. Communities who had but one family enrolled added several more, and many other farm families indicated they wanted to participate during the 1964–65 season. The commercial guest-keeping establishments noticed no ill effects as they were again filled to capacity, but many more hunters stayed in farm homes during the season plus many in private homes in the towns.

From 1,000 to 2,000 hunters from 29 States spent an estimated $50 each in the county during the 1965 hunting season. This included 350 to 400 farm-hosted hunters, who paid $10 per day for room, board, and hunting privileges. If they wished only to hunt, they paid farmers $1 for each day.

Many of the host families made over $100 per weekend. One host grossed nearly $3,000 for the season.

Interested farmers in the county have organized into the Custer Gameland Association. A constitution was adopted by the group, which investigated insurance needs and liability problems connected with both the hunting project and with farm vacations, which several in the group were interested in exploring. The sparkplug behind Custer Gameland has been, and is, Rancher Darrel Nelson of Oconto, who also served as chairman of the county's Rural Areas Development Committee.

289

Vacationing on the Crow Wing Trail

HERBERT A. FLUECK and HANS G. UHLIG

ADVENTURES in vacation pleasures reach their peak on the Crow Wing Trail 175 miles northwest of St. Paul, Minn. First designed for canoeing and camping, and then further developed for horseback riding, this big semiwilderness area now offers a full package of outdoor sports for both the natives and tourists. From the start, picnicking, hiking, bird watching, and fishing have added to the joys of canoeing. Now group activities are becoming popular—such things as saddle club rides and snowmobile races.

Basically, the Crow Wing is a clear water canoe trail with 13 campsites scattered along its 75-mile length. The infant river is narrow in most places, the water mild and slow moving, the shore scenery delightfully restful and natural. Canoeists paddle and float their way south from Blueberry Lake to the village of Staples. Boats are also available for fishing.

The river is just right for children—not too rough and something new to see around each bend. A wilderness atmosphere prevails, and wild animals are often seen along the shores. Canoe outfitters take the vacationers to any desired access areas and pick them up at a specified point downstream. The canoeists can therefore cover any distance and any part of the river. In fact, it is possible to travel the full distance to St. Paul by canoe.

The Crow Wing Trail is a local "bootstrap" project, part of a larger multicounty effort to perk up their economy through cooperative effort. The project's first promoter was John Rife—farmer, insurance salesman, and a supervisor of the Wadena Soil and Water Conservation District. Already concerned with the need for raising the market value of local resources, Rife got a further inspiration when he attended a Land and People Conference called by the Secretary of Agriculture in Duluth in 1963. There the late President Kennedy challenged delegates from upper Minnesota, Wisconsin, and Michigan to develop their human and natural resources.

Fortunately, Minnesota already had a going Resource Conservation and Development project sponsored by soil and water conservation districts and county commissioners of Kandiyohi, Swift, and Pope Counties. This project is one of several new national "pilots" to show how local citizens can team up with Federal, State, and county groups to stimulate economic growth. When Wadena and Otter Tail Soil and Water Conservation Districts were brought within the project boundaries, Rife was all ready to "hit the ground running" with his Crow Wing plans. He quickly contacted Don Benrud of the Soil Conservation Service, Biologist Ed Weiland of the Minnesota Department of Conservation, Miles Rowe, Extension

ⵣ   ⵣ   ⵣ

Herbert A. Flueck is *State Conservationist* for the Soil Conservation Service at St. Paul, Minn. He began his career in 1933 on the first soil and water conservation demonstration project in the United States.

Hans G. Uhlig is *Biologist* for the Soil Conservation Service, also at St. Paul.

Service, and other folks he knew would be able to help out.

While there are many canoe trails in the wilderness area of northeastern Minnesota, none were established with the enthusiasm and cooperation that the Crow Wing venture got from Wadena County folks. The county commissioners made available county lands adjacent to the river. The Northwest Paper Co. and private citizens contributed additional land. Boy Scouts in the village of Menahga, the Grange in Nimrod, a rod and gun club from Staples, and others cleared brush for the development of campsites. Future Farmers of America boys welded the grills for fireplaces.

Other materials for the tables and fireplaces were easily secured.

Using the facility designs and layouts obtained by the Soil Conservation Service, the Crow Wing Canoe Trail changed rapidly from a fantasy to fact. It took $3,000 hard cash to go with the enthusiasm and hard work.

With eyes to the future, three canoe outfitters started business. Twenty thousand brochures were printed to spread the word to the public. Jim Kimball, a staff writer for the *Minneapolis Tribune,* sampled the Crow Wing's pleasures and found them exceptional. So he gave the project a special boost in his column.

In 1964, Governor Rolvaag of Minnesota dedicated the trail and called it "one of the most exciting contributions to the art of resource management in our State's history."

The canoe trail met with almost instant acceptance from canoeists and campers throughout the State and beyond. John Rife received more than 1,200 letters, some containing additional contributions. In one summer season, at least 5,000 men, women, and children paddled down the river. One canoe party came from Japan.

The Crow Wing Wilderness Saddle and Hiking Trail started because of the success of the canoe trail. Natural trails adjacent to the river and through the jack pine forests were available, but little used. Imagination and a will to do were again needed. By 1965, Federal matching funds became available. Neighborhood Youth Corps boys were hired to brush out 15 miles of saddle trails, build corrals and hitching racks, and enlarge the campsites. Earning an average of $420 each, the 19 boys accomplished an outstanding job. Hubert Larson, Minnesota Department of Conservation forester, and Don Benrud, SCS, with local assistance, laid out the trail. On September 1, 1965, some 31 miles of trail were available. Now plans are underway for even further expansion.

The saddle trail fords the river at three points, and the campsites are used by the canoeists and riders together. On one occasion, 150 riders made camp, were served dinner, and concluded the day's activities with a square dance. During one event, three saddle clubs participated—young and old alike.

A wrangler stable has been established at Huntersville, and horses can be rented by the hour or day. Nonriders can participate. A buck and a half buys a ride on a buckboard.

To put the Crow Wing on a year-round schedule, snowmobile rides and races were started on the saddle trails during February of 1966.

Riders on the Crow Wing Wilderness Saddle and Hiking Trail, Wadena County, Minn.

Enjoying the Crow Wing Canoe Trail.

On one Sunday, 70 snowmobiles participated. The onlookers numbered an estimated 400 people despite temperatures slightly below zero. Use of trails is free, and any weekend finds snowmobiles winding their way over the saddle and hiking trails and through the jack pine woods. Multiple use of each resource adds to both income and pleasure, and this concept is not being overlooked.

While no survey has been undertaken, it is apparent that a substantial boost was given the local economy by establishment of the canoe outfitters and the wranglers' stable, increased trade, and a jump in restaurant business.

Plans are now underway for the Minnesota Department of Conservation to purchase wet lands a few miles south and east of Huntersville. SCS is studying the possibilities for constructing dams to create waterfowl areas. It appears that over 1,200 acres of wetlands could be developed and improved for production and harvest of waterfowl.

292

THEN YOU CAN CROW TOO

Do you have a good idea for a community self-help project?

If you do, sponsors of the Crow Wing Trails have the following suggestions:

Formulate your idea—write it down.

Talk with your soil and water conservation district board of supervisors and with several of your community leaders.

Hold a meeting. Write up the projects. Show the benefits to be derived.

Contact the local representatives from appropriate agencies (Soil Conservation Service, Extension Service, State conservation department, etc.).

Once the idea is accepted, follow on through. Get local community backing—financial, manpower, and other.

Publicize the project widely. Announce your intentions. Tell of your accomplishments. And extend invitations to other communities to join in.

The saddle and hiking trails will undoubtedly provide access to deer and grouse hunters. The combination of trails and wetland areas will make possible an increased protection against fires. It is anticipated that this protection will result in eventual establishment of improved woodland management and a base for an enlarged local wood products industry.

It should be emphasized that the canoe, the saddle, and the snowmobile developments, and the other projects mentioned above are not the only new enterprises. Well over 120 enterprises were proposed for the overall Resource Conservation and Development project ranging from an alfalfa processing plant to a tree nursery to a 70-unit senior citizens housing development. Five Minnesota counties—Otter Tail, Pope, Kandiyohi, Swift, and Wadena—or well over 3 million acres are within the project area.

In this Resource Conservation and Development project anything is possible. Leadership, imagination, enthusiasm, cooperation, coordination, and a willingness to work made the Crow Wing Trail a place to visit and to enjoy the simple pleasures of outdoor life.

Lands for Learning

HERBERT I. JONES

NORTHWEST of Santa Fe, N. Mex., a highway sign draws attention to a picturesque ranch spread of 21,000 acres whose origins, the tourist learns, can be traced to Charles III of Spain. This is "El Rancho de los Brujos"—The Ranch of the Witches.

A onetime object of superstition and fear, the setting for range fights, and an area shunned by even the weariest travelers, this ranch is now an oasis for vacationers, a living textbook of the land, site of the Ghost Ranch Museum, and a lesson in conservation for thousands of students and visitors.

Legend has it that the first settlers in the Ghost Ranch canyons lived in terror over reports of a monster called the "vivaron"—a rattlesnake-type creature, according to the telling, about 30 feet long. Cowboys and sheepherders vowed seeing it in the Badlands not half a mile from headquarters.

Over the years the legend persisted as the land changed hands. Once the title, in a game of cards, went to a cowboy and his eastern bride who operated their new property as a dude ranch. In the 1930's, the ranch was the site of a Civilian Conservation Corps camp and later was again operated as a real ranch.

The legend of the "vivaron" gained new credence when a group of university paleontologists discovered—in the same area where the "vivaron" once had been "seen"—the skeleton of a phytosaur coiled and giving hint of movement as the scaly armor plates and fossilized bones gave off heat waves in the sun. The skeleton of the prehistoric crocodile was excavated and displayed in the American Museum of Natural History in New York City.

Today the fossils of 180 million years ago are back home, housed in the Ghost Ranch Museum building near the place of their discovery. In the room, too, are the recessed cages of live kangaroo rats, tarantulas, turtles, lizards, snakes, and other native wildlife. Outside, a circle of "natural" cages house bigger species, including the wildcat, cougar, bear, and fox. Beyond are ecology exhibits, natural areas, trails, and the story of nature that can only be properly told outdoors.

Although this foundation-sponsored educational effort is scarcely 8 years in the making, over 75 schools within a radius of 125 miles send youngsters to study the exhibits, walk the trails, and supplement their classroom learning. Many return with their parents during vacations. Each year the number of participating schools increases. Not far from the educational center, on another picturesque part of the ranch, 5,000 persons each year camp at a Presbyterian Church center and enjoy the more recreational aspects of the Ghost Ranch property.

Nearly 4,000 persons visited the ranch in 1959, the year ground was broken for the interpretive teaching center. In 1966, a total of 110,000 visitors stopped to look

❀   ❀   ❀

Herbert I. Jones is *Assistant* to the Regional Director, Midcontinent Region, Bureau of Outdoor Recreation, U.S. Department of the Interior, Denver, Colo. He is former head of the region's cooperative grant program assisting States and local governments with acquisition and development of recreation lands.

and learn about land. And no one paid any admission.

On the "Walk Through the Ages," visitors use mounted telescopes to see geologic times reflected in distant 1,000-foot cliffs. They touch nearby samples of the rocks, read cleverly written informative signs, and listen to recorded explanations. Questions of teachers and students are answered by trained staff members.

One exhibit shows erosion in action with pushbutton rain falling on various kinds of terrain. Another reveals what the land once was, how man has helped cause deterioration, and how the land might be reclaimed through conservation practice. There is a model forest on a half-life-size scale complete with campers, lumberjacks, livestock, and fire control crews. There are soil and grass study plots and a walled prairie dog town.

A "talking beaver" relates his conservation role in both Spanish and English.

Federal agencies and State divisions combined forces in a growing watershed

demonstration to show the peak-to-river sequence beginning with the forest and followed by upland range pasture, irrigated lands, dams, multiple-use areas, and many other features of conservation practice. Half-size farm and ranch improvements and equipment complement the area.

From coast to coast, sound conservation ideas are being transformed into effective action through other "lands for learning."

On the edge of Denver, Colo., 2,000 acres of long neglected prairie land is open to youth groups, adult visitors, and school classes ranging from preschoolers taking the toddlers' nature walk to university graduates developing materials for advanced degrees. Though most Americans still think of Denver as the "wide open spaces," in 1967 there are a quarter of a million children of school age within a 45-minute bus ride of the Plains Conservation Center.

This center is the product of 18 years labor on the part of the West Arapahoe Soil Conservation District and, more recently, a community-spirited business, professional, and educational citizens' group of which the author is proud to be a member. More than 27 school superintendents—and 3 university presidents—helped to prepare the center's outdoor teaching plans.

At Tacoma, Wash., the Tomolla Tree Farm is the land for learning provided schoolchildren through the generosity of Mr. and Mrs. E. G. Griggs II. Cooperating are Federal, State, and local agencies and timber interests. Mrs. Griggs has long advocated the teaching-learning plan in effect. It provides repeated experiences beginning with the fourth graders on a 3-hour walk and picnic lunch along a "Youth Conservation Trail." Tomolla, Mrs. Griggs explains, is "tomorrow" or "the future" in Chinook Indian language.

Scout Leader Clem H. Dodson examines short-grass root structure with two Scouts at the Plains Conservation Center on the edge of Denver. The West Arapahoe Soil Conservation District worked for many years to set up the 2,000-acre Center, and has been assisted by a citizens' group and educators. Among those who use the Center's facilities are preschoolers, adults, and students.

Seattle, Wash., area school boards and educators have long been leaders in conservational activities. Beginning in the 1950's, the suburban Kent School Board adopted Trails End Ranch for its outdoor classroom. Every sixth grader and teacher follows the instruction guide developed by Albert C. Brown and 15 teachers.

Eighteen "units" of instruction are involved ranging from use of the compass to soil structure and formation. Teachers get intensive training on preparing the classes for outdoor work. The land is part of a major timber industry's holding.

Seattle was quick to build upon earlier efforts and open further opportunities for study and enjoyment through the State of Washington's early qualification for the matching funds from the Land and Water Conservation Fund. Matching money for the 50/50 Federal grant came from the trust fund held by the University of Washington.

By mid-1966, Seattle had planned and was developing segments of a metropolitan trail system. A pedestrian waterfront trail, in part of cedar plank, was laid out to skirt the Lake Washington Ship Canal and run through cattail marshes where opportunities to observe nature abound. Part of the trail takes students and those who walk for pleasure through the 153-acre University of Washington arboretum and an island bird sanctuary.

Eleven other major cities shared the first trail-oriented special grant. Atlanta, Ga., and New York City listed nature study as a principal feature. The other cities showed "education" as a secondary benefit from recreation bicycling, hiking, walking, and sledding.

Almost in the shadow of the spreading megalopolis of the east coast lies a wonderland—New Jersey's Pine Barrens. In 1967 it is still possible to drink the clean waters of the Oswego River—one of the few rivers in the East free of industrial and other pollution. Less developed than 125 years ago when pig iron furnaces and glassworks operated close by, the Barrens are a natural frontier within 50 miles of Philadelphia.

Students on field trips there see two rarities—the curly grass fern found nowhere else in the United States and the bright colored Barren's tree frog. They learn, too, how 90 percent of all the rainfall in the watershed soaks into the soil whereas 90 percent runs off the hilly sections of northern New Jersey. They learn how a billion gallons of water daily is yielded by one tract—a meaningful figure to future citizens of water-seeking Eastern States. On every side is an incredible variety of flora: Turkey beard, pyxie moss, cranberries, two score of wild orchids, laurel, golden crest, bog blueberries, and at least 400 other plant varieties. There are 150 species of birds, deer, and rodents. Pitch pines and scrub oak cloak the sandy soils.

To those who dash to and fro along the Garden State Parkway and railroads in the region, the fire-scarred trees, swamp water sour with pollution, and spoiled bog edges give little indication of the beauty and promises awaiting interpretation by trained teachers when one leaves the main routes to enter the Barrens.

Erling W. Clausen found the "Pine Barrens," in miniature, when he became superintendent of schools at Freehold, N.J., in 1963. Begun by Science Teacher Harold G. Smith and by a Soil Conservation Service staff conservationist, Neal Munch, the development was aimed at overcoming disadvantages of metrotravel by creating a "natural" area in the schoolyard. Altogether, 200 different plants, 28 types of animal life, and 2 ponds are handy for everyday class use.

Clausen says every community and school not blessed with a real natural area close by should create their own. He points out that State extension specialists in landscape design, game, fish, and parks personnel, and many others lent a hand with the Freehold land for learning projects. By 1967 standards, the cost of the effort was modest enough: $500. Plants were free for the digging—as they would be almost anywhere.

Rain gages, bird feeders, and similar equipment were made by the students.

Around the turn of the century, John C. Johnson was born in a sod hut on a homestead in eastern Colorado. As a boy he lived a pioneer life, close to the soil, plants, and animals, making himself useful in the family work. He carried water and gathered and stacked buffalo chips on the prairie so his mother could burn them and keep the cookstove hot.

John never dreamed of the smoke-filled industrial slums where boys his age had scarcely seen a plant. He was outdoors all day long tending livestock and the homesteader's meager fields. Rainfall was a scant 15 inches year after year, and most of what fell was lost through evaporation or, if greater amounts fell, in flash runoff. He learned about the rigors of dryland nature at every turn.

Getting to school was the chore that took extra effort. Once his father moved the family to a new home just to have the five children close to school. John learned his lessons well. Over the years, he successively became a college biology professor, dean, founded a teachers' college, and headed the science division of Pennsylvania State College. By 1920, he had begun the high altitude field trips that were to give him a unique place among our biologists.

Today, Dr. John C. Johnson is best known for founding the now far-famed Rocky Mountain Biological Laboratory at Gothic, Colo. The laboratory is nestled in the cradle of an alpine valley 10,000 feet above sea level.

Gothic has been the summer home of thousands of teachers and students who have applied, worldwide, the land for learning principles derived under Dr. Johnson's guidance. Most know little of the background which made the living laboratory-textbook theirs.

Dr. Johnson didn't tell me until late in 1966 how he bought and paid for the entire townsite of once silver-rich Gothic with his own money when college funds were not forthcoming. So convinced was he that the Nation should have a special place of beauty for high altitude field trips and study that he spent the entire summer of 1925, again at his own expense, driving through Kansas, Oklahoma, and Texas to visit every college science dean and educator whose support he might enlist. With the knowledge gained and their interests in mind, he returned to Colorado and bought the first four Gothic lots and an old hotel.

Johnson describes this move as "not a daring financial venture." He got title to the property for just $3. By 1928, he had made hundreds of acquisitions and succeeded in obtaining the first of three land-use grants from the U.S. Forest Service. Today, more than 1,100 acres of the Gunnison National Forest surrounding the townsite laboratory is designated for exclusive study use with thousands of acres of multiuse forest stretching to the 14,000-foot peaks that ring the laboratory.

Dr. Johnson eventually sold all his land, buildings, and the rights to the nonprofit laboratory corporation for what he paid for the properties years before. Between 1930 and 1960, the years he was an educator in Pennsylvania, Dr. Johnson and his family made at least one trip to Gothic each summer to serve the institution.

By 1967, more than 70 colleges and universities had become active members, and at least 1,600 teachers can look back to a land of learning unsurpassed in natural beauty and accomplishment.

The work of the center is reported in many publications, but its real mark is upon those who have trained there and have carried their experiences to countless thousands of others.

Dr. Johnson has retired half a dozen times, but in 1967 he is still not idle. He is president of the board of trustees of the Plains Conservation Center at Denver. Those of us who join him in that effort are awed by his vision, dwarfed by his plans, and ragged from trying to follow his swift pace.

The Plains Conservation Center is perhaps the only such venture in the Nation to be undertaken by a locally organized soil conservation district and an independent citizens' group.

The center has captured interest and drawn together as its subscribers farmers, public and parochial schoolteachers, a major cement producer, a leading private foundation, wildlife enthusiasts, one of the largest national nature conservation organizations, Members of the Congress, industrialists, and government staff and citizens from all walks of life. Being independent and self-sustaining is not an easy task, but a dedicated one of leadership for local conservation districts.

In Jefferson County, Colo., 35 miles

west of the prairie teaching center, is a mountainside tract and an interpretive teaching program which is the envy of school districts throughout the Nation. Each week throughout the school year four classes of sixth graders and their own classroom teachers arrive by schoolbus, laden with sleeping bags—some reluctantly, but most ready for 5 fun-filled days of learning they never forget. In the week the children get to know their teachers better than ever before, and their teachers get to know them too.

Eugene Herrington, conservation consultant for the Colorado Department of Education, and a teacher pointed out to me a boy who had been among the lowest in reading skills before the land-learning adventure. At the end of the year, he was reading everything he could find about "bugs that eat up forest wood."

Dr. L. B. Sharp told me of a similar experience in Illinois with a failing high school boy who went on to be a prominent biologist. His motivation: Discovering fish in a favorite creek were full of worms—a fact Dr. Sharp had known and had waited months to guide the boy to discover.

Herrington learned about the importance of outdoor experience quite by accident. Each week during his 11-year stint as principal of an urban elementary school, he walked with a class from the blighted neighborhood to a park a mile or more distant. The route that he chose was a suitable cross section of city life. Hundreds of times children called him to see a discovery they had made. When he responded a youngster would say, "Look, Mr. Herrington, people here have flowers in their yard."

Later he would learn that the child's family was moving from the blighted district to the neighborhood of better opportunity and better housing.

Signs of Good Hunting

LAWRENCE V. COMPTON

YOUR hunting may be easier and your success greater if you know some of the signs that mean good game land.

Like other American sportsmen, you very likely direct most of your hunting efforts toward small game like rabbits, squirrels, and quail. Sure, you would like to bag a deer or an elk if you can get away for a long hunt; but each year the bulk of your hunting time is spent on the nearby farms or ranches where you try to make out your limit of pheasants or rabbits or some other kind of farm game.

The wildlife you want to harvest is an agricultural crop. It is called "farm game" because it is grown on privately owned farms and ranches that are being used to produce the more conventional agricultural crops like corn, cotton, and timber which feed, clothe, and house us. While producing these essentials of our human existence, agricultural lands—if they are properly handled—also grow a crop of wildlife. Not all farms and ranches, however, are good producers of game—and for very good reasons.

The amount and the kind of game that an area of land can support depend upon the kind, the condition, and the arrangement of the plants growing upon it. Some

Lawrence V. Compton is *Head Biologist*, Plant Sciences Division, Soil Conservation Service.

235-917 O - 67 - 22

(above) The alternate bands of vegetation in stripcropped fields attract wildlife—and knowledgeable hunters. (below, left) Over 2 million farm and ranch ponds provide habitat for wild ducks and geese, and are important watering places for mourning doves and many other kinds of wildlife. (right) Pheasants find food and protection on a stubble mulched field, but they still have to take their chances with nimrods.

kinds of game require water, too. There must be food plants, there must be other plants for shelter, and the shelter plants must be close enough to food or water so that game can use either with safety. These are the essentials of wildlife habitat. Their presence upon agricultural lands is determined by the way the land operator decides to use his land.

Destructive methods of farming and ranching cause game to disappear. Overgrazing, up and down hill plowing, and unnecessary destruction of the vegetation in fence rows, field corners, and stream bottoms reduce and sometimes completely eliminate the food, cover, and water essential to the welfare of wildlife. Fields and rangelands that are gullied, windblown, and eroded are signs of poor game land as well as improper land use.

Good Game Habitat

Conservation farming, by comparison, results in greater numbers and variety of wildlife. Conservation farming means that the land operator is using the kind of agricultural practices that avoid erosion, restore and maintain the soil's fertility, and reduce rapid runoff of water. Among the more common of these soil and water conservation practices are contour farming, cover crops, field borders, grassed waterways, the hedgerows, stripcropping, stubble mulching, and windbreaks. These and many more such practices establish recognizable patterns of vegetation that are good game habitat.

Other types of conservation practices are mechanical in operation. These include ponds, terraces, water spreading, spring development, and others.

Soil and water conservation practices are the backbone of modern farming and ranching. And it is hard to find better game management practices or ones that are as acceptable to land operators. Let's take a look at a few of them to see why:

Fields stripcropped on the contour are so striking in appearance that they are almost the badge of conservation farming. These fields have wide strips or bands of crops planted on the contour to reduce water erosion. The crops are arranged so that a strip of a close growing crop like grass is alternated with a strip of clean-tilled crop like corn. Stripcropped fields have an enormous amount of "edge" where food and cover for farm wildlife are close together. In pheasant country these fields are especially good places to hunt. A farm with stripcropped fields is almost certain to have other conservation practices including a farm pond.

Ponds have spectacular benefits to wildlife. For the past 30 years, farmers and ranchers have been so busily constructing them that now there are more than 2 million ponds in our country, scattered from coast to coast.

Most of these ponds were installed for strictly agricultural purposes such as water for livestock. Regardless of their major purposes, they brought permanent water to places where such water did not exist or where it was available in only small quantities. The effect of this addition to wildlife habitat has been increased production of many kinds of game, but especially of ducks and mourning doves. Bobwhite, prairie chickens, and antelope are among the others also benefited by the additional watering places which are provided by the ponds.

A study of 91 farm ponds in Missouri revealed that every one was used by some species of game or furbearer.

Windbreaks a Boon

Windbreaks provide food and protection to many kinds of game including pheasants, mourning doves, squirrels, and deer. Windbreaks are used in the Great Plains and other parts of the country to provide protection to crops, livestock, and farmsteads. They consist of one to several rows of trees and shrubs planted at the edges of fields or around homesteads. The range of tree squirrels has actually been extended into our prairies by the planting of these bands of woody vegetation.

From these examples it is easy to see why wildlife is a natural byproduct of conservation farms. Stripcropping, hedgerows, field borders, and the many other practices which make up conservation farming have become the signs of good game land and good hunting.

Look for them.

Golf Becomes the New Crop

WILLIAM J. SALLEE

THE DAY before I arrived at the R. O. Brown farm in early June of 1964, R. O. Brown had sold the last of his 30 dairy cows. Instead of watching dairy cattle graze, I saw two men push golf carts to the next tee. A young couple was going from the clubhouse to the first tee. The golf course had opened up just the week before during the Memorial Day weekend, and several neighboring business people were taking time to enjoy the course this weekday afternoon.

The Brown farm, a few miles north of the small community of Brooks in central Maine, is now called the Country View Golf Course. One new to this area and to the Brown farm may gasp, as I did, from the scenic beauty. Country View is an appropriate name.

The farm is on a rolling hill from which you can look to the southeast and see the hills of Mount Desert Island. To the north and the west, you see the Rangeleys and Mount Washington. From several of the lofty putting greens, you look out over beautiful valleys of trees and farmlands to distant hills and mountains.

A visitor first goes to the clubhouse, a glassed-in porch of the farmhouse converted for this purpose. There you will have an enjoyable chat with Mrs. Brown, who is in charge of collecting green fees and selling refreshments. On my visit, Brown himself was waiting to tell about converting his dairy farm to the new recreation enterprise.

He acquired this farm in 1935 and through the years purchased additional land until he had 230 acres with 89 acres in cropland. He milked about 30 dairy

cows for which he grew forage and grain. Like most farmers in Maine, he had raised some potatoes and vegetables for market.

Brown said he could hardly justify the additional expense of acquiring modern equipment that he needed to survive as a dairy farmer.

As a young man, he had played some golf and through the years had visualized the possibilities of a golf course on this location. Upon hearing about the new Cropland Conversion Program (CCP), authorized in the Food and Agriculture Act of 1962, and its emphasis on converting cropland to recreational purposes, Brown conferred with his family on the possibility of a golf course. He discussed the project with the Waldo County Agricultural Stabilization and Conservation Committee and the Waldo County Soil Conservation Service office. The Browns then decided to hang up the milk pails.

A cropland conversion agreement was prepared, along with a plan outlining the proposed 9-hole golf course and the conversion of other land to camping and picnic areas. The agreement was approved by the Waldo County ASC Committee in July of 1963.

Under the CCP agreement, Brown received $1,558 in adjustment payments for converting 49 acres of cropland to a new use. He also received $577 in cost-share assistance for establishing grass cover on the fairways.

William J. Sallee is a *Land Use Adjustment Specialist*, Farmer Programs Division, Agricultural Stabilization and Conservation Service.

Golfers try their luck on the course developed by Maine farmer R. O. Brown under the Cropland Conversion Program.   Lady golfers review their score cards with Mrs. Brown (right) in the clubhouse on the side porch of the Browns' home.

Brown explains that the Federal assistance encouraged him to make the shift to a recreational income-producing enterprise. But since the program did not assist in establishing the putting greens, he was out approximately $10,000 in additional expense. Technical service for planning the course was furnished by the Waldo County Soil Conservation Service office.

Stories in the local papers and word of mouth reports had brought 100 golfers to the course the week before. The Browns established a membership fee of $35 for the first member of a family, $15 for the second, $10 for the third. Nonmember greens fees are $1 during the week and $1.50 on weekends and holidays.

In 1964, the Browns sold 35 annual memberships. Sixty memberships were sold in 1965 and 65 in 1966. Nonmembers using the course in 1965 and 1966 averaged about 100 per day on Saturdays and Sundays. Between 15 and 20 nonmembers used the course on weekdays in 1965 and between 30 and 35 in 1966.

Over 75 percent of the patrons of the fine Country View Golf Course are local people who never played golf until this course was built. Many admit that if they had been asked about playing golf prior to the opening of the course they would have replied, "No, we just aren't interested." But the course, located in their own community, had changed their minds.

When asked to compare his new enterprise to dairy farming, Brown points out that with a dairy farm the money came in every month, but with the golf course it is mainly during the summer.

However, the golf enterprise has many advantages, particularly that he doesn't have to work for long hours during the winter months. In 1965, his income compared favorably with income from his former farming operation. His 1966 income was even better, and Brown looks to more substantial returns when he makes improvements on the golf course and develops other recreational facilities on the farm.

The Browns hope to build a new clubhouse in 1967. In the meantime, Mrs. Brown will continue to greet golfers at the clubhouse on the side porch.

A Ranch That Produces Big Game *and* Cattle

VERNON HICKS and OLAN W. DILLON

THE HENRY WELGE family, ranching in Gillespie County, Tex., are descendants of pioneer ranchers who settled in the Edwards Plateau and Central Basin region—an area locally known as the "hill country" of Texas.

In 1967 the Welge ranch, 23 miles to the northwest of Fredericksburg, supports two families. Cattle and deer lease money produce the income. But before the advent of deer herd management, cattle alone could not support both families.

Since the first settlers came to the area in 1846, the hill country people saw the depletion of the native range and then its rebuilding. They also saw the near extinction of white-tailed deer.

By shortly after the Civil War, livestock numbers had greatly increased, and the native forage was dwindling. Deer were in competition for the grass. Cattlemen killed deer for home consumption and for the local market and drove their cattle to railheads in Kansas.

Soon after 1900 deer became too scarce for market hunting, but continued to be an important source of home meat supply. Deer were on their way to being eliminated from the area.

Texas deer hunting has gone through many stages of growth since the low population of the early 1900's. The State placed deer on the game animal list in 1909, and harvest was limited to bucks only.

But the harvesting of only buck deer then created a new problem. Overpopulation, especially of does, brought a deterioration of habitat.

The Texas Parks and Wildlife Department's biologists and a few progressive sportsmen and landowners recognized the problem as early as 1941. There followed a lag of 12 years before sound deer management began to be practiced. Many old wives' tales had to be overcome: "We cannot kill our does—they produce the bucks," or "We should never allow our graceful and beautiful deer to be killed."

Deer are important to the hill country. A large percentage of the 270,000 deer that Texas sportsmen take come from this country. The ranchers receive substantial sums of money for leasing hunting privileges to sportsmen who reside in urban regions. Some ranchers lease season-long hunting rights to groups, while others charge a daily fee. Either way, deer leases often equal or exceed net returns from domestic livestock.

The Texas Parks and Wildlife Department established deer census lines on the 2,138-acre Welge ranch during the early 1950's. The census reports, taken each fall prior to the hunting season, showed there was one deer to each 3 to 4 acres of this ranch. That added up to over 500 deer on the Welge ranch alone. No wonder the range was deteriorating—the ranch had too many deer.

With the domestic livestock the ranch

ʚ   ʚ   ʚ

Vernon Hicks is *Field Biologist,* Soil Conservation Service, Temple, Tex.
Olan W. Dillon is *Regional Biologist,* South Regional Technical Service Center, Soil Conservation Service, Fort Worth, Tex.

had a severe overpopulation, resulting in deterioration of forage resources.

In 1961, Henry Welge started up a day hunting arrangement. He built several hunting blinds with old lumber so that it would not take a lot of capital to get going. A hunter charge of $10 per day was made the first year. Texas law allows three deer per hunter, of which not more than two may be antlered. Welge was issued doe permits each year, based on the fall census figures. He in turn issued these permits to his hunters.

The first year of operation produced 225 man-days of hunting. The kill was 100 bucks and 162 antlerless deer. A very good year, but what about the next year? The old question popped up again, "Did I kill too many does?"

Removal of 262 deer allowed the food supply to recover. And what the biologists had been saying would happen actually did—the 1962 fall census figures showed just as many deer as the previous census.

Again an old wives' tale cropped up, "Deer were moving in from several miles away." But the biologists found that deer on southwestern ranges do not migrate. The home range of deer in the Texas hill country is, normally, 1 to 1½ miles. They will starve to death upon the home range rather than move into unfamiliar places. In fact, hunters on the Welge ranch harvested deer that, because of overpopulation conditions, would have perished due to natural causes.

Welge had turned natural losses into a recreation resource for urban people. This meant cash for him because city people were willing to pay for the privilege of hunting on private land. The privilege of hunting deer returned a net of $1 per acre to the ranch the first year.

With this experience, Welge reoriented his ranch's management objectives. Deer were not something that contributed little to the ranch. He took a greater interest in his deer herd. Now he plants three 20-acre fields to oats, spelts, or other small grain just for the deer.

Juniper, a poor food for both deer and cattle, has been removed from about 1,300 acres to increase the better forage plants. Welge was careful, however, to leave post

Herd of buck deer feeding in a hill country clearing.

Henry Welge takes a deer hunter to a blind on his ranch in the Edwards Plateau region of Texas, an area which is locally known as the "hill country."

oak and live oak, elm, hackberry, and any shrub that produces mast or browse. He also left shrubby and tree cover in escape, bedding areas, or travel lanes for deer.

Welge has improved his road system to facilitate travel by hunters to the blinds. Most Texas hunters prefer blinds since the country is open enough to make stalking difficult. Fifty new blinds have been built since 1960. Three types—ground level, tree, and tower—give the hunter a choice. Welge accepts only 20 hunters a day on the ranch at any one time. This allows for both hunter safety and a better chance to kill a deer. The price is now $20 per day.

Has this enterprise been successful, and has it maintained a healthy deer herd? The 1965 season gives the answer. Hunter days have increased in the 5 years to 250 man-days. The take was 147 bucks and 163 antlerless deer.

Welge is still improving on his skills in managing deer and cattle upon the same range. He has in effect become a game and cattle man. Weights of the deer have increased due to better yearlong forage resources. The bucks taken in 1961 averaged 53 pounds each and during the 1965 season averaged 73 pounds. He watches the better native deer foods to see if they are increasing or decreasing, the same as he does for the key foods of his cattle.

Henry Welge is managing the resources of his ranch to keep the deer and cattle in a healthy condition and to maintain his resources of range forage. Many urban people are benefiting by the hunting method being used. It is important to Welge that ranch income has increased enough to support two families. Had it not been for this extra income, his son would have had to leave the land that his ancestors settled.

Research and information showed the way. Henry Welge and son are benefiting from the hunting method now used.

Trails That Tell Stories—
You Can Build One

ELLSWORTH R. SWIFT

HAVE you ever walked along a trail and had your curiosity aroused by something you saw—perhaps a beautiful flower which was new to you, a strange growth on a tree trunk, or the mystery of a long deserted building? These things and more may have raised many unanswered questions in your inquiring mind. Remember your frustration from not knowing the answers?

Most people have had experiences like this, but today more and more trail walkers are getting answers to their questions. They are finding a wealth of information along trails that tell these stories—trails that tell their stories through small signs or a leaflet keyed to the interesting features along the trail. Usually trails of this sort are called self-guiding trails or simply "nature trails."

Story trails are now quite common in such places as national parks and national forests, but why limit them to this type of area? The inquiring mind does not stop functioning on a trail located outside of a large public park or forest. For this reason, landowners and managers who have an interest in recreation and in informing the visitors are discovering the value of the self-guiding trail in a variety of situations.

Would this type of trail be useful to

a school? Dr. Howard Owens, science supervisor for the Prince Georges County school system in Maryland, answered that question by enthusiastically pointing out their goal—a nature trail for every school in the county. Even school grounds without a woodlot contain a wealth of nature lore material, he explained. Dr. Owens suggested a visit to West Lanham Hill Elementary School in the Washington, D.C., suburbs to see a trail.

With the company of two 6th grade students, I passed under an arch bearing the name Raccoon Trail and into a small woodland upon the school grounds. We stopped at rock specimens whose labels

Sign identifies spice bush for youngster on nature trail in Bethel, Conn.

Ellsworth R. Swift, a former Interpretive Officer for the Forest Service, is *Chief*, Exhibit Planning Section, National Park Service, U.S. Department of the Interior.

305

Along a nature trail you may meet a new friend as this little girl did on a visit to Gifford Pinchot National Forest in Washington. She met a turtle.

explained the difference between igneous, sedimentary, and the metamorphic types. The other labels revealed a variety of facts about plants, animal homes, and conservation. It was soon evident that this trail had a considerable influence on students. They helped build it, and they helped maintain it. It was their trail. They knew what President Johnson meant when he had talked about a beautification program. They had one right here.

Mrs. Leo Bennett, school principal, told me that this nature trail was built in 1957, partly on weekends when parents, students, and teachers all pitched in to remove the accumulated trash from the woods and to build trail. The State forestry commission helped select points of interest and identify plants all along the trail. The trail still isn't really finished, and won't be since it's a changing thing. Every year the students have new ideas for revisions or additions to the trail.

Mrs. Bennett explained some of the benefits of the trail—the development of

respect and appreciation for nature and natural beauty, the opportunity to learn about nature firsthand and to see how it relates to all the subjects taught in school, and the tranquilizing effect upon emotionally disturbed children.

Can the nature trail be an asset to the private landowner? Ross Raum thinks so. He has a ranch in northwestern Nebraska near Crawford. The idea of rural recreation as a business (publicized through Secretary of Agriculture Freeman's Land and People Conferences in 1962) made sense to Rancher Raum. He built campgrounds, cabins, and trout and bass fishing ponds, made other modifications to his ranch, and went into the recreation business himself.

In September 1965, with the technical assistance of the Soil Conservation Service, Mr. Raum planned and built two nature trails to add to his recreation development. Now vacationers on his ranch have an opportunity to walk or ride along trails that pass through flowering fields and wind up the wooded slopes to a crest that offers a view of the beautiful Nebraskan "Pine Ridge" country. For most visitors, these walks or rides are get-acquainted sessions where the signs along the way introduce trees and flowers that become personal things, each with a name; "that big evergreen tree" becomes a ponderosa pine, "those showy yellow flowers"—prairie thermopsis, and so forth.

The ranch visitors like these trails, and Rancher Raum knows that they have been a good addition for his vacation ranch. The addition of a self-guiding trail might be considered wherever a landowner is in the recreation business, and the natural scenery or historical setting can be part of the recreational experience.

The nature trail project on Ross Raum's ranch is just one of many similar projects underway in Nebraska. With the technical assistance from the Soil Conservation Service, nature trails have been established on ranches and a variety of other places, such as Opal Springs Boy Scout Camp, Fairbury City Park, and the campus of Chadron State College. These trails in Nebraska are typical of those that have been built or could be built in other States.

Private industry is finding that nature trails can be good business. These trails are worthwhile public service projects whose dividends are good publicity and good public relations.

The Southwestern Electric Power Co. set aside 2,000 acres of its land in Marion County, Tex., as an encampment, primarily for the agricultural youth groups. W. J. Sedberry, vice president of Southwestern Electric, suggested to Rip Loftis, a district agent, Agricultural Extension Service, that a nature trail be developed for the camping groups, and the idea sounded good to Rip. By March of 1965, the project was underway.

The Soil Conservation Service, U.S. Geological Survey, Texas State Forest Service, and Texas Agricultural Extension Service worked with Southwestern Electric to turn a trail concept into reality. It is a beautiful and informative trail.

At about the same time the Texas trail was being built, the Richwood Rangers 4–H Club was working on a trail project 1,200 miles to the northeast in Gloucester County, N.J. These eager youngsters were doing the job with a minimum of technical assistance from adults and doing the job very well—proof that developing a nature trail is no impossible task. The theme of their nature trail, in the 35-acre 4–H forest near Aura, is "learning to know the trees." Trees along their trail have been numbered to correspond with the index numbers from the bulletin, "Common Forest Trees of New Jersey," prepared by the Extension Service. By picking up this bulletin at the start of the trail, anyone can not only identify the trees along the trail, but also learn many facts about them.

The self-guiding trail doesn't have to be limited to the subject of nature. A variety of subjects or themes have been used successfully for trails of this type, including history, Indian lore, and land management.

For example, Hard Bargain Farm in Maryland—administered by the Alice Ferguson Foundation—features a self-guiding trail that explains the management of a farm woodlot.

With help from the Director of Conservation Education, U.S. Forest Service, this trail was planned and a brochure written so that the visitor sees the woodlot through the eyes of a forester.

Pausing before a sweetgum tree, the visitor reads that ". . . It is an important timber tree, second in production among the hardwoods, the leading furniture wood, and second in veneer production." At another point along the trail the visitor has a chance to learn about and to try measuring the height of a tree and scaling a log. The youngsters and adults who use this trail will surely leave with a better understanding of the forest as a resource, forestry, and the relationships between conservation and economics.

You don't need to have land to participate in a nature trail project. Many groups have participated by sponsoring trails on public land. Here are three of the self-guiding trails on national forests which have been built with the financial assistance of sponsoring groups:

• Pig Iron Trail—George Washington National Forest, Va., sponsored by the Children of the American Revolution.

• Buffalo Nut Trail—Chattahoochee National Forest, Ga., sponsored by the Garden Club of Georgia.

• Rim Rock Forest Trail—Shawnee National Forest, Ill., sponsored by the Illinois Federation of Women's Clubs.

In addition to the Federal land, State, county, or municipal land is often made available to sponsoring organizations for their nature trail projects.

The examples described above can only open the door to the opportunities that exist across the country for the self-guiding trail—a trail intended to satisfy curiosity, to educate, and to entertain. Does one of these opportunities exist on your land or in your community? If so, consider developing a self-guiding trail. The task is not difficult. In fact, it can be fun.

SURPRISE, SURPRISE!

A friend who was principal of a large city elementary school quizzed a third grade class about the nature walk they had taken with their teacher. One little girl said it was fine—"They had learned lots of things they didn't intend to. . . ."

Here are the basic steps you will need to take to get the job done.

1. Explore the area and identify the main features of interest.

2. Plan and lay out a trail route to take advantage of the features.

3. Build the trail.

4. Prepare written descriptions of the trail's features.

5. Put the written descriptions on signs at proper places along the trail or in a brochure keyed to numbered posts located along the trail.

There are many sources of technical assistance you can draw upon. Check your local community for talent. Usually there will be one or more people who have the special knowledge you seek help with, perhaps a botanist, an ecologist, a forester, or a geologist. Generally they are happy to assist in projects of this type. Local

A poisonous fungus, Amanita muscaria.

schools and universities are good sources of help, and some State agencies also are prepared to help out.

Assistance is available from the Federal Government. The Soil Conservation Service in cooperation with local soil and water conservation districts will provide technical assistance on plant identification, trail construction, and label preparation to rural landowners, rural organizations, and municipalities. Contact your local Soil Conservation Service representative for this help.

Your county extension agent or other land-grant college official will give assistance or help you secure the services of qualified officials.

You might also visit a nearby national forest, national park, Office of the U.S. Geological Survey, or other Federal agencies. Representatives of these agencies will be happy to share their special knowledge as their work schedule permits.

Are you ready to start? Good luck!

For further reading:
Trail Planning and Layout. Information-Education Bulletin No. 4, National Audubon Society, 1130 Fifth Avenue, New York, N.Y. 10028. $2.50

U.S. Department of Agriculture, Developing the Self-Guiding Trail in the National Forests. Miscellaneous Publication 968, U.S. Government Printing Office, Washington, D.C. 20402. 20 cents. (This booklet is not limited in application to national forest land.)

Happiness Is a Week
as a Young Wrangler

LEO M. SCHAEFER and ROY M. CLARK

NINETY-ONE boys and girls can tell you that happiness is a week at the H–M Vacation Ranch near Lake City, Iowa. In the old western tradition, these youngsters from 8 to 16 have enjoyed the sunshine, horsemanship, and outdoor living there.

The H–M Ranch—located in the Iowa corn, hog, and cattle country—had been a farm in the Morrow family for 40 years. Harlan Morrow decided in 1963 to transform the 160-acre farm to a boys camp and horsemanship training activity.

This decision was made possible under the pilot Cropland Conversion Program of the U.S. Department of Agriculture. The program assists farmers in diverting cropland from the production of crops in ample supply to recreational and other income-producing uses.

During our visit, the ranch had been completely converted to riding trails, campgrounds, and outdoor recreation. A bunkhouse had been built, and a group of boys had spent a week on the ranch. Morrow and his family were enthusiastic about the new operation.

Harlan Morrow, head wrangler of H–M Ranch, is assisted in managing this project by his wife Ruth and two children, Rocky and Dee. Ruth Morrow has the understanding it takes to solve the problems that arise with young wranglers in everyday camp life. Her love of ranch life

❧ ❧ ❧

Leo M. Schaefer is Chief, Land Use Programs Section, Farmer Programs Division, Agricultural Stabilization and Conservation Service.

Roy M. Clark is Information Specialist for radio, television, and visuals, Agricultural Stabilization and Conservation Service. During a fact-gathering visit to the H–M Ranch, he took the photographs that illustrate this chapter.

Wagon wheel frames bunkhouse (left) at the H–M Vacation Ranch near Lake City, Iowa. At right, Mr. and Mrs. Harlan Morrow, ranch operators, talk to young wranglers in Western hats. Stagecoach (below, left) gives flavor of Old West for youngsters at the H–M. Horsemanship training (below, right) is a key activity.

Roping practice at the H–M Ranch.

and her personable manner help make their stay happy and exciting.

This farm formerly produced corn, soybeans, oats, and tame hay. A beef cattle and swine operation is being continued.

The H–M Ranch is bordered by extensive timberlands, to which the young wranglers have access. This land includes part of the winding Coon River. Rainbow State Park is within a short canter for fishing, swimming, and riding galore.

Besides training in grooming and riding fine saddle horses, the ranch offers trail riding, camping, fishing, swimming, and rodeo exhibitions, as well as several other outdoor sports.

A messhall, kitchen, restrooms, and showers have been built.

The head wrangler gives riding lessons and teaches all aspects of horsemanship. After the young wranglers have passed their basic riding tests, supervised short and long trail rides are organized for them. The horsemanship training season opens in June for 10 weeks, closing in the middle of August.

In 1965, a girls camp and horsemanship training activity was organized on the ranch. The boys and girls camp alternately on a weekly basis.

In conjunction with the horsemanship training camp, there is a riding stable with 25 horses and ponies. Families may rent horses and ponies to take trail rides along the Coon River.

The H–M facilities have become very popular for weekend group activities. Organizations that use H–M facilities for weekend outings include Boy Scout and Girl Scout troops, church groups, and civic clubs.

H–M Ranch had its start in this new enterprise in 1963 when Morrow signed a 10-year cropland conversion agreement with the Calhoun County Agricultural Stabilization and Conservation Committee. Under that agreement, Morrow has received $8,269 for diverting 146 acres of cropland from crop production to this new use and $2,730 cost-share assistance for establishing conservation practices on the land diverted. Practices carried out included seeding of grasses and legumes and fencing.

Access to Farmers' Lands
for Hunting and Fishing

WADE H. HAMOR

SOME of my earliest memories are of hunting on our home farm. Hunters from the town nearby often came by to enjoy Dad's company and the abundant farm wildlife.

But I recall, too, the time my father

Hunter calling ducks in a flooded "green tree reservoir," near Fairoaks, Ark.

asked two hunters to leave our farm because they had not asked permission to hunt. Dad never denied permission to any hunter who first stopped at the house. Yet he always insisted on knowing who was on the farm and for what purpose. I've hunted most years since that time and have found that Dad's displeasure with uninvited guests is shared by most men who till the soil.

Today's farmer has more legal backing in the control of trespass than he had 40 years ago. Laws are more restrictive on the sportsman and are more widely publicized. Enforcement of trespass laws is much improved.

Some farmers post their lands as a means of encouraging sportsmen to ask permission before going onto the land to hunt or to fish. Others feel that the signs give them an additional legal backing in trespasser control. This is true in some States, but in others the trespasser is subject to prosecution whether the land is posted or not.

Basic in a posting is the landowner's desire to know who is on the land. Also, if damages result from the presence of sportsmen he wants to talk to those responsible. Imagine the frustration of the farmer who finds dead stock, broken fences, or other mischief and can't find out who did it!

I am sure it never occurred to my father

🌱　🌱　🌱

Wade H. Hamor is a *Regional Biologist* with the Soil Conservation Service, Lincoln, Nebr.

to charge a fee for hunting or fishing. Even today some farmers appear reluctant to charge for access to publicly owned crops of wild game. Others, however, use fees as a means of controlling the numbers of those who want to hunt and fish on the farm. By doing so, the farmer can better regulate the harvest of wild animals to assure a continued supply. A few farmers charge as compensation for past or anticipated property damages. Others charge a fee to pay the cost of improving wildlife habitat on the farm.

Farmers and ranchers produce the bulk of the wildlife and much of the fish that is harvested each year and usually without undue expenditure of their time or funds. But game production is intentionally promoted by thousands of farmers across the Nation who devote land and water to the exclusive use of wildlife. These farmers are protecting natural habitats of squirrels, ducks, deer, and many other game and nongame species from damage by livestock and other agricultural activities. And they are improving additional thousands of acres by providing food, cover, and water for the use of wildlife. In this way they help meet mounting pressures for hunting and fishing opportunity.

Despite present efforts of management,

In English and in Spanish, the message is just the same: "Stay Away."

the size of the annual wildlife crop may vary widely.

Game crops are high or low and hunting and fishing success good or poor depending upon the weather and a great many other factors.

Although good management cannot

A bird's-eye view of hunting for bobwhite quail in Charlotte County, Va.

guarantee abundance every year, it tends to assure better crops from year to year.

Farmers can get Federal cost-sharing aid through the Agricultural Stabilization and Conservation Service for selected habitat improvement practices—such as planting food patches, planting trees and shrubs, or building ponds, marshes, and watering places for wildlife.

Technical help for habitat improvement on farm and other rural lands is available through the Soil Conservation Service and other Federal and State agencies. Some agencies provide materials such as fish for stocking ponds, planting stock of trees and shrubs, seeds, and—in some cases—fencing materials.

Farmers cooperating in the Cropland Adjustment Program can receive payment for permitting hunting, fishing, and other recreational activities upon land removed from the production of certain crops.

With the technical and financial help now offered, farmers and ranchers are creating and improving wildlife habitat at a growing rate. Sportsmen who respect the landowner's rights and property—and particularly those who help pay for wildlife improvements—are increasingly welcome to harvest the wildlife produced.

When the Recreation Bug Bites

ROSS H. MELLINGER

THE HOTTEST THING right now is the use of land for recreation! This is good news for the city dweller who wants to get out into the great outdoors. It means fishing, swimming, and boating, horseback riding, picnicking, camping, and hunting for him and his family and perhaps for a club he belongs to."

That's Tom Simpson speaking. He's a professional in the land use field, and he knows what he's talking about.

Tom is a soil conservationist for the Agriculture Department's Soil Conservation Service. But he deals with lots more people than farmers.

He has advice for folks who buy land for part-time country living, for weekend retreats, or even for full-time country living. Many of these people buy farmland, but don't want to farm it. Neither do they want to chop it up into subdivisions because they like the beauty of their outdoor landscape and want to preserve it. And farmers, too, are doing things with their land besides growing crops.

But let Tom tell about it. Farming is close to his heart, and he likes to take farmland as an example of what can be done by landowners to make money from outdoor recreation. And his advice can be used by any landowner with enough property to give folks outdoor elbowroom close to home.

"I'd like to tell you about the Burton place," Tom commences, tipping back his smart field cap.

"The place is owned by Sam Burton— the third generation of Burtons on their 250-acre, 40-cow dairy farm up the Little Kanawha River a bit from Parkersburg, W. Va. The Burtons have always been kind to their land. In fact, Sam was the

✿   ✿   ✿

Ross H. Mellinger is *Woodland Conservationist* for the Soil Conservation Service, Morgantown, W. Va., serving West Virginia, Maryland, and Delaware. The soil conservationist and farmer in his chapter are fictitious, but the setting and place names used are authentic.

first farmer to develop and apply a conservation plan with the help of the newly organized Little Kanawha Soil Conservation District.

"But things are changing now on the Burton place. Sam and his wife Mildred, bitten by the recreation bug, asked me to come up and talk about recreation as a possible main source of income.

"We started with the soil map for their place. It showed the suitability of soils for different kinds of recreation facilities.

"The Burtons made it plain that they weren't going to give up farming entirely. They did want to change from dairy to beef cattle if the recreation angle looked promising. Sam told me the family had spent evenings talking about the problems involved. They had asked themselves such questions as:

• Would they enjoy working with all kinds of people and enduring the many problems that were sure to crop up?

• Could they give up their Sundays and holidays and reconcile their deep religious beliefs with Sunday work?

• Could they depend on their children to help out, and how long would it be until they would be off to school or taking other jobs?

• Would the additional income and kind of work attract their oldest son John

to stay on the place under a two-family arrangement?

• How much would the changeover cost, and what would be the expected financial returns?

"With these basic questions partially answered, Sam was interested in what kinds of enterprises would best fit their land, resources, and personalities.

"We started down at the river which stretches for more than half a mile along the Burton place. This is a good fishing stream, but not big enough for operation of powerboats or water skiing. One place offered possibilities for a small bathing area. Boat rentals for fishing and pleasure could be included.

"For float fishing, Sam said he could use his truck to haul boats and fishermen up to Creston or Grantsville so they could float and fish back down to his place. A boat launching area would be easy and cheap to put in. Sam could do this himself. We noted the location on our aerial photo map.

"Next, Sam suggested we look at an area nearby where he felt tent and trailer camping sites might be developed. The site, including several big trees, was on a flood plain, however, and flooded quite frequently.

"But just above was a well-drained

Opening day of the trout fishing season on the Musconetcong River near Hackettstown, N.J. The demand for outdoor recreation generally far exceeds the supply—which is why farmers and other rural residents may find it rewarding to provide recreational facilities.

terrace out of flood danger. Spreading crowns of trees cast afternoon shade all along the edge of the field. I pointed out that campers liked morning sun and afternoon shade. The area looked like a real good bet for what Sam had in mind.

"Little more than a half mile of access road would be needed to reach the terrace, and all the area was on level, well-drained soil. I showed this to Sam on the soil map and explained why it was also a good area for septic tank disposal fields. That was important in locating toilet and bathhouse facilities and would help keep the cost down.

"Starting up toward the pastureland we passed by a half acre pond. The Burtons had put the pond in above the barn a few years before to furnish water for the barn and winter feedlot. Stocked with bass and bluegills, it was the source of fishing fun for family and friends.

"Sam asked about the possibilities of enlarging the pond and using it on a fish-for-fee basis. My hand level indicated the pond could be enlarged to about an acre. "I suggested that if this were done, he might build his income by stocking it with larger fish on a 'put and take' basis. A picnic area, located around the pond, would be an added attraction.

"While I was checking out the pond, Sam wandered over to a nearby pasture where three riding horses and two ponies were grazing.

"As I came up, Sam explained that his whole family loved horses. He had recent inquiries from townfolks about hiring horses for riding, but had not given it much thought until now.

"This brought up the subject of horse rentals and bridle trails as another kind of recreation. It would mean adding a string of horses, a few more ponies, and a pony track for small fry. A road system used for timber harvest and fire protection already laced through the 60-acre woodland. This woodlot had supplied the lumber and posts needed on the farm for several years. It also was a good squirrel woods, and each member of the family had his favorite squirrel tree which was never singled out for cutting. If the low-hanging limbs were removed, the woods roads would make good bridle trails. This

kind of recreational use of the woods would not conflict with its major use— that of growing continuous wood crops for the farm and for sale.

"Well, I left Sam at the end of the day with a lot to think about. He kept all the maps, plus our field notes. The family planned to spend their spare time during the next few weeks discussing the ideas, the problems, and the changes that would be needed in their lives and their farming operation."

Tom Simpson lit his pipe, puffed away for a moment, and then resumed.

"Sam has three main areas of concern. He would need to discuss liability problems with a lawyer. Costs and returns economics of recreation needed to be researched. Costs of recreation facilities are not well known and good figures on returns are highly variable. The Soil Conservation Service cost-return information will be very useful to him in making up his own estimates.

"Sanitation is another important item. Water supplies, toilet and bathing facilities, sewage, garbage and trash disposal must be carefully planned. Using SCS soils information, Sam will need to work these problems out with the local health and sanitation department.

"If the Burton family decides to go into this new recreation business, I'll bet you a new hat they'll make a go of it. The whole family gets along well with people. They all have outgoing personalities, and they don't mind hard work."

Tom Simpson stared off into space meditatively, then turned back to me.

"Helping plan the use of land for recreation makes my conservation job a lot more interesting, though harder," he said. "I'm sure this recreation trend will help the economy of the area, too. Outdoor recreation is a scarce item here in this part of West Virginia where practically all the land is privately owned. When landowners like the Burtons start thinking about filling this need, the results could benefit the whole area.

"That's a long story, but it's an example of a day in the life of a soil conservationist in 1967. Every tract of land has different possible uses, and every owner has needs and ideas for the use of his land."

Lassoing the West's Rampaging Dunes

A. L. HAFENRICHTER

ASK PEOPLE about rolling, billowy sand dunes and the torrid Sahara wastes—the setting for a Lawrence of Arabia intrigue—flash to mind.

Not so well known, but perhaps just as spectacular and imposing, are the large "sandpiles" common to our seashores, lakeshores, and areas of the semiarid interior of the West. These dunes and their ever-changing ridges, slopes, and valleys are a natural showplace and playground enjoyed by millions of vacationers.

Destructive Too

But dunes aren't all fun. They can be destructive too. Sand dunes move actively and relentlessly—when their vegetative cover is destroyed. They can spell trouble to highways and railroads, fill harbors of navigable streams, push into homes and communities, and encroach on farmlands and forests.

When these things happen people want something done about it. But people themselves are the chief cause for the growth of dunes and the high damage toll that dunes cause.

The onward surge of civilization has destroyed good plant cover by fire, overgrazing, excavation, trampling, vehicular travel, cultivation, and jetty building.

We can stop dunes from growing up and stabilize ones that are active. The job can be done with a good vegetative cover, using a few adapted plants.

The methods are quite simple and relatively inexpensive. But any communities with dune problems must understand and rigidly follow these methods. There can be no compromise. And once the dunes are controlled, there must be community action to maintain the plant cover.

Coastal dunes along the Pacific coast cover more than 55,000 acres, with the largest areas at mouths of principal rivers. At the mouth of the Columbia River near Warrenton, Oreg., accelerated erosion was caused by excessive use by vacationers and horseback riders, jetties built out into the ocean from the mouth of the river, building of resort homes, and the unrestricted livestock grazing of dune areas. Some 3,000 acres of sand moved toward resorts, highways, military reservations, farmlands, and the river, menacing 26 million tons of shipping. The eroding area was 20 miles long and as much as 1.5 miles wide in some places.

The assistance of the Soil Conservation Service of the U.S. Department of Agriculture was requested to control the dune areas, and Work Area Camp SCS–0–7 was set up, at Warrenton, in 1935. SCS nurseries were established to find, develop, and grow plants that the Civilian Conservation Corps camp could use to tie down the dunes.

Only a few usable plants were found among thousands studied. And only a few good methods for growing them on the

A. L. Hafenrichter is *Regional Plant Materials Specialist* (West), Soil Conservation Service, Portland, Oreg.

infertile sands proved necessary. Within 10 years the 3,000 acres were stabilized with permanent vegetation. Since then many other coastal sand dune areas along the Pacific coast have been successfully treated with the same plants and methods that were used in Warrenton.

Three simple, direct steps were used to restore a good plant cover and tie down the dunes at Warrenton.

First, a foredune was built to reduce the large amount of sand that was moved inland by winds averaging 16 miles per hour, with winter gales in excess of 55 miles per hour. The old foredune had been destroyed along most of the 20 miles of coastline.

The foredune was started in the fall and winter 50 feet above the high tide line with two rows of picket fence 30 feet apart. Fence pickets were 4 feet high, 4 inches wide, and spaced 4 inches apart. In early spring a year later, sand-stilling European beachgrass (*Ammophila arenaria*) was planted between the pickets and 50 feet to leeward and 100 feet to windward. These plantings were fertilized with nitrogen.

The dune was built back in several years to a height of 30 feet and was about 300 to 500 feet wide at the base. This was the size of the old eroded foredune.

Plantings in Hills

European beachgrass was planted over the eroding area, except where standing water existed. Plantings were always started to the windward side of any area and progressed to the leeward. They were made in hills, each of which contained three culms (a culm is a single stalk taken from a clump; it will produce a new clump). The culms were from selected stock and were grown in bare sand nurseries. Culms are strong and when dug for planting are cleaned and topped back to 20 inches. American beachgrass (*A. breviligulata*) and American dunegrass (*Elymus mollis*) were tested, but were inferior to the selected strain of European beachgrass on the Pacific coast.

Hill survival is the key to success when planting beachgrass. Survival must exceed 60 percent or the planting will fail to hold the sand. Each hill of the culms must be planted 12 inches deep and solidly tamped. Spacing between hills averages 18 inches. Spacing must be reduced to 12 inches if the conditions are severe. Only rarely are plantings spaced at 24 inches.

European beachgrass must be planted between November 1 and March 30. This is the time when air temperatures for 72 hours after planting do not exceed 55° F. Newly planted European beachgrass does not survive temperatures higher than this.

Plantings of European beachgrass are fertilized in early spring, just as buds on nodes at the base of culms begin to grow. Single applications of 60 pounds of nitrogen in the inorganic form, preferably as ammonium sulfate, give the most consistent results at the least cost.

$325 Per Acre

Cost of initial stabilization with European beachgrass averages about $325 per acre, including outlays for planting stock, labor, and fertilizer.

But plantings of European beachgrass provide only initial control of sand movement upon coastal dunes. Once the sand is stilled, beachgrass plants die and must be followed up with one of two kinds of a permanent vegetation: Grasses and legumes or shrubs and trees.

The grasses and legumes are preferred where fire is frequent or cannot be readily controlled. Clatsop red fescue (*Festuca rubra*) or Alta fescue (*F. arundinacea*) and purple beach pea (*Lathyrus japonicus*) are drilled into stands of European beachgrass after the sand has been stilled. Hairy vetch (*Vicia villosa*) is added to the seeding to provide extra nitrogen and shade for the new grass seedings the first year or two. An application of 300 pounds of 16–20–0 fertilizer is made at seeding time. Many other grasses and legumes have been tried, but none is as successful as these. An average cost of planting is $18 to $25 per acre.

Shrubs and trees are also planted into stands of European beachgrass for permanent control. Among many that have been tried on the dunes on the Oregon and Washington coasts, none compares with the leguminous shrub Scotch-broom

318

Tying down sand dunes with newly planted culms of European beachgrass in the Siuslaw National Forest, in Oregon.

(*Cytisus scoparius*) and shore pine (*Pinus contorta*). The shrub provides nitrogen necessary for establishment of the shore pine, and it is shaded out when overtopped by the pine.

Shore pine is planted as 2-year seedlings spaced 8 by 8 feet and is alternated with 1-year seedlings of Scotch-broom. These are planted after beachgrass has stilled the sand. Sitka spruce (*Picea sitchensis*), a native of the northern Pacific coast, gradually volunteers into the planting.

Pacific coastal dunes in California are planted to Monterey pine (*Pinus radiata*), but without the Scotch-broom.

Seashore dunes are used largely for recreation. Carefully planned campsites on public or private lands provide places where food can be cooked and have containers for papers and trash. Provision is made for adequate parking, toilets, and bathing facilities to prevent undue wear and destruction of ground cover.

Roads leading to the beaches are of gravel, rock, or blacktop to prevent any breaks in the ground cover.

Fire protection can be provided by building fire trails and restricting smoking and fires to camping areas. People should not cut or destroy the vegetation growing on dunes.

Special precautions also are needed to restrict traffic by vacationers, horseback riders, motorcycles, and sand buggies to areas specifically designed for these uses. Unrestricted traffic over stabilized dunes quickly destroys plant cover. Blowouts occur and become larger, and soon the dunes again become active.

Many dune areas along the coast have inland lakes where migratory waterfowl provide hunting. Hunters need to be told that destruction of grass or tree cover must be avoided. Some coastal dune areas provide good sites for upland game and for big game. Roads and trails should be provided to make these areas accessible. The roads can also be used for fire control.

Construction of homes on coastal dunes should be in the back of the foredune. Any destruction of the vegetation around buildings should be limited, and exposed sand in and around them should be planted immediately.

Some dune areas that are tied down with native grasses may be grazed. When livestock use these areas, all good pasture and range management practices become necessary to keep the pasture in good condition. Proper stocking rates, season of use, deferred and rotation grazing, and proper utilization of feed must be rigidly adhered to. Should any blowout occur, these areas must be excluded from grazing and immediately repaired.

Inland Dunes

Inland dunes in the West are of two kinds: Those in semiarid areas and those in the desert. Dunes in semiarid areas are in cool winter wet—summer dry climates in the northern part. Those in the desert regions of the south receive very scanty winter rainfall.

Inland dunes in the semiarid north are pinned down with Volga giant wildrye. Volga, a selected strain of *Elymus giganteus,* is the best plant the Soil Conservation Service found among 35 native and introduced grasses for controlling inland dunes. Plantings grew and prospered in semiarid areas. Volga stilled the sand and also spread and became the permanent vegetation. This strain was used by the U.S. Army Corps of Engineers to control dunes along new rights-of-way near McNary Dam. Later, the Bureau of Reclamation planted this grass on a large area of dunes in the heart of the Columbia Basin irrigation project which was encroaching upon farmlands.

Volga wildrye plants are produced in nurseries and dug, cleaned, and planted exactly as is European beachgrass, but in early spring. Density of planting is two culms per hill in 2- by 2-foot spacings. They are fertilized with nitrogen at the rate of 60 pounds per acre when planted.

Dunes in the desert areas of the Southwest can be controlled with vegetation only if they are artificially watered. The Southern Pacific Co.'s mainline across the desert near Indio, Calif., was plagued with severe sandstorms moved along by winds up to 30 or 40 miles per hour. So severe was the damage to equipment and tracks that 10 miles of track had to be replaced—at a cost of several million dollars. Here the company accepted the

SCS recommendation to plant a single row of tamarisk trees (*Tamarix gallica*) along each side of 10 miles of track. This planting is often called the longest windbreak in America.

Trees were planted as cuttings and spaced 18 inches apart. Tamarisk is evergreen, adapted to temperatures up to 120° F., and has an extensive root system. But even these trees must be irrigated in the scanty rainfall of the desert. At first they were watered from pipelines at 5-day intervals. The windbreak grew to a height of 30 feet in 6 years, and now no more than 5 acre-feet of water per year is required. Cost of maintenance of windbreaks and railroad equipment is small compared to the cost of repairing damage before the tamarisk trees were planted.

Sand dunes are menacing highways in the general vicinity of the Southern Pacific railroad, and they are a recognized deterrent to planned urban developments. Annual damage to automobiles traveling the highways in the area has been estimated at $12 million. The California Highway Department has now started plantings similar to those made by the Southern Pacific Co.

The sand dunes in the southern Great Plains can be controlled by establishing a cover of native grasses. Dunes occurred when man destroyed the grass cover to grow crops on land that should not have been plowed. Dunes, blown up by the wind, endangered public property and encroached on other farmlands.

The dunes are controlled in the Great Plains by smoothing them mechanically, planting sorghum crops, and then seeding native grasses into the standing stubble of the sorghum crop. The best native grasses are Indiangrass (*Sorghastrum nutans*), switchgrass (*Panicum virgatum*), sand bluestem (*Andropogon halii*), big bluestem (*A. gerardi*), little bluestem (*A. scoparius*), and side-oats grama (*Bouteloua curtipendula*).

These grasses are seeded in the spring when the soil moisture is favorable to germination and growth.

When the seedings of native grasses are protected, they effectively stabilize the sand dunes.

Eternal vigilance is necessary to keep sand dunes tied down. Constant and careful management is necessary to maintain a permanent cover of vegetation. If even a small amount of the plant cover is removed or destroyed, the forces of erosion quickly increase the size of the area.

Community Basis

Maintenance in any large section of stabilized dunes is best when organized on a community basis. This is most important if the dune area is used by the public or if it is a complex of individual properties. The Warrenton Dune Soil Conservation District adopted a land use regulation provided by the State of Oregon to protect the 3,000 acres of stabilized dunes at the mouth of the Columbia River. With the aid of the county court and the sheriff's office, SCD supervisors have been eminently successful in preventing damage to the area.

Landowners or communities throughout the United States can get technical help in dune stabilization through their local soil conservation district.

For further reading:
Brown, Robert L., "Permanent Coastal Dune Stabilization With Grasses and Legumes." *Journal of Soil and Water Conservation*, Vol. 3, No. 2, 1948.
———— and Hafenrichter, A. L., *Stabilizing Sand Dunes on the Pacific Coast with Woody Plants*. Miscellaneous Publication 892, U.S. Department of Agriculture, Washington, D.C. 20250, 1962.
McLaughlin, Willard T., and Brown, Robert L., *Controlling Coastal Sand Dunes in the Pacific Northwest*. Circular 660, U.S. Department of Agriculture, Washington, D.C. 20250, 1942.
Smith, Orlie W., Jacquot, H. D., and Brown, Robert L., *Stabilization of Sand Dunes in the Pacific Northwest*. Washington Agricultural Experiment Stations Bulletin 492, Pullman, Wash., 1947.

Outdoor Recreation — How to Find It

KARL F. MUNSON

SO YOU are thinking of a holiday in the great outdoors. Anticipation of some fine weekends and afternoons in the outdoors is running high. But where do you go? What is available?

Ask your friends, neighbors, and the people you work with. Studies show they are the number one source of information

Cosmos Blubaugh and his hunting dog, Knox County, Ohio.

on outdoor recreation. This method alone, however, will miss some high-quality opportunities.

Which State or States do you plan to visit? All States maintain tourist information offices where you can obtain free travel and descriptive recreation materials. They will provide State highway maps and information on State parks and fishing areas. Most also offer pictorial brochures, descriptions of places to go and things to do, as well as a calendar of special events. Since the specific agency varies greatly by States, a listing is at the end of this chapter.

Be as specific as possible in asking for information. For example, are you looking mainly for good camping sites? Are you interested in the historical sites of the State? Do you want to know about the fishing laws and seasons? If you say what your main interests are, they can send you more specific materials.

Tell the State's agency what your planned final destination is (if any), how much time you are going to spend in the State, and when you are planning to go. All of this information makes it easier for the agency to furnish you helpful information.

If you are going to one particular part of the State, be sure to mention it. Many area tourist organizations have printed material with the cooperation or direct

Karl F. Munson is *Program Leader* for Outdoor Recreation, Federal Extension Service.

Outdoor recreation possibilities range from water fun for a family in a national forest, riding a mule to a fishing and swimming spot during a farm vacation, to improving putting skills at a recreation area converted from a dairy farm, or even fishing from a "floater" on a lake.

(above) Pulling in a rainbow trout at fish-pond along Wilson Run, Garrett County, Md. (right) An air sled on Deep Creek Lake in Garrett County.

support of the State. The State will be happy to send this material or will refer your letter to the area tourist promotion agency for action.

You may want to know what Federal recreation areas are close to where you are going. The Forest Service maintains 10 regional headquarters. Each region has detailed, colored maps of specific national forests. These maps show lakes, trail areas, campgrounds, picnicking areas, points of information, and in addition roads, towns, drainage, and elevation.

Special publications available are (*a*) *National Forest Vacations,* (*b*) *Skiing,* and (*c*) *Backpacking.*

The addresses of these regional headquarters are:

Northern Region, U.S. Forest Service, Federal Building, Missoula, Mont. 59801.

Rocky Mountain Region, U.S. Forest Service, Federal Center, Building 85, Denver, Colo. 80225.

Southwestern Region, the U.S. Forest

Service, New Federal Building, Albuquerque, N. Mex. 87101.

Intermountain Region, U.S. Forest Service, 324 25th Street, Ogden, Utah 84401.

California Region, U.S. Forest Service, 630 Sansome Street, San Francisco, Calif. 94111.

Pacific Northwest Region, U.S. Forest Service, Post Office Box 3623, Portland, Oreg. 97208.

Northeastern Experiment Station, U.S. Forest Service, 6816 Market Street, Upper Darby, Pa. 19082.

Southern Region, U.S. Forest Service, 50 Seventh Street NE., Atlanta, Ga. 30323.

North Central Region, U.S. Forest Service, Carpenter Building, 710 North Sixth Street, Milwaukee, Wis. 53203.

Alaska Region, U.S. Forest Service, Post Office Box 1631, Juneau, Alaska 99801.

Answers to specific questions about national parks can be obtained by writing to: National Park Service, Office of Information, U.S. Department of the Interior, Washington, D.C. 20240.

The U.S. Army Corps of Engineers has a listing of all their reservoirs. A free map that shows the recreation facilities available at any reservoir can be obtained by writing to the headquarters for that reservoir. Write to U.S. Army Corps of Engineers, Washington, D.C. 20310, for a list of their reservoirs.

Are you going where the Tennessee Valley Authority (TVA) has its lakes? Write the TVA Map Library, Knoxville, Tenn. 37902. They can send you a free map of all TVA reservoirs or a detailed map of the specific areas with recreation facilities for 10 cents each.

Now let's suppose you are particularly interested in family camping grounds. Several excellent commercial guides are available at newsstands or directly from the publishers. Some of these have as many as 11,000 listings.

Some States and areas have private campground associations. The associations have printed listings available. The State tourist agency generally will have copies of those listings.

Are you interested in a farm vacation? There is a national *Farm and Ranch Vacation Guide* that sells for $1.50. It is published by Farm Vacations and Holidays, Inc., 36 East 57th Street, New York, N.Y. 10022.

A family paddles down Juniper Creek through lush, semitropical greenery in the Ocala National Forest, Fla. Fresh, clear water flows from spring at Juniper.

Some outdoor recreation booklets.

Many States and regions have farm vacation associations. Association listings are generally available through the State tourist agency.

Many areas have special pageants and annual events. An inquiry to the local chamber of commerce will bring you a list of these special events.

Many chambers of commerce can also supply you with descriptions of places of scenic or historic interest, tours, and local places to stay.

Winter sports areas have much material available. The State will often send you this material.

Of course, each State has material on its own hunting and fishing areas.

Perhaps the best single source of information is the Bureau of Outdoor Recreation's *Guides to Outdoor Recreation Areas and Facilities.* It lists both commercial and governmental sources of information, and it is organized by four types of outdoor recreation. It is available for 20 cents from the Superintendent of Documents, U.S. Government Printing Office, Washington, D.C. 20402.

And don't forget the numerous special interest magazines.

Magazines on camping, fishing and hunting, and boating are chock full of articles describing good places to go for that specific type of experience.

Anticipation is one-third of a good outdoor recreation experience. The other two-thirds are participation and reflection. Browsing through maps and descriptive materials is a very important part of the anticipation and planning experience. Maps and descriptive material are important in successful participation, and they certainly add to the satisfaction of reflection.

Have fun planning your trip!

STATE INFORMATION OFFICES

Alabama—The Division of State Parks, Monuments, and Historical Sites, Department of Conservation, 711 High Street, Montgomery, Ala. 36100.

Alaska—Department of Natural Resources, Division of Lands, 344 Sixth Avenue, Anchorage, Alaska 99503.

Arizona—Arizona Development Board, 1521 West Jefferson Street, Phoenix, Ariz. 85007.

Arkansas—The Arkansas Publicity and Parks Commission, 412 State Capitol, Little Rock, Ark. 72201.

California—Division of Beaches and Parks, Department of Natural Resources, Post Office Box 2390, Sacramento, Calif. 95811.

Colorado—Colorado Department of Public Relations, 40 Capitol Building, Denver, Colo. 80201.

Connecticut—Connecticut State Park and Forest Commission, Hartford, Conn. 06115.

Delaware—Tourism Division, Delaware State Development Dept., 45 The Green, Dover, Del. 19901.

District of Columbia—National Capitol Parks, the National Park Service, U.S. Department of the Interior, Washington, D.C. 20240.

Florida—Florida Development Commission, Caldwell Building, East Wing, Tallahassee, Fla. 32300.

Florida Board of Parks and Historical Memorials, New State Office Building, Room 311, Adams and Gaines Streets, Tallahassee, Fla. 32300.

Georgia—Georgia Department of State Parks, 7 Hunter Street SW., Atlanta, Ga. 30303.

Hawaii—Hawaii Visitors Bureau, 2051 Kalakaua Avenue, Honolulu, Hawaii 96815.

Idaho—Idaho Department of Highways, Box 879, Boise, Idaho 83701.

Illinois—Illinois Information Service, Room 406, State Capitol, Springfield, Ill. 62706.

Indiana—The Division of State Parks, Indiana Department of Conservation, 616 State Office Building, Indianapolis, Ind. 46204.

Tourist Assistance Council, Department of Commerce and Industry, 333 State House, Indianapolis, Ind. 46204.

Iowa—Division of Lands and Waters, State Conservation Commission, East Seventh and Court Avenue, Des Moines, Iowa 50309.

Kansas—Tourist-Travel Division, Kansas Industrial Development Commission, Room 122–S, the State Office Building, Topeka, Kans. 66603.

Some vacation farms cater to the special interests of a particular clientele, such as artists, musicians, or photographers. Here an art instructor gives pointers at a farm pond in Prince George County, Va.

Kansas Forestry, Fish, and Game Commission, Box 581, Pratt, Kans. 67124.

Kentucky—The Kentucky Tourist and Travel Commission, Room 66, Capitol Annex, Frankfort, Ky. 40601.

Louisiana—State Parks and Recreation Commission, Box 2541, Old State Capitol Building, Baton Rouge, La. 70801.

Maine—Department of Economic Development, State House, Augusta, Maine 04331.

Maryland—Department of State Forests and Parks, State Office Building, Annapolis, Md. 21404.

Massachusetts—Department of Natural Resources, Division of Forests and Parks, 15 Ashburton Place, Boston, Mass. 02108.

Michigan—Michigan Department of Conservation, Parks and Recreation Division, Lansing, Mich. 48926.

Michigan Tourist Council, Stevens T. Mason Building, Lansing, Mich. 48926.

Minnesota—State Parks Division, Department of Conservation, Centennial Office Building, St. Paul, Minn. 55101.

Mississippi—Travel Department, the Mississippi Agricultural and Industrial Board, 1504 State Office Building, Jackson, Miss. 39201.

Missouri—Missouri State Park Board, Post Office Box 176, Jefferson City, Mo. 65101.

Montana—Advertising Department, the State Highway Commission, Helena, Mont. 59601.

Nebraska—Information and Education Division, State Game, Forestation, and Parks Commission, State Capitol, Lincoln, Nebr. 68509.

Nevada—Department of Economic Development, Carson City, Nev. 89701.

New Hampshire—New Hampshire Forestry and Recreation Department, Recreation Division, Concord, N.H. 03301.

New Jersey—Department of Conservation and Economic Development, 520 East State Street, Trenton, N.J. 08609.

New Mexico—Tourist Division, Department of Development, State Capitol, Santa Fe, N. Mex. 87501.

New York—State Conservation Department, Division of State Parks, Albany, N.Y. 12226.

North Carolina—State Travel Bureau, North Carolina Department of Conservation and Development, Raleigh, N.C. 27600.

North Dakota—Division of State Parks, State Historical Society, Bismarck, N. Dak. 58501.

Ohio—Ohio Division of Parks, Department of Natural Resources, 1500 Dublin Road, Columbus, Ohio 43212.

Oklahoma—Tourist Division, Oklahoma Planning and Resources Board, Room 533, State Capitol Building, Oklahoma City, Okla. 73105.

Oregon—State Parks Department, Oregon State Highway Department, Salem, Oreg. 97301.

Pennsylvania—Department of Commerce, Travel Development Bureau, Harrisburg, Pa. 17101.

Rhode Island—Rhode Island Development Council, Publicity and Recreation Division, the Roger Williams Building, Hayes Street, Providence, R.I. 02908.

South Carolina—Division of State Parks, State Commission of Forestry, Post Office Box 357, Columbia, S.C. 29202.

329

South Dakota—Department of Game, Fish, and Parks, Pierre, S. Dak. 57501.

Publicity Department, Department of Highways, Pierre, S. Dak. 57501.

Tennessee—Division of State Parks, Department of Conservation, 203 Cordell Hull Building, Nashville, Tenn. 37219.

Texas—Travel and Information Division, State Highway Department, Highway Building, Austin, Tex. 78701.

Utah—The State Park and Recreation Commission, 19 West South Temple, Salt Lake City, Utah 84101.

Vermont—Department of Forests and Parks, Montpelier, Vt. 05601.

Virginia—Virginia Travel Council, The Robert E. Lee House, 707 East Franklin Street, Richmond, Va. 23219.

Division of Parks, State Department of Conservation and Economic Development, Suite 403, Southern States Building, Seventh and Main Streets, Richmond, Va. 23219.

Washington—Washington State Parks and Recreation Commission, 522 South Franklin, Olympia, Wash. 98501.

West Virginia—Division of Parks and Recreation, Department of Natural Resources, State Office Building, Charleston, W. Va. 25305.

Wisconsin—Recreational Publicity Section, Conservation Department, State Office Building, Madison, Wis. 53701.

Wyoming—Wyoming Travel Commission, Room 60, Capitol Building, Cheyenne, Wyo. 82001.

Sand Fortresses
Tame Atlantic Surf

WILMER W. STEINER

FOR 3 DAYS during March 1962 a coastal storm raked Atlantic beaches and shore communities from the Carolinas to New England. Maryland, Delaware, and New Jersey bore the brunt of tides topped by pulverizing 25-foot waves. Rampaging waters took precious human lives, and property losses were staggering.

As the wind and waves subsided, town officials and property owners began to assess the scene. Debris was strewn up and down the coast as far as one could see. Skeletons of beachfront homes filled the horizon. Yet, one contrast stood out: Where properties had been nestled behind protective sand dunes there was little or no damage. But on the stretches of shore where bulldozers had leveled dunes to create more house lots or play areas, destruction was often complete. Similarly,

little protection was provided by low dunes which had been eroded by wind after the heavy foot traffic of summer vacationers destroyed the vegetation. The crashing surf had overwhelmed the low, irregular dunes and had swept through a number of communities.

Two days after the storm, a USDA Soil Conservation Service team of specialists drove along New Jersey's Long Beach Island toward the seaside community of Loveladies. After clearing police checkpoints, they picked their way through the shambles of what had been the beautiful town of Harvey Cedars.

֍   ֍   ֍

Wilmer W. Steiner is *Regional Plant Materials Specialist*, Regional Technical Service Center, Soil Conservation Service, Upper Darby, Pa.

330

They had a special interest in what had taken place. Since 1956, they had been working with local groups in the testing of plants and techniques on Loveladies' dunes. Dr. E. E. Evaul, SCS technical leader in New Jersey, selected a stretch of beach and encouraged the owners to help the SCS team conduct the tests. Entering the Loveladies community, the specialist team had some anxious moments until they spotted the test area and found its houses still intact.

Six years of sand fencing, planting, and fertilizing on the test plots built and held the dunes high and wide in front of the houses. The churning seas had not breached the test dunes. Granted, waves chewed into the seaward side for 30 feet or more. They left a vertical wall of sand festooned with hanging beachgrass roots where gentle, grassed slopes once existed. But the houses were intact.

Neighboring properties fronted by low or narrow dunes were not so fortunate. There was damage and loss from waves and flooding as sea water poured through many a living room. A Philadelphian who "summered" in Loveladies declared, "My place is wiped out. I planned to retire here, and I still want to. But something has to be done to make sure this doesn't happen again. The future—that's what's important now."

The Great Storm of March 1962 set in motion a host of new preventive activities. Immediately, the U.S. Army Corps of Engineers marshaled bulldozers and dredges to build a protective sand dike from Maryland northward through Delaware into New Jersey. This dike was designed for the normal storm tides; sand fences were erected, and plantings made here and there to fortify it.

There remained a need to build and stabilize a massive frontal dune system.

Using the guidelines from their early studies on the dunes of Long Beach Island, Soil Conservation Service specialists intensified their search for better plants and planting techniques. Marshall T. Augustine, field plant materials specialist working in four coastal States, established cooperative test plantings at New Jersey's Island Beach State Park and on a scoured area of former dunes near Lewes,

Del., controlled by the Delaware State Highway Department. Elsewhere, SCS cooperated with State research workers assigned to dune work in North Carolina, Massachusetts, and Rhode Island.

A wealth of information soon began to accumulate. American beachgrass (*Ammophila breviligulata*) proved to be the best species for building and holding frontal dunes from Maine to North Carolina. In North Carolina, American beachgrass and sea-oats (*Uniola paniculata*) solved the problem; and, farther south, sea-oats proved the dominant frontal dune species.

Fence "Backbones"

Armed with new knowledge of what to do and aided by fresh memories of the Great Storm, SCS technicians set forth to encourage and aid seafront communities. Working through soil conservation districts and cooperating State and Federal agencies, they recommended erection of sand fences to build dunes higher and wider. Under certain conditions, sand nearly 4 feet deep can be trapped during a single windstorm. Another set of fences, set on top of the new sand, causes the process to be repeated.

In this way, sand fences become the "backbones" of new dunes.

Seaside workers drove posts in parallel lines 40 to 60 feet apart, running along and above the sea's edge. To these, they fastened lines of snow fencing or pickets or brush to form the sand-trapping fences. Where the edge of the surf was not at a right angle to the prevailing winds, a single line of fence was constructed parallel to the sea and perpendicular spurs of fencing 30 feet long were attached, spaced 40 feet apart. In other more critical areas, dunes were built rapidly by bulldozing or through dredging.

Next came the job of "tying down" the newly formed dunes. The SCS specialists showed the community groups how and when to dig American beachgrass plants from nearby sandy flats and how to prepare planting stock for use on the dunes.

As SCS men worked with groups and agencies, interest in dune building and in stabilization mounted. Planting "bees" were organized by community leaders,

331

with old and young alike pitching in. Such popular terms as "Operation Greendike" promoted an atmosphere of importance and urgency. Typical of community action, more than 1,000 "greendikers" swarmed onto New Jersey's Long Beach Island to make plantings at Barnegat Light, Harvey Cedars, and Shipbottom on a single weekend.

The U.S. Navy began dune building and planting in Virginia and Delaware.

The Delaware State Highway Department and State Parks Commission joined private citizens in a massive sand trapping and planting program.

Various agencies of the U.S. Department of the Interior planted some 14 miles of dunes along the beaches of the Chincoteague (Va.) National Wildlife Refuge, and they were active elsewhere along the Atlantic with their beachwork.

100 Miles of Barriers

The result was more than 100 miles of renewed, vegetated protective barriers—sand fortresses standing guard against the sea. Much remains to be done. But where the dune grasses have been established, they will continue to trap sand and reach ever higher and wider if they are properly protected and managed.

Soon after this flurry of dune planting started, it became evident that better sources of American beachgrass were needed. Grass on the sandy flats was being exhausted. "It's folly to rob any of the barrier dunes of their mantle, and hand-digging good planting stock from the old beachgrass stands is laborious," observed Robert B. Thornton, manager of SCS's National Plant Materials Center, which is in Beltsville, Md.

After studying various beachgrass production methods at the center, Thornton developed practical methods of producing nursery-grown seedlings.

The vigorous young plants responded to the improved cultural methods. Stems multiplied nearly a hundredfold the first year, ample quantities for propagating material. The next logical step was to use these methods and materials to encourage commercial nurseries to take over plant production.

The SCS plant material specialists approached soil conservation district leaders. The latter found a number of cooperators interested in trying out commercial beachgrass as an enterprise. Beltsville's American beachgrass planting stock was then shipped to the district supervisors who, in turn, shipped to the cooperating growers.

SCS also followed up with technical advice upon planting and growing techniques. By 1965, several million stems of the nursery-grown beachgrass were being produced commercially. Following suit, some State and Federal agencies secured stock for nurseries that now produce stock for their own lands. Prior to 1965, there had been no nursery production of American beachgrass along the entire Eastern United States.

In the spring of 1966, a new dunes-related project was established. It was at least partly stimulated by the "Great Storm of '62" and its aftermath. With funds from Congress, and land provided by the State, SCS built and put into operation the Cape May Plant Materials Center at Cape May Court House, N.J. One of the center's main objectives is to develop better plants and techniques for Atlantic coastal dunes from Cape Cod to North Carolina. The center's men gather and test suitable grasses for the ever-changing pioneer zone of the frontal dunes; and better herbaceous and woody plants for the more stable climax zone of the back dunes.

Also of concern to Plant Materials Center specialists are plants to add beauty and wildlife food and cover around dune-based homes.

Thus the 3 devastating days in March 1962 may well have been the prolog to a new era of secure shoreline beauty backed by plant science that the seas inspired.

For further reading:

Jagschitz, J. A., and Bell, R. S., *American Beachgrass (Establishment—Fertilization—Seeding)*. Bulletin 383, Agricultural Experiment Station, University of Rhode Island, Kingston, R.I., 1966.

Thornton, R. B., and Davis, A. G., *Development and Use of American Beachgrass for Dune Stabilization*. Miscellaneous Publication, U.S. Department of Agriculture, Soil Conservation Service, National Plant Materials Center, Beltsville, Md., 1964.

County Planning Counts
When You Buy a Home

ERLING D. SOLBERG

MRS. HOMEMAKER stormed into the builder's office where my wife and I were waiting and exploded to the builder: "I just won't take that house we were looking at. It was nice, but I don't want any house in Haphazard County. The county seems to have grown without any kind of plan.

"The business center is a crazy mixture of stores, gas stations, homes, and other land uses. Streets are narrow. There's no place to park. The center is rimmed with autowrecking yards. Even the country-side is ruined—with junkyards, dumps, and billboards.

"Your subdivision site was bulldozed clear. All the trees are gone.

"I have three school-age children. Yesterday, I visited the community's elementary school. I could hardly believe my eyes. It's a new school, but located across a main highway from a large residential area. Children must cross the highway going to and from school."

The tornado of words continued: "I looked for recreational facilities—parks, ball fields, swimming pools. There were none within miles. My oldest boy likes to go fishing. So, I drove him down a lane to the river. A farmer told me there aren't any fish left in the river. The stream was just filthy—poisoned with industrial and municipal wastes.

"My next stop," she said, "was at the county courthouse. I was looking for the planning and zoning office. There wasn't any. I was told that community land use planning was a waste of tax money.

"So I don't want your house," she shouted at the builder. "I wouldn't think of living in such a helter-skelter community." And with that Mrs. Homemaker flounced out, slamming the door.

By this time my wife had lost some of her enthusiasm for a new home in this area. She suddenly remembered an urgent appointment.

We found the irate Mrs. Homemaker in her car studying a roadmap. She was going to the planning office in neighboring Planwell County. She wanted to talk to their planning director and to examine their land use plan.

My wife's appointment now became somewhat less urgent. We went along to the planning office too.

We arrived at the office of the county planning commission and were fortunate to find the director there. Yes, he would be happy to show us the county land use plan and to tell us how it was prepared.

He motioned toward a large multicolored map on the wall. "That," he said, "is the county land use map. Each color is for a different kind of land use area. There are areas for residences, for business—including local shopping centers, for industry, for parks and schools, for forestry, and large areas for agriculture."

Here the director hastened to explain that the purpose of a land use map and

Erling D. Solberg is an *Agricultural Economist* in the Natural Resource Economics Division, Economic Research Service.

plan is to direct and guide future community growth into suitable areas. "All the areas indicated for residential uses on this land use map, for example, are not now built upon. But, as the community grows, more space will be needed for homes. We are suggesting," the director added, tapping four areas on the map, "that the new homes be built here, and here, and here, and here."

The director went on to discuss some of the qualities considered when locating desirable areas for residential uses. "First," he said, "we look for well-drained land, possibly sloping for a better view. We avoid land that may flood or is unusually wet. We also avoid steep slopes and land with many boulders or high bedrock. It's more costly to dig basements and trenches for utilities on such land.

"The other factors to consider," he continued, "are the location of existing residential areas, schools, parks, and shopping centers. Planners also are mindful of the location of present roads, sewers, water mains, and other public facilities. Next they consider proposed public improvements planned for the future. These are programed ahead for several years as needed. Our taxpayers object to wasteful duplication and excess capacities."

Mrs. Homemaker was becoming restless. "Something is missing," she objected. "You haven't mentioned those appealing qualities that cause women to want to live in a residential area."

"I know," the director agreed, "I was coming to that.

"Yes, the areas for homes should have ample room for green open spaces. And the air should be free of soot and grime.

"We need to have parks, playgrounds, schools, and churches nearby. Shopping centers should not be too far away. We also need convenient ways to get to work. But residential areas should be away from the noise and bustle of business and industry. Heavy traffic through the residential streets must definitely be avoided."

Mrs. Homemaker now focused her

A Soil Conservation Service man points out features of a watershed project as he gives technical advice to the Grafton County Development Council in New Hampshire.

Recreation can be the principal purpose of a small watershed project or a byproduct of reservoirs built for other purposes. This 7-acre lake is in Virginia's Shenandoah Valley.

attention on business areas. "Why," she inquired, "do we tolerate business areas stretched out along the main roads and streets? Through traffic is slowed. Parking space is limited. The areas are dangerous, both for shoppers who want to cross the roadway and for motorists."

The director strode over to the county land use map and picked out the locations of existing business areas and of some that are proposed. He pointed to the central business districts and to the several neighborhood shopping centers of about a dozen stores. These centers cater to the shopper's everyday needs. Then he indi-

cated some larger community shopping centers. These contain a greater number and variety of stores and serve a wider trade area. Finally, he showed where a much larger regional center is proposed.

The planning director turned to Mrs. Homemaker to answer her question. "Ribbon business areas strung along main roads and streets are out of date. They are an older form of business area. We would like to get rid of them.

"Shopping centers, like ribbon business areas, are highway oriented. They need to be close to busy highways and important crossings. But shopping centers are placed well back from the roadside. Ample off-street parking spaces are provided. There the shoppers can park, shop, and load bundles with safety and convenience."

"Why," Mrs. Homemaker wondered, "are factories and homes often found side by side? Why are smoky industries often located on the windward side of a town? Isn't it possible to plan our communities better than that?"

The planning director paused and then began his reply by discussing the kinds of locations that are best for industry. "Suitable transportation is the first essential," he said. "I look for vacant land fronting on navigable waters. I look for areas 500 to 2,000 feet wide between a main highway and a railroad. I look for sites near important crossings of freeways and locations near major airports.

"Industrial land should be fairly level and free from flooding. The soil must be suitable for bearing heavy structures. Modern factory buildings of one or two stories require a large acreage. Also, land is needed for landscaping and for parking for employees.

"Industry prefers areas with adequate water, sewers, and power facilities," he went on, "and with fire and police protection. The prevailing winds should be considered, especially for certain types of industries."

He concluded with a warning. "Good industrial land is often scarce. It should not be taken for other uses. Existing industries need room in which to operate—and to expand. If new industries are expected, more space will be required. Foreseeable future land needs for industry are reflected in this county's land use map and plan."

Mrs. Homemaker still wasn't satisfied, she had still more questions. "Why," she demanded, "shouldn't the subdivisions be located out among the farms? The countryside is so pleasant; there is green and open space. The soils are fertile for growing flowers, shrubbery, and shade trees."

"I am afraid," the planning director replied, "that idea isn't as good as you think. Scattering subdivisions and non-farm homes out among the farms is certain to increase taxes for everyone. New highways will be needed and new schools of all kinds. Water and sewer mains must be constructed and other public facilities and services provided."

He walked over to a large land use capability map on the wall. "This map," he commented, "tells us the locations of eight classes of soils in Planwell County, ranging from the most fertile land to the very poorest.

"Agriculture needs fertile soils. Little is gained by farming poor land. Also the

Wheaton Plaza shopping center in Maryland.

This muskrat house shows that marshlands may have important values as wildlife habitat.

land should be level or gently sloping to permit use of farm machinery and prevent erosion. Sometimes overlooked—but of increasing importance in this age of changing agriculture—are the industries which process farm products, the people who work there, and the many firms that supply or serve agriculture.

"These related industries, often located in town, would decline with the loss of agriculture's fertile soil base.

"Fertile soils," he stressed, "are a priceless heritage of any people. They should be reserved for agriculture to feed a growing population. Other less fertile land, if equally suitable, can be used instead for nonfarm purposes."

The director turned again to Mrs. Homemaker. "Besides, homes and some kinds of agriculture do not get along well side by side," he said.

"Housewives become very, very un-

happy if their homes are near hogpens, livestock feed yards, commercial poultry operations, or even modern dairies. Residential values may suffer."

Mrs. Homemaker described the dirty, lifeless river she had seen that morning in Haphazard County. She wanted to know if the land use plan for Planwell County included areas where her husband could hunt and her boys could fish and swim.

The director stepped over to the wall maps again. On the land use map he found the areas suggested for forestry and for city watersheds. He outlined other smaller areas proposed for recreational uses and for wildlife uses. He located the same areas on the land use capability map, which shows whether the soils are fertile or not. "The areas reserved for forestry," he said, "consist of soils that are poor for farming, but good for growing trees. The watershed areas are mountainous and steep. Both of these kinds of areas are good hunting grounds."

He walked to a third map—a map which tells whether or not the soils are good for a number of nonfarm uses. "The soils in these areas," he said, circling several locations with a finger, "are suitable for recreational uses. Also, the areas contain groves of trees, clear streams, and a number of good sites for dams." He circled other sections. "These lands," he explained, "are swampy and wet. We are suggesting forest and wildlife use."

The planning director sat down at his desk. He gave us a few parting thoughts. "A land use plan only serves to guide future growth in the county," he said. "The plan merely suggests. It does not direct. The county has other ways for assuring that the plan is followed. Among these are zoning and subdivision ordinances and building and sanitary codes.

"Most important, however, is the exercise of great wisdom in scheduling and in selecting the locations of new public improvements."

Our Family's Farm Vacation

JOHN L. SBARBARO III as told to LLOYD E. PARTAIN

HAS your family ever taken a farm vacation? Ours did and I would like to tell you about it.

Mother suggested that a farm vacation, even for a family of six, might not be very expensive. As a little girl she had spent summers on her grandmother's farm. She had talked to us many times about how wonderful it was. Relating her memories of the animals, birds, swimming hole, good food, and many others now became even more interesting than ever to brother Jim, 8, and me; I was 10. This even captured the imaginations of our sisters, Kathy, 5, and Carol, 2.

Dad said we should go West and see a lot of the country we had only heard about. So we decided upon southwestern Oklahoma near the Wichita Mountains. We learned about a place where we could have an air-conditioned farmhouse all to ourselves and be close to lakes, mountains, Indians, many wild animals, and interesting farming and ranching. The Salt Fork of the Red River ran right through the 440-acre farm. Arrangements were made to go and stay for 2 weeks.

I want to tell about our farm vacation myself because I kept a diary. I'll let it tell you some of the more exciting things that happened on this 1965 vacation.

July 31—Left our home in Radnor, Pa. The countryside through Pennsylvania, Maryland, West Virginia, and Virginia—with the Appalachian Mountains, Shenandoah Valley, and the Blue Ridge all around us—was beautiful and interesting. We made good time and drove a long way into Tennessee.

August 1—We drove from Tennessee to Oklahoma. Between Memphis and Little Rock along a great cyprus swamp, we spotted great blue herons, snowy white egrets, red-wing blackbirds, and so many other birds. We saw fields of soybeans and cotton for the first time.

Arrived a day early at my great uncle's country place near Oklahoma City, where we planned to visit and rest before going on West to the ranch.

🌼   🌼   🌼

Lloyd E. Partain is *Assistant* to the Administrator on Recreation, Soil Conservation Service.

A sampling of what a farm vacationist can see in Oklahoma. At the right, a prairie dog. (left) Honey bee on cotton flower and a cotton boll. (bottom) Longhorn and calves, Wichita Mountains Wildlife Refuge.

We kept it to play with, and we soon caught some more.

Our uncle took us for a ride on his tractor—what a thrill when he let each of us drive it a little. While on the tractor ride my dad said, "What's that running under the brush pile?" We stopped to see. It was a black snake about 4 feet long. Uncle said it was not poisonous, and it ate field mice and insects—a friendly snake.

Then we went fishing in a farm pond. Had to buy bait from a neighboring farm—but no one was tending the bait stand, so my uncle just dropped the money in the coin box for the bait. They call this the honor system. Kathy caught the first fish. Soon we were all catching fish.

Near uncle's barn Jim and I found an old log about 2 feet long with many holes in it. In the holes were bullets. With a knife we started digging them out. Our uncle said the log had been used for rifle and pistol target practice. He got an ax and split the log so we could get the bullets out easier. Just as I put my fingers in a crack in the old log, he said, "Look out!" There was a long scorpion in the crack.

We learned that a sting from him would be very painful. Uncle put a stick on the scorpion to show how he would

August 2—Right after breakfast, Jim found and caught a horned lizard near an anthill—an ugly but an interesting and harmless anteating creature.

curve his stinger over his back and strike the stick; and then killed him.

August 3—Early in the morning we caught a June bug in the tall grass near the barn—a big, beautiful green and blue bug with strong legs and wings. Uncle tied one end of a string about 6 feet long on the bug's hind leg and handed the other end to me and said, "Turn him loose and follow him." The bug sailed up in the air, and as he tried to fly away I ran to follow him. What fun! All the others—even little 2-year-old Carol—had to have a June bug with a string on it.

Then we went to visit some very interesting places. Our first stop was a quarter-horse-breeding farm where we saw the fastest horse in the world for a 400-yard race. He was bought for $100,000.

On the way out of this farm we saw a flock of rare birds—the upland plover. The land conservation work on this farm and others in the region is helping this bird to thrive there.

Our next stop was the Cowboy Hall of Fame near Oklahoma City. I could spend a week here studying the pioneers, the cowboys, and their troubles and joys in winning the West. We then visited Frontier City nearby where there was a lot of realistic cowboy-and-Indian stuff. This is a restored village with old saloons, the sheriff's office, country store, stagecoach, hitching posts, and everything else of the frontier times. A faked but exciting robbery was staged on the dirt street with the two robbers losing the gunfire battle.

August 5—We left uncle's early to go to our vacation ranch about 140 miles farther west. We stopped at Indian Village near Anadarko. This replica of Indian life and culture was built under supervision of the University of Oklahoma. An Indian guide with braided hair and native costume took us on a hiking tour through the village.

The Indian dances to the tom-toms were very exciting and colorful.

We visited the different kinds of homes the various tribes once lived in—thatched huts, adobes, hogans, tepees, thatched hogans, earth covered log houses, summer arbors, etc. The guide told us how various tribes learned to live off the land—how they had built their homes, collected and preserved the seeds, the fruits, and nuts, and hunted animals for use as food, clothing, and shelter without exploiting the countryside.

We drove through the Wichita Mountain Wildlife Refuge on the way to the ranch. Here we saw buffalo, Texas longhorns, deer, and other animals. We arrived at the ranch late in the afternoon. We had stopped at a farm produce market and in town to stock up on some food and other supplies.

August 6—I woke up early and started exploring the farmstead. Jim found me at the barn where we saw many things we wanted to learn more about—in the hayloft, the saddleroom, the bins, the machine shed, and other places. After a big breakfast, including the best vine-ripened cantaloups we had ever eaten, we went on a long hike in the fields, pastures, and woods. Most of this farm, or ranch as we called it, grows grass. Then we had our first yellow-meated watermelon—um—good! Dad had always thought Mother was "pulling his leg" about yellow-meated watermelon until now.

About midmorning we were off to the lake on the nearby Quartz Mountain State Park—a big lake in the edge of the mountains—for water skiing. The skis

A prickly pear cactus in bloom.

A Plains Indian war dancer.

were too heavy for me to handle, but Mother was up and skiing the first time she tried. Dad saw to it we all wore our "Mae Wests" and obeyed the other safety rules. After skiing a couple of hours, we had lots more fun swimming and enjoying the sand beach.

August 7—The man at the farm—we call him Uncle Bob—taught Jim and me about gun safety and finally let us shoot a real .22 target pistol. We both learned to hit the target. We spent most of the day at the lake and in the park.

August 8 (Sunday)—Following early church we went to the riverbed on the farm. Footraces on the sandbar were fun. Mother collected interesting driftwood, and Jim collected mussel and snail shells.

Then we learned about quicksand. Mother first stepped in the edge of it to show how you could sink, then let each of us wiggle our feet in it down to about our knees to show us that it was dangerous because we had to have help in order to pull ourselves out.

There was more water skiing in the afternoon—Mother was tremendous!!!—followed by a cookout back at the farm.

August 9—We had learned about the fields, the pastures, and the lanes, so we were permitted to saddle up Apache, Uncle Bob's big, beautiful horse, and take turns riding him with Dad leading him. Mother rode him alone. We were jealous, but had to learn before we could have a horse to ride by ourselves.

August 10—This is the day we have been waiting for. We had the use of two more riding horses, Della and Kay, and a Shetland pony, Buster. But we had to practice on Buster who had been trained to walk in a circle at the end of a long rope. Jim, Kathy, and I took turns taking our lesson. Mother and Dad rode Della and Kay, and I got to ride Buster on a short ride in the lane to the big pasture. Jim and I were learning to groom and feed the horses by now.

It was interesting to see them wallow in the sand and drink at the windmill tank after they were unsaddled. We also had a lesson on how to place the saddle, blanket, bridle, and ropes in the right places in the harness room.

Another cookout on the farm that evening with paper plates and cups, outdoor grill, etc.—our meal preparation was not a very big job.

Mother read in the newspaper about the showy display of shooting stars due in the western sky. We set up cots outside to watch. There were millions of stars in the clear sky. They look so much lower, and there are so many more of them than we had ever seen in the East.

About 9:30 we began to see the shooting stars. Some of the meteorites seem to have long flashing tails of fire.

August 12—Mother needed some more

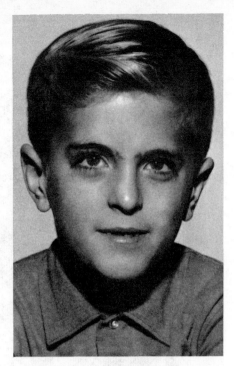

John L. Sbarbaro III, of Radnor, Pa., whose diary describes his family's farm vacation.

fresh peaches, vegetables, and melons, so our first chore was to go and pick them. There is nothing better than a soft ripe

If Shorty egret asks, "Where's Pa," his big brother might reply: "Out scratching for a living for us."

A golden eagle.

peach right from the tree. We put the melons in the windmill tank to keep them cool—there was no room in the refrigerator.

We rode horses most of the rest of the day. Even Carol got to ride Buster with Dad leading him. Jim and I had our first lesson in using the lariat rope. A post about 5 feet high was our target. It's fun, but not so easy.

The gypsum hills are about 2 or 3 miles distant. We explored these and collected interesting gypsum rock, some with copper ore. We climbed one high hill. On the way up we flushed some scale quail—a beautiful game bird the conservation department started in this area a year or so ago. We collected some ripe fruit of the prickly pear cactus—had to be careful about the needles and fine spines.

Tonight we were invited out to the 4–J Ranch, another summer vacation place near the Wichita Mountains, for a big cookout. We arrived in time to hike along some of the trails in the jack oak-covered sandhills on this ranch where there were numerous wild turkeys. Since this was molting time, Jim and I had fun collecting turkey feathers.

On the way home that night we stopped for a quick dip in the lake.

August 13—This was our day to return to the Wichita Mountain Wildlife Refuge. After a drive through the mountains, we stopped at several points in the refuge. We saw a prairie dog town. These members of the squirrel family do all kinds of antics. There were several herds of buffalo and longhorn steers. At other places we saw deer and elk. From the highest mountain inside the refuge, which has a scenic drive up it, we saw several hawks, one golden eagle, and many other interesting birds. We could look for miles around—the mountain range, lakes in the foothills, and ranches and farms beyond.

August 14—More horseback riding. Kathy now rides Buster without someone leading him. Jim and I practiced galloping our horses while on a very long ride through the fields with Mother. In the evening we went to gocart races at the park and then for a swim.

August 15—Mother's brother who lives in Oklahoma City visited us. He and his wife both love horses; so there was more trail riding and fun. I am learning to throw the rope pretty well. It makes me feel like a real cowboy. Jim and I both have lariat ropes and western hats now.

Another big dinner followed by watermelon and more stargazing, and we were ready for bed—we thought. But someone heard a coyote howl. Out of the house everyone came to listen to the sound.

Cotton and Jack Rabbits

August 16—We took a long tour in the area to learn more about farming and ranching. Cotton, alfalfa, and grain sorghums were growing upon irrigated land. We saw huge fields of dry wheat stubble where many jack rabbits live. Dad saw a U.S. Department of Agriculture pickup near a gulch. We stopped and had a nice chat with the Soil Conservation Service man.

He told us his survey crew was staking out a damsite. The dam would create a big lake to help prevent floods on a creek about a mile away. There were mesquite trees, sagebrush, and cactus everywhere around. He said in 2 or 3 years the lake would be a good place to find water birds and go fishing.

The conservationist told us about the many things being done in the county to conserve the soil, water, range, and wildlife. He was headed for another place in the soil conservation district down by Red River on the Texas border, and said if we would follow he could show us several kinds of land and the different crops and grasses suited to them. We did and stopped at several places.

Jim and I asked if we might collect samples. The farmers were glad to have city boys take one plant out of a big field so we got samples of cotton, milo, alfalfa, sweetclover, sudangrass, peanuts, and guar. Nothing is more beautiful than a field of alfalfa in bloom—pink-purple on top of dark green and alive with honey bees. On some fields the hay had been cut and was curing in the sun. It smelled like something good to eat.

On the way back to the ranch we saw ground squirrels, road runners—the bird that does not fly, terrapins, horned and

345

Horned lizard.

green lizards, hawks, and a beautiful Mississippi kite soaring overhead.

August 17—All of us were up early. The scissor-tailed flycatchers in the trees around the house were our alarm clock as usual. This is a colorful, but noisy long-tailed bird that catches insects in the air and drives away hawks, crows, and other large birds. We heard bobwhite quail calling from beyond the shelterbelt area north of the big barn.

Jim and I saddled up and bridled our horses without help for the first time— after feeding, currying, and brushing them. We rode to a sandhill area on the ranch to collect long yucca stems with seed pods for Mother.

Uncle Bob found and gave Dad an old branding iron with his initials—J-L-S— as the brand. What a find! Mother visited an antique place and got a leather horse collar with hames and straps. She is going to fix it up for a mirror frame for our recreation room at home. She also got a set of old cotton weighing scales, a cow yoke, a milk can, and other things to take home with us.

We found time to go fishing and swimming in a large farm pond in the afternoon and have an outdoor fish fry and chicken barbecue in the evening.

August 18—This was a very sad day for us kids. We had to pack up to leave the farm. We are going to miss Buster the pony the most; then Uncle Bob and the horses, Della and Kay. We talked about the good food, the water skiing, fishing, horned lizards—everything that makes a vacation on the farm a happy one for the whole family.

We had to pack and crate our many collections for our recreation room to be shipped; our car wouldn't hold them all. "About what does it cost for a farm vacation?" My mother keeps good records, so she says about $140 a week for our family of six where we supplied our own food and did our own laundry.

If you have meals with the farm family and get other housekeeping services, the cost would be $30 to $35 a week for each child and $40 to $45 for each adult.

This is the deal we want for our next farm vacation so that Mother can have a full vacation, too.

These costs do not include travel and swimming or horseback riding lessons.

A farm vacation does not end with going back home. I have written a little story about ours that was printed in the school paper. The many farm vacation items and photographs which decorate our recreation room inspired me to write a poem about it for English class. And Jim and Kathy use a lot of the things for "Show and Tell" in school.

Careers in the Outdoors

CARL B. BARNES

EVERY year the Jones family hauls out camping gear, piles it into the family car, and heads for the wide open spaces. It's vacation time and like as not the family's goal is some national forest or park, either close to home or somewhere across the vast expanse of the U.S.A.

Somebody has to see that the Joneses—and the thousands of families like them—are safe and sound and that there are no flies in the ointment to mar their happy vacation expectations. Who is this "somebody?" It's Uncle Sam, of course, and his army of workers serving in careers in natural resource management.

These workers are the foresters, outdoor recreationists, soil scientists, soil and range conservationists, park rangers, farm management supervisors, the wildlife biologists, engineers, horticulturists and landscape architects, plus a host of people in other professions who conserve, develop, and protect our natural resources.

Today, the careers in natural resource management are in a period of evolution brought about by new advances in science and technology, increased demands for outdoor recreation, and new emphasis on natural beauty. And the field for recruits is wide open.

Startling gains in agricultural production in our country since the 1940's have freed men and land for other uses. During the 1950's, the program of multiple use of forest lands for recreation, wildlife, water, forage, and timber was conceived.

The increased income of the American public, as a whole, combined with more leisure has created big new demands for recreational facilities.

Our greatly increasing rate of population growth has brought about a concern

❁   ❁   ❁

Carl B. Barnes is *Director*, Office of Personnel, U.S. Department of Agriculture.

A range conservationist (above) helps the owner's wife develop a conservation plan for a guest ranch. At left, a district forest ranger talks over a sheep grazing permit with a ranch foreman. Right, the depth of an irrigation reservoir is being checked, a task which humor helps make more bearable. The man is reported saying: "Hurry up and read this stick, I'm slipping off my brother's shoulders."

for man in his environment. This has brought increased demands to preserve and enhance the beauty of the outdoors before it slips through our fingers and is lost forever—and to end pollution that defiles our lakes and streams and the very air which we breathe.

These are but a few of the factors that have focused attention on the need for conserving and making better use of our natural resources; beautifying and retaining areas with scenic, historic, and esthetic value; a concern with domestic and industrial water supplies and abatement of air and water pollution; and increasing use of our land and water areas for recreation and fish and wildlife enhancement.

Forest Rangers

One of the most popular natural resource careers is that of the forester. The U.S. forest ranger, in his olive green uniform, works closely with the State and the Federal fish and game departments to provide better fishing and hunting for sportsmen. He recommends development of new campground and picnic areas to serve the ever-growing number of recreationists who visit the national forests. He works to maintain the natural beauty of the land for the enjoyment of all by screening "ugly" areas like work centers and powerlines with trees, by enforcing regulations to prevent the destruction of wildflowers and flowering trees, and by using construction techniques that blend rather than clash with rustic settings.

Timber and range management are, of course, among the major concerns of the forest ranger.

In everything the forest ranger does, he is concerned with good soil and water management. Water flowing from the Nation's forests is becoming one of our most valued resources.

The first soil conservationist was employed by the Federal Government about 30 years ago. Originally, he helped landowners and operators combat the ravages of erosion on their land. Over the years new challenges have arisen.

The soil conservationist has met them by taming floods, holding water on the land and in reservoirs, using it both for irrigation and for recreation, or helping nature establish vegetation upon eroded hillsides and transforming them, once again, into productive pastureland.

The conservationist, also, is becoming more involved with the urban, as well as rural, areas. His work has broadened to include planning activities for complete watersheds, irrigation projects, entire river basins, and leading the fight on water pollution through fostering practices that effectively control erosion.

In all of his work, the conservationist helps to maintain beauty where it exists, restore beauty where it has been marred, and to create beauty by using land, water, and the forests in ways that enhance the quality of man's surroundings.

Lots of rural would-be hosts to the Joneses do not have the "know-how" and the financial backing required to provide

Conservation Biologist Bill Hollister, of the New York State Conservation Department, tacks up a poster marking a cooperative hunting area on the Alexander Ewing farm near Millbrook, N.Y.

349

facilities for the vacationers. Farm management supervisors are building satisfying careers giving technical and credit assistance which benefit both the would-be hosts and the Joneses.

These specialists in farming and rural management furnish the guidance and needed credit to enable rural families to develop recreational enterprises like golf courses, campsites, hunting areas, and fishing ponds. Through loans, and assistance in farm and money management, they help farmers to use their land and water resources to produce more food and to improve their homes. They also help small communities develop water supply and sewage disposal systems. Working in close cooperation with foresters and soil conservationists, they provide credit for producing trees, developing irrigation systems, and draining farmland.

Insect Pest Control

Those using our outdoor recreational areas might also give a prayer of thanks to the entomologist for the blessing that he bestows by controlling insect pests.

Because the entomologist has learned the behavior of insects, his knowledge aids the manager of recreational areas in controlling pests like the mosquito whose sting is very annoying, but whose greater danger lies in its transmittal of diseases such as malaria.

The entomologist has discovered that certain insects are weedkillers. Through these discoveries, the Klamath weed, formerly a scourge to our Western States, was controlled, as were also the alligator weed in our Southeastern States and the puncturevine in California.

It was also the entomologist who discovered that a substance, taken from the abdomen of the female gypsy moth, could be used as a lure to trap and destroy the male moths which had ravaged a New England forest. Without this and other means of control, millions of acres of wildflowers and timber would become desolate landscapes.

Then there's the wildlife biologist. He develops wildlife management systems for the most efficient use of resources and methods for revegetating depleted habitats. He also determines the effects of timber growing and harvesting practices on these wildlife habitats, the effects of wildlife upon timber production, and the interrelations of livestock and wildlife to obtain optimum production of both.

The landscape architect plays an important role in the selection of lands that have important features of interest and beauty to the American public. He helps make the national forests enjoyable by his design of recreation areas and other installations that will withstand intense long-range use. Through his designs he also provides for natural growth and beauty. New campsite development plans averaging 3,000 per year for the next several years will challenge the young landscape architect and tax our colleges' ability to produce the numbers of such professionals which are needed.

Another worker in resources conservation and management is the program specialist who also serves the agricultural price support and production adjustment programs. He helps administer the Agricultural Conservation Program (ACP), through which the farmers and ranchers receive payment for part of the costs of carrying out soil, water, woodland, and wildlife conservation practices on their land. He is also involved in expanding the cropland diversion programs which move eligible acreage from the production of surplus crops to more economic uses. The newest Cropland Adjustment Program (CAP) encourages farmers to open up farmland to the public for hunting, hiking, trapping, and fishing, with additional benefits from increased protection of water supplies.

Under a special feature of the CAP, popularly called "Greenspan," local communities can apply for Federal funds to help them purchase and develop former cropland to provide more open spaces for public recreation, wildlife habitat, natural beauty, or other uses that control air and water pollution.

Most people employed by the U.S. Department of Agriculture in such careers are at the professional levels. They are graduates of the colleges of agricultural engineering, forestry, and other schools that specialize in resource management curricula. Just a few years ago, a majority of the students entering these colleges came principally from the rural areas. In 1966, about half of the students entering these colleges came from nonfarm homes.

This reflects the impact and emphasis on forestry and wildlife management, outdoor recreation and parks management, water pollution control, and the other off-farm agricultural occupations.

According to the National Science Foundation's Commission on Education in Agriculture and Natural Resources, 20 of the 50 land-grant colleges and several other universities which offer courses in agriculture are now offering options and curricula in outdoor recreation and park management.

A majority of the 40 forestry schools offer options in forestry recreation and/or park management. These options are in addition to the standard curricula and major areas of study already provided by the schools of agriculture and forestry to prepare students for careers in the natural resource management area.

Any young man or woman who wants to follow a career in the natural resource management field should write the dean of agriculture or forestry at the college or university he plans to attend.

He might also refer to the U.S. Depart-

These two rattlers were spotted by members of a soil survey team in Lea County in New Mexico. Natural resource careerists get close to nature.

ment of Labor's "Occupational Outlook Report" series. These are made available for reference by college counselors and placement directors and at public libraries.

For natural resources careers in the Federal Government, information can be obtained from the Office of Personnel of either the U.S. Department of Agriculture, Washington, D.C. 20250, or the U.S. Department of the Interior, Washington, D.C. 20240.

An individual can get information on similar careers in State governments by writing to the head of the agricultural, conservation, or forestry departments of the individual's State or to his State employment service.

A soil conservationist, with his know-how on soils and drainage, can give good advice to forestall problems like this golfer has at Folkston, Ga. See ball in water at far left.

Bicycle Trails
and Trail Riders

WILLIAM W. VETTER

THE FIRST marked bikeway within the United States was established in Homestead, Fla., about 6 years ago, and the idea spread not only to other communities in that State, but to many areas around the country. Other examples may be seen in Boston, with its path along the Charles River to Cambridge; New York City, which has many miles of paths in 28 parks; and Chicago, which has extensive bike paths along the lakefront, as well as others in outlying parts of the city. It is estimated that as many as 10,000 cyclists have used the Chicago facilities in the course of a single day.

Milwaukee has a loop trail which completely encircles the city for a distance of 64 miles. Adjacent to it is the Waukesha County Bicycle Route—and these now connect with others to make up the cross-Wisconsin bicycle route which completely spans the State. The Kettering section of Dayton, Ohio, has a cycle route which covers 18 miles and passes through some neighboring communities, while several other cities in Ohio offer facilities.

Maryland opened its first bikeway in Patapsco State Park in 1964 and its second the following year in one of its parks within the city of Baltimore. California is a hotbed of cycling activity, yet paradoxically it has few bikeways at present. The situation is changing, however, and more are beginning to appear. Washington, D.C., has no bikeways within the city, but several park areas are conducive to cycling, and the historic Chesapeake & Ohio Canal towpath has been a favorite

habitat for cyclists for a number of years. Silver Spring, Md., a suburb of Washington, D.C., has recently opened a path in its Wheaton Regional Park, with provisions for expansion if needed. This is just a small sampling of the facilities available around the country.

Special cycling events include the semiannual ride from Palmyra, N.J., to Mount Holly and the Pennsylvania Dutch rallies. The Mount Holly run, a 35-mile round trip, has been held for well over a half century and takes place on the first Sundays of May and October. The Pennsylvania Dutch rallies were held in 1965 and 1966. Both usually draw well over 100 cyclists from many areas in the East.

Difficult terrain has been traversed by cyclists of a relatively limited experience and ability, like cyclists who belong to the International Bicycle Touring Society. This all-adult group is made up of persons from many parts of the United States, besides a few from Canada and overseas. Most of the group consists of professional people, white-collar workers, and civil servants, and ages range from the mid-20's to over 70. During the early fall of 1964, some members embarked on a 12-day, 600-mile tour through the hills

William W. Vetter, a scientific photographer at the Goddard Space Flight Center, Greenbelt, Md., has been a cyclist for about two-thirds of his 44 years. He planned and led the 14-day tour through the Appalachian Mountains which was sponsored by the International Bicycle Touring Society in 1966.

352

Cycling through the rolling farmland of Lancaster County, Pa.

and mountains of Connecticut, Massachusetts, Vermont, and New Hampshire amid the splendor of the autumn foliage.

The group became more active in 1965 and ran two fall trips, one along the coast of Maine followed by another along the upper Mississippi Valley through Illinois, Wisconsin, and Minnesota. In 1966, three big tours were successfully completed: A repeat of the 1964 New England tour, a tour of the Appalachian Mountains of Maryland, Virginia, and West Virginia, and a fantastic tour through France which attracted 25 Americans.

The groups and individuals who venture away from urban areas by bicycle include hostelers, those who hold membership passes in the American Youth Hostels, Inc. AYH, a member of the International Youth Hostel Federation, was established in 1934 with the idea of providing inexpensive accommodations for those traveling under their own steam, by bike, canoe, on foot, and so on.

Hostels have been established in many parts of the country and may be located in a school, camp, church, student house, mountain lodge, farmhouse, converted barn, or specially constructed building. They usually come equipped with dorms, washrooms, and kitchen facilities. The whole operation is "do it yourself," and the hostelers cook their own meals and do the cleaning up.

The word "Youth" in the title does not imply age but rather, spirit, and the slogan is that anyone from "4 to 94" may participate in the U.S. program.

Further information about cycling programs can be obtained from the following four sources:

• The League of American Wheelmen, 5118 Foster Avenue, Chicago, Ill. 60630 (touring and the general promotion of cycling activities).

• International Bicycle Touring Society, 846 Prospect Street, La Jolla, Calif. 92037 (extended tours for adults).

• American Youth Hostels, Inc., National Headquarters, 20 West Seventeenth Street, New York, N.Y. 10011 (hosteling activities for all ages).

• Bicycle Institute of America, 122 East 42d Street, New York, N.Y. 10017.

An abandoned beaver dam alongside a quiet road in Hidden Valley Creek, Rocky Mountain National Park, Colo. These dams, chinked with mud, are so strongly built that men seeking to clear watercourses have been forced to use dynamite.

Shunpiking Is for Fun

KATHARINE N. MERGEN

SINCE the automobile joined the family circle in America, the Sunday or holiday drive into the country has become as much a part of our family traditions as Thanksgiving turkey.

Shunpiking is the modern-day term for Sunday driving and is a word that might have been coined by some turnpike-weary driver seeking a change of pace from the speedway scramble. Indispensable as they are to transportation and travel, today's high-speed roads are not only lethal, but in most cases illegal for the leisurely pace of the Sunday drive.

Shunpiking is first of all for pleasure, for freedom to follow a whim, for time to stop and enjoy the sunlight on a field of grain, a chipmunk frisking over a rock, or the lilting song of a meadowlark. Many shunpikers gear their trips to wildflower hunts in spring and color jaunts in autumn, to bird watching, rock hounding, or photography.

Other shunpikers find their chief joy simply in following tree-lined roads or watching the changing pattern on a countryside made beautiful through the harmony of care and long use.

The people of Manitowoc County in Wisconsin added a new twist to the country drive with "Reading the Landscape" tours, complete with a self-scoring list of things to see and with bonus points for spotting a glacier-deposited esker, a forest plantation, a gully, and specified trees.

✤   ✤   ✤

Katharine N. Mergen is an *Educational Relations Specialist,* Information Division, Soil Conservation Service.

This is shunpiking with a conservation flavor, and it has all the excitement of a sports car rally.

I know of one dedicated shunpiker who loves the desert country of a Western State where trees are scarce. For several years, he has planted small trees at his favorite roadside stops and watered them in dry seasons. At last he had the satisfaction of seeing his trees come under the protection of the State highway department.

Pennsylvania, the State first with the modern turnpike, now features shunpiking as a tourist attraction throughout the State. One of the favorites with visitors is a loop that starts and ends at the Blue Mountain Interchange of the Pennsylvania Turnpike. This route offers such

Offbeat bird watching. Anhinga (snakebird) spears a bluegill in the Everglades of southern Florida.

A farm in the valley near Folsom, W. Va.

diverse scenes as Gettysburg Battlefield, the picturesque Amish and Dutch country, and vistas of rich farmlands whose contoured crop rows and curving grassed waterways are living studies in pattern and perspective.

Shunpikers on the other side of the country in southern California can have their choice of desert, mountain, or seashore just off the freeways.

Within the city limits of Los Angeles lie 800 acres of chaparral and boulders where Big Tujunga Creek spreads over the flatland of Tujunga Wash during the course of its winter rampages.

100 Bird Species

Here is a miniature wilderness, alight with flowers in spring and lively with more than 100 species of birds.

North of Los Angeles, off Highway 101, a winding drive along State Highway 33 from Ojai brings the shunpiker to the Sespe Creek turnoff and, by way of a primitive road, to the Sespe Wildlife Area where the last of the California condors have taken refuge. Farther north on Highway 33, for the same back-country feel but on less primitive roads, the Lockwood-Ozena route leads through piney country to Highway 99, and so home.

Chicago shunpikers have a wealth of choices. They can follow the Black Hawk Indian Trail through the beautiful Rock River country along Route 2, south of Rockford. Or they can visit the Indiana dunes country, where the steady march of the towering sandhills can be plainly seen. On Highway 74, Kickapoo State Park with its 2,000 acres of outdoor playground stands on formerly depleted strip mine land, now reclaimed through good land use management.

Shunpike trips are waiting all across the land, to suit every interest and taste. All it takes is a little curiosity, imagination, and a road map.

Some shunpiking sights. (right) Red fox pup, Kettle Moraine State Forest, Wis. (upper left) Cactus. (left) Sign outside a shop at New Market, Md., inspires a question: Where can you find the "new line" antiques? (below) Pelicans near Klamath Falls, Oreg.

357

Clean, Pure Air, *Anyone?*

C. STAFFORD BRANDT

AIR POLLUTION can blight a community as surely as poverty. What good are "paint-up fix-up" campaigns if a freshly painted wall becomes grimy in a few months? Why fix a broken gutter if you know it will corrode in a year? We would not expect much civic pride from residents surrounded by an open garbage dump, and the air of some of our communities is just that—a garbage dump.

Air pollution can despoil any valley as effectively as a polluted stream. An open sewer is not very attractive in a recreational area, regardless of how lovely the trees are along it. A crystal-clear brook running through a woods blighted and discolored by air pollution is also not very inviting. All too often the polluted stream and the polluted air go hand in hand to spoil an area.

Air pollution can reduce farm productivity as surely as soil erosion. There is a difference. If a farmer loses productivity because of erosion, it is his shortsighted actions that are to blame. But if a truck farmer in New Jersey loses a crop of lettuce because of smog, it is everyone from D.C. to Boston who's to blame.

Any explosion demands attention. But slow corrosion may pass unheeded until in time the result is just as destructive.

Some years ago many realized that soil erosion was a waste. Few realized how serious a waste. Fewer yet dared nag our conscience. Even the "earthquake" of the Dust Bowl left many disinterested. Now, almost too late, most people recognize the essential need of sound soil conservation practices. Much progress has been made, but much remains to be done.

Today the quality of the air is beginning to nag our conscience. Many realize that air quality is deteriorating. Much has been written recently about the disgraceful, costly, unpleasant, unnecessary, and potentially hazardous problems of air pollution. But effective action requires more than words.

There have been few "earthquakes" to attract our attention. The little desert around Ducktown, Tenn., stands as a continuing monument to the destructive influence of air pollution. Donora, Pa., attained unwanted fame when 20 people died because of air pollution. And then there is Los Angeles and its smog.

Some areas have obtained a degree of fame through solving air pollution problems. While Ducktown still has its desert because of effects created early in this century, the smelter that caused the damage now has its emissions under good control. Pittsburgh has made a dramatic recovery from the smoke and grime for which it was once noted.

And again, there is Los Angeles. The efforts of this area to clean up smog have been well publicized. The gains that have been made are frequently not noticed in the smog which remains. Of even greater concern is the fact that this problem of smog is no longer unique to Los Angeles.

The symptoms of photochemical smog are now common to all our metropolitan

❧ ❧ ❧

C. Stafford Brandt is an Agricultural Research Service *Chemist* assigned to the Division of Air Pollution, Public Health Service, U.S. Department of Health, Education, and Welfare, Cincinnati.

areas. For smog severity and extent, the coastal belt from Washington, D.C., to Boston can now claim the unenviable title of "first in smog"!

In the 1963 Yearbook of Agriculture, *A Place to Live,* I outlined some of the problems of air pollution and its control. If I were rewriting that chapter today, I would make only minor changes. The primary causes of air pollution—people—have not changed. In essence this problem is the result of more and more people demanding more and more services.

How does air pollution affect the needs and desires of people? Some points are obvious yet they need to be restated.

Accept the obvious: Air pollution fouls the area we want for shelter, corrodes the beauty we seek for relaxation, and erodes the productivity that we require for living. What more do we need for action?

Many places have cleaned up obvious sources of air pollution. Pittsburgh has reduced its dirt and grime so that the golden triangle can gleam in the sun.

There is really no reason for any community, regardless of size, to tolerate the smoke, grime, and dust aspect of air pollution. Some do tolerate this waste as a price for prosperity. Waste is hardly justifiable at any time and certainly not as a product of prosperity.

That smelter at Ducktown destroyed thousands of acres of wooded hill. The corrosion of the natural beauty of this area was so complete that recovery has been almost impossible despite good controls. Although few isolated sources are so totally destructive as the original Ducktown smelter, far too many sources are needlessly degrading the natural beauty of large areas. An isolated location should not be an excuse for permitting air pollution. The best air pollution control procedures available should always be required regardless of location.

The problems of reduced productivity due to air pollution in areas like the belt from Washington to Boston are serious. If we were able tomorrow to install the best air pollution controls technology available upon every single air pollution source in this area, the situation would not be eliminated, but would be greatly improved. The lettuce farmer would still have some troubles. But to do nothing because we cannot do everything is more than ridiculous.

The problems of our large metropolitan areas and belts put a great strain on our air resource over large areas. Many smaller problems as well strain our air resource beyond need. Even with the best of controls the clean, pure air of the remote wilderness is unattainable. However, this does not mean we must accept foul air.

We must recognize that the air is just as much a limited, essential resource as our soil and our water. If we are to continue to satisfy our needs and our desires, we must practice air conservation.

As of now we are having some "earthquakes" which should shake us all into action. If we do not act, we may have a Donora-type earthquake on the destructive scale of Ducktown.

Smoke from open burning of refuse at the District of Columbia's Kenilworth Dump becomes a backdrop for the Capitol of the United States.

Six-foot-two man at left is dwarfed by strip mining shovel near Marissa, Ill. Shovel picks up 250 tons of earth and releases it as far as 400 feet away.

Returning Strip Mined Areas to Use

THEODORE B. PLAIR

IN THE VALLEYS of the upper Mississippi and the Ohio, machines as tall as a 21-story building are clawing up more than 200 tons of earth and rock in a single scooping motion and dumping it in thunder hundreds of feet away.

Other equipment being used in strip mining—the harvesting of minerals after removing the covering rock and dirt—has grown in recent years to giant proportions. A truck will carry as much as 140 tons of coal or of ore. Augers 7 feet in diameter bore 200 feet into the seams to drag coal from the mountainsides.

Public Interest Rises

With new efficiency in this industry, the acreages mined are greater, pits are deeper, and the spoil piles are higher. The cost of reclaiming mined lands has kept pace as well.

Public interest in using the strip mined land for crops, pasture, timber, wildlife, recreation, and for residential and industrial sites has grown, too, as has a concern on the part of many people over the leaving of blight on the landscape. This has resulted in new demands upon the skills of those who make the plans for and who rebuild these areas.

In the infancy of strip mining, a hundred years ago, acreages disturbed were relatively small. There was little demand to return them to use.

An expanding population, with broadened requirements for space, has changed this. Newer generations have developed a keen awareness of the values of land—land for livelihood and good living, for play, and the restorative effect of a pleasing outdoor scene. New leisure has helped to intensify this need.

As a result, landowners are seeking improved ways to reclaim and repair, to reshape and replant, and to find profitable uses for strip mined areas when the machines have moved away.

In the interior coal province—Indiana, Illinois, Missouri, Kansas, and western Kentucky—from 10 to 15 percent of the mined area is now in water surfaces. Land by water has a high potential for homesites. Water surfaces offer recreational opportunities in the form of fishing, boating, swimming, water skiing, and hunting. Water storage in strip mined areas, too, has an effect on streamflow, tending to increase it in dry seasons.

Trees, shrubs, grasses, legumes, and cultivated plants will grow successfully on strip mined areas, in some cases better than they grew before. In Virginia, for example, hay production was 50 percent greater after reclamation than before mining. Some of the fastest growing yellow pines in the Nation are on land hydraulically mined in the gold rush days in the Sierra Nevadas.

Trees are growing in strip mined areas for erosion control, for pulp, for saw logs, and for the living room at Christmas.

❧ ❧ ❧

Theodore B. Plair is *Assistant Director*, Plant Sciences Division, Soil Conservation Service.

In most reclaimed strip mined areas, it is usually possible to develop additional wildlife cover and food. Water for fish and migratory fowl has been brought, through surface mining, to hundreds of new sections.

Some of the upper Mississippi valley's best fishing is on the lakes that have been created by strip mining.

In some areas, mining companies follow a policy of restoring strip mined lands. For some the policy was established well in advance of legislation. A Pennsylvania company has mined more than 2,000 acres and has kept pace with the mining in the planting of grasses and legumes and more than 2 million trees.

Machinery and methods have been developed to replace the dirt and rubble, leveled with topsoil on top, as the mining operation proceeds.

In a growing number of areas local landowners—with soil conservation districts and the Soil Conservation Service providing leadership and technical know-how—are bringing new order to lands jumbled by strip mining. This work is often in cooperation with industry.

In West Virginia, soil conservation districts began in 1953 entering into contracts with mine operators on a voluntary basis to do revegetation work. In such cases, a Soil Conservation Service technician lends guidance in the development of a conservation plan for each landholding where mining has been carried on. Most of the planting work is being done by the districts. In a single year, the soil conservation districts of West Virginia revegetated 3,238 acres of strip mined lands, as part of the conservation use and treatment of landholdings.

For best final results, with minimum cost to all concerned, a joint mining and reclamation plan is a most useful tool. In most areas much information is available to guide the mining engineer, the soil scientist, and the geologist in deciding how best to move and to use the waste material. Knowing, before mining, what the site limitations are helps in deciding on the uses of the area. These uses can be

Good fishing in an Indiana lake created by strip mining. Tree planting along the banks enhances the area's recreational value.

both temporary and permanent. For example, a reservoir may be developed for storing water for ore processing and later used for domestic and recreation needs.

It is still necessary to find remedies that are more satisfactory and more efficient for the use of the mined areas. Research by government and by industry has opened the way to swifter return of profit and beauty to mined hills and pastures and to the return of clear, clean streams.

Today there is a pressing need for more knowledge of this kind. Mining minerals and restoring the mined areas to the best use for the greatest number of our citizens will be a continuing challenge.

In this Nation, we have the ingenuity and resources to turn most strip mined areas into useful and attractive portions of our landscape. It is not necessary to invite the censure of those who follow us because we, in our haste to gain wealth and comfort, left ruin in our countryside when we might have kept it beautiful.

Trees and My Country Place

JAMES L. HARRISON

ONE ACRE of waterfront woods may not seem to offer sufficient challenge to a dedicated woodland enthusiast, but I can assure you that the opportunities for a weekend hobbyist to explore the fascinating mysteries of forestry, beautification, and woodland management are legion. Five years ago, after tramping over most of the Chesapeake Bay watershed, I found an acre of property on Mill Creek, a stone's throw from its juncture with the Patuxent River, and bought it. This act began an affair of the heart between me and a small corner of the "land of pleasant living" which has not diminished.

Less than one-third of the tract was cleared. A small one-room cottage stood in the center of the open area, and the view from this point—30 or more feet above the creek—offered a vista of simple beauty and great charm. The existing tree cover was typical of the region—shortleaf and loblolly pine, red and turkey oak, a few hickories, sassafras treelings, dogwood, and hundreds of American hollies.

On the creek side was a high, rather steep bank—moderately eroded. I could see the soil fully exposed. There was no topsoil—just a clayey gravel for as deep as I could see.

However, the bank, in addition to weed clumps, was grudgingly supporting several dozen pine seedlings. A large, rough seed pine, occupying a precarious perch about midway down the creek bank, was obviously responsible for this.

For a year or more, I occupied myself with making the small cottage not only livable, but comfortable. I added a breezeway and a garage wing, installed year-round comfort conditioning, then nursed a lawn into respectable greenery, and planted a garden. I did find the time to clear off undesirable underbrush in the woods area, cutting away the stunted hardwood and pine growth.

The advantages of an organized plan for a plot of ground are obvious—and I prepared mine early. I enlisted the help of my wife, who was—and is—an enthusiastic partner in this undertaking. The feminine touch in bringing beauty to

✤   ✤   ✤

James L. Harrison is *Public Printer* of the United States.

an enterprise like this simply cannot be overemphasized.

The shape of the tract, the ground contour, the character of the neighboring land, and the existing growth all enter significantly into the total organization of your country place. Our plot is roughly trapezoidal, with the south and north boundaries parallel—the south limit being a macadamized, high-crowned road and the north the bank of Mill Creek. A natural screen of shortleaf pine, dogwood, holly, and mixed hardwoods lay between the road and the house clearing. This screen is penetrated by a crushed-bluestone driveway.

Our plans called for this to remain virtually as we found it, except for underbrush removal and periodic clearing to reduce the inherent fire hazard of an accumulation of leaves and needles. The screen would be carried back to the rear line of our cottage along the west property line. Here, an area was cleared for my garden—about 50 by 100 feet.

The slope to the creek was left uncultivated. And still another natural belt was preserved along the east property line joining the roadside belt of pine and local hardwoods.

This plan gave privacy from the roadway and the abutting property and permitted us to enjoy the prevailing northerly breezes and the cooling evening flow of air from the water. Keeping the underbrush down, and the area under larger trees open, allowed air to circulate.

Our tree-management plan had three objectives—to beautify and enhance the setting for our home, to screen for privacy, and to control the waterside erosion which had scarred the creek shoreline.

As an emigré from rural living many years ago, my knowledge of tree selection and planting, to say the least, hardly induced an overwhelming confidence on either the part of my wife or myself. But, happily, I was intimately familiar with one of America's contrived resources for such information—Department of Agriculture publications. I obtained a subject price list and ordered a boxful of books, pamphlets, and bulletins from the Superintendent of Documents. The range of the subject matter was enormous—from a 5-cent leaflet on American holly to the

The author's country spot in Chesapeake Bay "land of pleasant living" area of Maryland. Bank planted with treelings protects against erosion of tide and drainage.

$2.75 Yearbook of Agriculture for 1949—with nearly a thousand pages of material on trees. I read them all and made my plan for my country place specific.

We carefully selected trees whose adult size and shapes would complement, as well as ornament, the cottage area. Two hollies were transplanted from the woods to the cottage grounds proper. Those chosen were small-to-medium sized and were root pruned a full year before I attempted relocation. I took a large ball of earth and prepared an oversized hole to receive the transplant. After replanting the holly, the hole was refilled with the spoil mixed with peat moss. I wrapped the trunks with burlap and cared for them as I did the other trees. They are now thriving alongside the several older hollies that were already there.

Since holly is a smallish, triangular-shaped tree, we decided to plant several tulip trees for height and ornamentation, and also some magnolia for the elliptical roundness it assumes. Chinese chestnut was also picked for its well-proportioned shape and pinkish-white blossoms.

A lone mimosa was permitted to dwell on the lawn area and was cultivated carefully by root-feeding.

I obtained a number of small Norway spruce treelings, and planted a line of them to screen the garden area from the house. I used more than 100 white pine seedlings to plant in the open areas close to the natural wood line on the plot.

I have been quite partial to Scotch pine for our annual Christmas tree. I learned that this bushy, irregularly shaped import would thrive on even the poorest soils and would give good annual growth. So I decided to try these, also. I obtained 200 seedlings and scattered them throughout my ever-more-bountiful tree farm.

One of my earliest and, I might add, my most successful enterprises was the use of 700 loblolly pine seedlings to supplement the natural treeling population on the creek bank to check the wasting away of soil. I made an important discovery as I planned this project. In speaking to the State forester's office in Annapolis, Md., I learned that as a landowner, I was entitled to free seedlings—providing my use of these seedlings was

for control of erosion. Seedlings are also available, free of charge, to landowners engaged in timber farming and to those who expect to plant for the purpose of creating game cover. For decorative or ornamental use, the landowner does not qualify for this service and must turn to commercial nurseries for stock. In Maryland, the State maintains a nursery in Anne Arundel County, where all sorts of evergreen tree seedlings are cultivated.

When I received my seedlings, I borrowed a planting tool and set to work. Although I was advised to plant the seedlings about 6 feet apart, I placed them every 3 feet. In doing this, I hoped to provide extra protection in a short period of time. Young loblollies were reputed to grow 2 to 3 feet per year and, while my stand did not quite equal this growth the first year, they had grown to 3 or more feet within 2 years.

At 2 years, I used a hedge clipper and trimmed each tree to a height of 24 inches. After 5 years and regular pruning, the entire bank is stabilized, and I have beautiful, year-round green cover on the waterside of my property. Keeping the tops clipped, together with the dense planting, has created a hedge effect of which I am inordinately proud.

My reading recommended against fertilizers, but I cheated a little here. I used my hose-connected, liquid fertilizer dispenser to water the young seedlings during the dry first summer, and they appeared to prosper. Late the first fall, I noticed that my seedlings were being gnawed by some animal. The small side branches and some of the tops were the parts favored. Early one morning, I spied two cottontails feasting on my young trees, and I chased them away.

The suggested procedures for repelling a rabbit invasion were inappropriate for my use so I ignored this incident, hoping my unwanted visitors would locate better fare. Apparently they did, because I never saw them in my tree patch again. All the damaged trees lived, and I congratulated myself upon my restraint in not applying sterner measures.

After 5 years, my country place shows the effects of early organization and planning. Woodland management is rather a

(above) Skipjack and the Chesapeake Bay Bridge, near Annapolis, Md. (below) Thomas Point Light on the Bay.

366

grand term to apply to one acre. But I make no apologies since, on an abbreviated scale, all the principles which are used to manage a 1,000-acre tree farm are still largely valid when used to manage a single acre. The rudiments of tree care are simple to learn and easy to understand.

I am happy to report that, from my experience, the hardest work occurs early in your program—when your enthusiasm is apt to be at its peak.

Although less than 2 hours' drive from the Metropolitan D.C. area and accommodating a welter of "weekenders," the natural beauty of this region is relatively unspoiled. Highway rights-of-way (to the everlasting credit of the State) are broad, regular, free from natural and manmade clutter, and shoulders are given doses of a weed inhibiter. By and large, land development has been restrained and free from wholesale preparation scars.

The natural beauty of this area is not the spectacular variety, but runs more to the tranquil side—soft, undulating hills of incredible greens, cool riverborne blues, and the ever-changing play of light and color reflected on the lazy tidewaters. No manmade embellishment could enhance this quiet land, and only a careful husbanding of the bounty nature lavished on it is needed to preserve its native beauty.

When Fire Strikes Your Woods

OSAL B. CAPPS

THAT March was a rough forest fire month in Missouri. We received practically no rain or snow, and a strong wind blew day after day. Fires were bigger than normal. Fire crews were bone weary. We had expected April to be worse, but widespread showers fell on the parched soil the Thursday before Easter and fire danger was reduced.

April became a normal fire month in Missouri. Farmers worked the fields, and city people began to think about outdoor recreation. Some wanted to go fishing, some hunting, but most just wanted to drive the ridge roads and see the lovely spring scenery.

One beautiful day in late April shortly after lunch I was driving along a rural road admiring the redbud and dogwood. The oaks and hickories were just beginning to take on new life, but the redbud had been in full bloom for a week or two and was on the wane. Dogwood was nearing its peak beauty. Almost every patch of woods was vivid with color.

Suddenly on my two-way radio I heard a fire towerman report a fire to the district dispatcher. Almost immediately a second tower gave an azimuth reading on the fire. The dispatcher, who had fire danger information at hand, quickly directed a crew of three men to proceed to the fire.

I knew this crew would be in a ½-ton pickup truck with handtools consisting primarily of broom rakes and 5-gallon backpack water cans. Remembering my time as a district forester, I could visualize the dispatcher taking a look at his fire plan and the district map with the red crosses where he had crews on fires. He

Osal B. Capps is *State Forester*, Missouri Department of Conservation, Jefferson City.

would be planning to send more crews or tractor-plow units if this hand crew could not extinguish the fire.

Then I saw the smoke! It was boiling up about a half mile behind a farmhouse in what appeared to be a young white oak stand. Since there was not much wind and the fire was burning along a ridge, I knew it would not spread very rapidly. I talked to the crew leader by radio, told him I was near the fire, and found out he was 10 miles away. I decided to talk to the farmer. I drove to the back door of the farmhouse, spoke soothingly to a very large dog, and knocked on the door.

After being invited in, I asked the farmer about the fire. He said he had burned a brush pile in the edge of a field that morning, but had checked it before he came to the house for lunch and it had burned up. I told him a crew was coming to help him with a wildfire. He was amazed, but pleased to know that we had located a wildfire on his farm before he even knew about it.

About this time the crew arrived and the farmer and I piled on the pickup and rode with the crew to the fire. Sure enough the fire had started from the burning brush pile. The crew leader quickly sized up the situation. He gave me a backpack and the rest broom rakes. We started raking a line in front of the fire's hot end.

The wind was blowing about 10 miles per hour. This is not much wind from a fire danger standpoint. Fires are really hard to control when the wind is blowing 30 to 50 miles per hour.

A fire tends to create its own wind and this fire was fairly hot.

Fires move faster in the direction the wind is blowing. Firefighters call the part that is moving the fastest the head of the fire. The line which is to be made to stop the head of the fire is built far enough away so a control fire can be started at the line to burn back into the head.

Locating the line is always a critical point in the control effort. If it is too far away, timber is needlessly burned over. If it is too close, the head fire will sweep over the line before the backfire can be started. This line was built about 50 feet in front of the head which was burning on a rather narrow front. Oak leaves were about 6 inches deep, and the soil was damp underneath. We backfired from the line and stopped the fire. We then raked the leaves directly into the burned area on the cooler sides of the fire.

Often in heavy fuel a line will have to be constructed around the entire fire. Line construction can be very difficult, depending upon the kind of material that has to be removed to get down to mineral soil. On larger fires tractor-plow units or bulldozers are often used to make the line. The width of the line varies also with the fuel conditions. It has to be wider for very inflammable fuels. And it has to be broad enough so that the backfire does not jump it and become another wildfire.

Water units are used to patrol the lines to put out spot fires caused by blowing embers. In light fuels a 5-gallon backpack pump is good enough. In heavy fuels large pumpers are required to cool down the burning material inside the line.

The line for this fire was only about 2 feet wide. While the crew was cutting some burning snags, I explained to the farmer that a fire could be stopped by cutting off its fuel as we had done; by cooling it below the ignition point with water, as we did with the backpack on a spot fire where an ember blew across the line; or by cutting off oxygen as the crew was then doing by piling dirt on a burning stump.

I had trouble holding the farmer's attention. He finally asked me to go with him to check a den tree to see if it had

A fire tower.

Smokey, the fire preventin' bear, appeals to the emotions of all of us. Many foresters believe that Smokey's effectiveness compares favorably with the best of our technical advances in wildfire prevention and control.

caught fire. He said the tree had some young fox squirrels in it—and he had hunted near this same den tree for years. Fortunately the fire had been stopped before it got to his favorite tree.

I began to think highly of this farmer. I reflected on his woods with good squirrel hunting and maybe even wild turkey. I knew there were deer in the area. I thought about the beauty of the redbud and dogwood. I also mentally visualized the fall colors. I thought of the fishing in the two well-designed farm ponds we had passed going to the fire. Here was a farmer whose sons would love the land. If they left to seek their fortune, they would come home as often as possible. Life for this family looked good to me.

The crew leader paced the fire to determine acreage burned for statistical purposes. It only burned an acre. I told the farmer he was lucky since in late March a fire would probably have burned his 75 acres of good oak timber along with that of his neighbors.

I thought this a good time to point out that he probably had the tools on hand to extinguish fires of this kind. I mentioned that even a wet burlap bag could have been used to beat out the flames while they were creeping through the short grass at the edge of the field. He could also have used a garden rake or a hayfork to rake the line in the oak leaves.

The main thing is to be careful with controlled burning. A person should have a backpack pump or a bucket of water and other needed tools on hand before he starts burning brush piles. He should then watch the fire closely until it burns completely. Many fires start each year from burning brush piles that farmers think are burned up. Actually, a bed of coals with ashes on top is an invitation to disaster when a strong wind suddenly starts blowing as it often does in March or April.

A fire of this type which burns onto a neighbor's land and causes damage can also bring a civil lawsuit.

While we walked to the truck the crew leader cautioned the farmer to walk the fireline several times on that afternoon. As the truck moved slowly across the fields toward the farmhouse, I heard the crew leader urge the district dispatcher to be sure the fire patrol aircraft checked the fire site each time it was in the area. At the farmhouse I complimented the crew for doing a thorough job because the time to completely control a fire is while the crew is there the first time. Breakovers can cause large fires—not only on the fire that is not completely extinguished the first time, but also because crews called back are not available to hit the next fire while it is still small.

I spent a few minutes pointing out to the farmer that he had some fine young white oak. For his part, he expressed an interest in starting a Christmas tree plantation. We discussed the economic possibilities of this, and I ended up by giving him the name of our local farm forester. I promised to mail him some literature and assured him the farm forester would be glad to help him get started if he decided favorably. He was already aware that we would furnish the young trees from the State nursery since a neighbor had started a plantation.

Just as I started to leave we were called into the kitchen for hot apple pie and coffee. I finally did leave and as I got into the car the dispatcher was sending the crew that had been with me to help on a fire out of control about 20 miles distant.

I drove away feeling pleased to be a part of the private-State-Federal effort that was helping to insure a timber supply for the future, as well as to preserve the other values of the woods such as wildlife and natural beauty.

Pine Trees and Profits
From a Family Forest

ROBERT E. NIPP

THE FIRST TIME I saw youthful Bob Murphy at his 950-acre farm near the town of Washington down in Wilkes County, Ga., he was jabbing a chemical injection gun deep into the trunk of a deformed old tree. The purpose, Bob explained, was to kill the unwanted vines, brush, and hardwood trees with but little commercial value and to make room for his young 3- to 5-foot pines which needed more moisture and sun.

Three years before, Bob, his wife, and some hired help had wound their way through this field of nondescript trees and underbrush and hand planted about 900 loblolly pine seedlings on each acre. Seedlings were spaced every 6 feet in rows 8 feet apart. Most had survived. Now they needed more room to grow.

Bob said the brush and hardwood trees killed by the chemical injection lose their leaves and then gradually rot and fall to the ground. The resulting debris provides a thick moisture mulch for the young pines and protects the soil from erosion.

Crewcut and sporting a healthy tan, Murphy at age 26 typifies today's younger generation of farmers.

✿   ✿   ✿

Robert E. Nipp is an *Information Officer* with the Farmers Home Administration.

The Murphys have found that credit is an important tool in today's agriculture, and like many young families, they had little in the way of property which they could offer as a collateral on loans from conventional lenders. In early 1963, they turned to the Farmers Home Administration of the Agriculture Department

A forest plantation in Mississippi.

and qualified for one of the first forestry-purpose loans by that agency.

With this assistance, the Murphys have been able to work over and improve about two-thirds of their 800 acres of woodland. Around 200 acres of previously unproductive woodland have been planted with loblolly pine seedlings, and the undesirable brush and hardwoods removed from about one-half of this newly planted area.

Besides this, they have carried out conventional timber stand improvement work—mostly killing off the undesirable brush and the poor quality trees—on more than 300 acres of other land. This area had a fairly good stand of pine trees intermixed with other tree growth when the Murphys purchased the farm. By removing the unwanted growth, the remaining pines could grow fast and straight.

By 1970, the Murphys hope to have all 800 acres of woodland producing a maximum growth of pine trees.

Bob and Carole Murphy's records show that timberland they have replanted to loblolly pine seedlings, or otherwise improved, is producing about $8 an acre a year compared to $2 an acre before. On 540 acres renovated, that adds up to an income improvement of $3,300 a year.

An untapped resource on the Murphy farm consists of recreational and hunting rights which they could lease out to city people. Quail, turkey, raccoon, pheasant, and deer abound on the farm which now represents a wildlife paradise. Horseback riding, camping, picnicking, and nature study are among the recreational possibilities on their meadow and timberland.

The Murphys' woodland is one of 4½ million of our Nation's family forests, 75 percent of which are farmer-owned. What has been done on the Murphys' property can be repeated on many others.

As Tom K. Wilson, the Farmers Home Administration's credit technician for Wilkes County, points out, "The Murphy story points up some solutions to a number of national problems:

"Farm people need more income.

"City people need more space to play.

"Our wood-processing industries need more timber to meet ever-increasing demands from an energetic Nation which will see 330 million people living within its shores by the year 2000."

The Alexander Ewing family walks through a hardwood stand on their Overlook Farm near Millbrook, New York.

A Town Recreation Center—
Play Pays Its Own Way

ROBERT S. CRITES

A RECREATION CENTER doesn't cost—it pays." This was the view expressed by a young minister of Lake View, S.C., where a nonprofit association had borrowed $40,000 from the Farmers Home Administration in 1963 to build a recreation center that included a swimming pool, tennis courts, basketball courts, and a miniature golf course. And then the minister told me how this town of 900 had benefited from the center.

"It has given a new lift to the spirit of the community," he said. "There has been a very marked reduction in juvenile delinquency problems and in vandalism."

During the 5 years preceding the building of the center, not more than five new homes were built in the town. In the 2 years after that, 15 new homes were constructed and 5 more planned. Two new industries located in Lake View, and the recreation center was an important factor in their decision.

A different type of development is close to completion near Terra Alta, W. Va., where a nonprofit association was formed, with some 1,200 members. Each member agreed to put in $100 to enable the association to secure a loan of $820,000 from the Farmers Home Administration so it could develop a recreation complex designed to draw tourist dollars to this sparsely populated region.

꙼   ꙼   ꙼

Robert S. Crites is *Recreation Specialist* for the Farmers Home Administration. He is the author of FHA's "Handbook of Outdoor Recreation Enterprises In Rural Areas."

The new development centers around a 42-acre lake nestled in the bowl of a 2,000-acre tract of woodland. The lake is fed by artesian wells, cold enough for trout production. The complex includes a ski chair lift and ski slopes, opened for the 1966–67 season.

Ready for 1967 vacationers are lodges, cabins, picnic areas, a golf course, sports fields, and a swimming pool.

A Mesquakie Indian maiden adds exotic atmosphere to a campground development financed by USDA near Tama, Iowa.

The operation includes deer, turkey, and duck hunting in season.

The complex is surrounded on all sides by large population centers which are within a reasonable traveling distance.

These specific examples of recreation centers illustrate attempts to meet two different types of needs. Any rural town or community that is considering whether or not it needs a recreation center ought to consider first what it hopes to achieve. Is it (1) principally concerned with improving the quality of living for its own residents—and possibly attracting more residents, or (2) is it interested primarily in attracting tourist dollars?

Any community can benefit from the first type of development if it is presently lacking. The second type must depend on some natural attractions as a base from which to develop, and it is essential to consider where the customers will come from to make the project feasible. No community wants to embark upon a recreation development simply because others are doing so. A study of prospective use should be undertaken.

One of many golf courses converted from cropland—the Riverlands Golf and Country Club in Louisiana. The greens are Tifton 328 bermudagrass planted as part of a conservation plan for the course.

Rider in Kennedy Park, Fort Dodge, Iowa. An adjacent tract is to be acquired for public use as a golf course, under USDA's Greenspan program.

The Federal Government, through the U.S. Department of Agriculture, is taking many avenues to assist rural communities in developing more recreation opportunities to benefit rural people as well as those who seek respite from the asphalt jungles.

The Farmers Home Administration can make loans to nonprofit associations of farmers and rural residents—or to local public bodies.

Besides this, the Agricultural Stabilization and Conservation Service can now make grants to local public bodies that wish to take cropland out of production and convert it to recreation. Under this program, called Greenspan, communities buying cropland may receive financial aid similar to that for farmers who sign Cropland Adjustment Program agreements.

Campsite and picnic area on the south shore of the Snake River Canoe Trail, Kanabec County, Minn. The campsite is being developed and improved by the Sheridan 4–H Club of Whited Township.

The Secretary of Agriculture can also help local governments and States invest in conservation practices needed on this land to protect, improve, and renew soil, water, woodland, and wildlife. This is handled very much like conservation cost sharing on private farmlands.

While the Government offers help in many forms to those communities that want it and can qualify, somebody locally has to ask for the assistance. Somebody has to care enough to be willing to spend countless hours, without compensation, to overcome the inertia which often overtakes the communities—large or small. Someone has to decide what is practical for the town and set it down on paper and prod the local citizens to raise funds for needed studies and plans. Someone has to have the boundless optimism that will keep all the others encouraged when the going is rough. Some person or some event has to get the thing started.

A small Colorado town talked about installing a swimming pool for many years, and did nothing. Then one summer day the weekly newspaper reported the drowning of three youngsters in one afternoon in a stock pond.

The article went on to recall the stories of the youths who had drowned in stock ponds and treacherous river currents in the region during the preceding 5 years. This was the spark which ignited community spirit. Some residents furnished labor; others donated money.

They built a $60,000 swimming pool with $35,000 cash. And using their rediscovered strength of working together, the people went on to construct a new hospital, a nursing home, and new schools.

Interclub Group

The residents of Putnam County in northern Missouri were worried because their county had lost 26 percent of its population between 1950 and 1960. So four of the most active clubs each selected four members to form an Inter-Club

375

Cooling off at a recreation enterprise.

Service Council and see what could be done to arrest the population downtrend. The story of how the ideas generated by this council took shape and moved, step by step, to the beginning of construction is told in the headlines of the weekly newspaper of Unionville, the county seat.

Altogether 117 stories appeared in the paper during this period. Here is a sampling of the headlines:

Sept. 18, 1963—"Study Possibility of a Large Lake"

Oct. 9, 1963—"Lake Meeting at Yount's Cafe" (The community stirs.)

Nov. 6, 1963—"Lake Project Corporation Being Formed; Meeting Next Monday To Formulate Plans"

Nov. 27, 1963—"Over the Top With $20 Donations for Lake Project"

Feb. 5, 1964—"Corporation Papers to FHA; Countywide Meeting February 26" (Things are really rolling!)

June 24, 1964—"Tentative Approval of $800,000 Lake Loan Granted by FHA"

July 15, 1964—"These 277 Have Signed Lake Memberships"

Sept. 16, 1964—"FHA Grants Final Approval of 1,500-Acre Recreation Lake"

Jan. 13, 1965—"Check Cashed—Land Paid for—Lake Project in High Gear"

Feb. 2, 1965—"Name the Lake Contest Is Gaining Momentum"

July 28, 1965—"Lake Project Open for Bids; Will Let Contract Aug. 18"

Aug. 25, 1965—"Our Lake Is Named"— ("Thunderhead, the word itself creates a challenge; let's meet the challenge by each doing everything possible to make our lake project a success.")

Sept. 1, 1965—"We've Waited 2 Years for This" (Picture of the first piece of equipment going to work at the lake site clearing timber.)

Sept. 29, 1965—"Readying for the Big Task at Lake Thunderhead" (Picture of heavy equipment being moved in to build the dam.)

The FHA gets many letters each week

asking about help for a recreation development. Most of these are seeking ways whereby some individual or organization can make a profit for themselves.

Many such inquirers, when they learn that the organization must be chartered under the nonprofit laws of the State, are ready to drop the whole idea.

Some, however, decide that the idea is bigger than their own self-interest and are willing to forgo personal profit for community betterment. If they are able to get several hundred of their fellow citizens to invest money upon the same altruistic basis, this is a pretty good sign that the project will have strong local support.

Letter From Montana

Occasionally we get a letter like this one from a woman in Montana where community betterment appears to be the motivating factor from the beginning:

"Dear Sirs:

"We live in a rural area that decreases in population each year. There are less and less job opportunities. A number of bars comprise the total recreation availability. . . . The people here would like to have a center where they could swim, bowl, and have the use of a gym. . . .

"Send Any Information"

"Would you please send us any information on what your office can do to help us with this? Also, if there is any help that you can give toward individual or cooperative recreational facilities, to bring in more money to the area, to create more jobs, we would appreciate that information. Thank you."

This could be the beginning of another recreation center which will rejuvenate a rural community.

Whether it was profits, shock, civic pride, or just a plain restless energy that sparked the first move, 345 rural communities across the Nation had borrowed $44,137,370 to develop outdoor oriented recreation centers through the end of March 1967. These covered a big range of facilities. The most popular were golf courses, followed by swimming pools,

An Indian rodeo.

377

tennis courts, marinas, snackbars, trailer and tent camping areas, ball fields, fairgrounds, ski slopes and ski lifts, rodeo grounds, youth camps, fishing and hunting areas, and curling rinks.

Despite the wide range, however, the needs are even greater.

For example, the United States as a whole is surprisingly deficient in many of the sport facilities which are needed for Olympic contestants to practice on. We have only one skating rink of Olympic size for speed skating. There's only one bobsled run of Olympic standard.

Not every town can have an Olympic size swimming pool or skating rink or ski run or bobsled run, but every State can have at least one Olympic size facility to fit its climate.

Modern developments permit enclosed swimming pools at reasonable costs so that swimming can be extended the year around. Enclosed rinks today make possible a longer ice skating season. Snowmaking equipment has extended ski areas

farther south than ever before—and has made possible an almost continuous ski season during the winter months in areas formerly plagued with spotty snowfall.

New sports are gaining acceptance among the general population.

Rodeo on the Rise

One sport now growing in local communities and in college competition is rodeo, including such events as bronc riding, calf roping, and bulldogging.

This is a sport which is indigenous to the United States, and one that is possible in all climates and areas. It requires great skill and toughness.

One researcher has predicted that in a few years we will have many popular sports which are not even known at the present time.

So, if your community doesn't now have a recreation center, it's a matter worth considering. It might pay in more ways than one.

This pool is part of extensive recreation facilities developed at Lake View, S.C., with a USDA loan and technical assistance.

The Tattletale Tree Ring

WILLIAM J. ROBINSON

ON A WARM, cloudless day in the summer of 1904, two men stood near a cleared field on the outskirts of Flagstaff, Ariz. One man was the farmer who owned the land, and the other was a young astronomer whose interest in the regularity of astronomical events had led him to the study of tree growth.

"Do you know what year this tree was cut?" asked Dr. A. E. Douglass as he and the farmer rested briefly on an old stump. "Why, yes," replied the farmer, "I cut this tree myself the first year I farmed this land." Douglass studied the stump for a few minutes, seemingly lost in thought, then said, "That would have been the year 1887." Astounded, the farmer exclaimed, "That's right, but how did you know?"

How Dr. Douglass was able to tell the farmer the exact year the tree had been cut was his discovery of the principle of cross-dating—the foundation of dendrochronology or the study of tree rings.

For a decade or so previously, Douglass had been investigating the relation between certain astronomical events and the climate on the earth. He thought he detected weather changes that occurred not only at regular intervals, but coincided with the same intervals in the astronomical events. To be sure of this, however, he needed weather records that went into the past longer than the Weather Bureau had been in business. He thought maybe tree growth would provide this record.

So Douglass started his study of growth rings in trees—mainly pines—in northern Arizona near the Lowell Observatory, where he worked. Soon he noticed that the pines growing in this land of great yearly differences in rainfall had rings that varied in size. Some were thick and some were thin. He also noticed that the same pattern of thick and thin rings recurred in tree after tree. This similarity Dr. Douglass termed as "cross-dating." After some years of recording the patterns in trees, he was ready for a test of the method; to establish the year of death of a tree of unknown age. This ability was what so astounded the farmer in 1904.

For more than 10 years following his discovery of cross-dating, Dr. Douglass worked on the patterns of ring widths further and further back into time. Since the pine trees near Flagstaff rarely live longer than 300 to 400 years, he turned to the redwoods of California. Then in 1914 a new use for tree rings was found.

Dr. Douglass had gone to Washington, D.C., to present a paper on the results of his studies. Sitting in the audience, quite by accident, was Clark Wissler whose institution, the American Museum of Natural History, was engaged in the excavation of two large Indian ruins in northwestern New Mexico.

"Would it be possible," Dr. Wissler later asked Douglass, "to date the beams used in the construction of these large pueblos?" Douglass was not sure since nobody knew how old the ruins ought to be, and his growth patterns based on the trees near Flagstaff only extended backward from 1914 for about 400 years. He

❀ ❀ ❀

William J. Robinson is *Research Associate* in the Laboratory of Tree Ring Research, University of Arizona, Tucson.

Patriarch Grove of bristlecone pines at 11,000-foot elevation in the Inyo National Forest, Calif. "The Old Ranger" in the center is a study in grotesque beauty, although the tree is now dead.

would try, however, and over the next 15 years Douglass and his colleagues painstakingly identified the patterns from ancient beams until they had a chronology nearly 600 years long.

But nowhere did the patterns of the old beams fit with the patterns based upon the living trees whose age was known. There was a gap between these two chronologies which might be 1 year, or a thousand; nobody was certain. Gradually more and more pieces of wood were dated, and their patterns added to one or the other chronology until finally, on another warm and pleasant day, near the small town of Show Low, Ariz., a piece of wood was dug from a ruin.

This piece proved to hold the key; the outer rings matched the patterns of the oldest parts of the chronology based on living trees, and the inner rings matched the latest pattern of the ancient chronology. Success! With that piece, a tree ring chronology more than 1,200 years long was established, and exact dates could be given for over 40 large ruins in Arizona and New Mexico. In recent years, this ruin chronology has been extended backward in time to 59 B.C., and many hundreds of ruins in the Southwest have been dated by tree rings.

Although Douglass worked for many years with the redwood trees in California because of their great age, the tree ring patterns were not altogether satisfactory. And their age, although over 3,000 years, proved to be less than other recently discovered trees. In the dry eastern mountains of California, on the Nevada border and at a high altitude, grow the bristlecone pines.

Since 1954, it has been known that these trees not only live longer than the redwood, but provide finer chronologies. The oldest living bristlecone is over 4,600 years. By cross-dating the ring series of long dead bristlecone with inner portions of living trees, the chronology for bristlecone pine now is over 6,600 years long! There is every hope that this may eventually be extended back as far as 10,000 years, near the time of the last ice age.

Why are rings from the bristlecone, from the ruin logs, and from other old living trees of importance? Remember that Douglass was originally interested in the relationship between tree growth and climate. He thought, and for many years other dendrochronologists believed, that the growth reflected rainfall from year to year. This is only partly true.

Since 1961, many experiments have been made with living trees, and hundreds of hours have been spent with computers to show which of all the things needed for growth are reflected in the size of the ring. Trees have literally had their pulse and their blood pressure taken throughout the year! Now we have proof that the climate, namely precipitation and temperature, influence the growths of trees on dry or cold sites. The ring record which may one day go back as far as 10,000 years can be used to reconstruct past climate.

Tree rings have been collected from many old trees throughout arid areas of North America. These have been transformed by computers and plotted as maps of past climate for each decade since A.D. 1500. Such information helps meteorologists study past weather.

Hydrologists also use tree ring data to reconstruct flood and drought sequences in river basins. Geochemists are checking radiocarbon dating, and the geologists are measuring erosion rates by means of tree rings. Astronomers and geophysicists are interested in tree rings as the possible recorders of a past variability in the sun's activity. Foresters use tree rings to measure age and the growth of their forests.

The tree rings are becoming accepted sources of information in a variety of sciences. However, many tree ring problems still baffle the researchers. There are likely many secrets still locked up in limbs and trunks of trees.

Through all the ages, trees have been responding to their environment by laying down thick and thin layers of wood each year. It is the job of the tree ring scientist to extract this information and apply it to today's scientific problems.

Create a Small World—
In Your Own Backyard

JAMES L. BAILEY

LET'S assume you are an edge-of-the-city or a suburban homeowner. The house and lot are yours to do with as you will. Is yours to be a well-manicured lawn with a few shade trees, the usual ornamental plantings and flowerbeds, and a seldom frequented window feeder and birdbath? Or is it to be a place where a wide variety of plants and animals live together—a haven for the birds, squirrels, chipmunks, rabbits, bees, and butterflies? Your place can be either one or the other, or some of both.

If you choose to make your homesite attractive to wildlife, you will be well rewarded for your efforts, both in the process and the product. Working in the outdoors with soil, water, plants, and animals has many compensations. As you plan and work with nature, you learn and develop fresh, and deep, appreciations. Because you feel you are helping to create a natural microcosm in your own backyard, you become increasingly absorbed.

Our home place in Tennessee is such a place, and we are fortunate in having neighbors who, too, are attentive to the needs and values of wildlife. This is important because many species require a territory larger than a single backyard. Obviously, the wildlife found in a neighborhood is affected by the attitude of all of the property owners and the natural features of their holdings. Important, too, is the control of cats, dogs, and, sometimes, irresponsible youngsters.

We like to look out our kitchen windows at the goldfinches and cardinals feeding on the sunflowers. The sunflowers were planted in 1960. Each year since, they have grown from seeds scattered by the birds. Across part of our backyard is a hedgerow which, incidentally, screens our compost pile. Rabbits emerge from the briar patch and brush pile behind the hedgerow at twilight to nibble upon the clover on the lawn.

Squirrels "sniff out" walnuts they have planted in a neighbor's yard, dig them out of the ground, and climb to their favorite perches to eat them. A number of walnut trees growing in our yard were planted by squirrels. A pair of brown thrashers

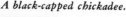

A black-capped chickadee.

ʊ̯   ʊ̯   ʊ̯

James L. Bailey is *Supervisor*, Educational Service, Tennessee Department of Conservation.

nest in the clump of coral berries (buck bushes) growing around a post which supports the clothesline or in the multiflora rose. Field sparrows and a yellow-breasted chat are heard in the brushy area behind the hedgerow. Blue jays fuss at one another in the mulberry tree and around the birdbath. We like the animal creatures and the plants that provide food and protection for them.

What are some of the factors to consider in creating a community of plants and animals? How do you go about it?

You must recognize first of all that the wild animals require food, water, shelter (cover), living space, and a place to raise their young. Remember that among the birds there are permanent residents, summer residents, winter residents, and the transients. For the permanent residents (as with the mammals), there must be an adequate day-to-day, week-by-week, year-round food supply. The presence of seasonal residents and transients depends, too, upon the availability of food during the appropriate season.

Plants, also, have certain requirements and must be suited to the environment: Soil, exposure, moisture and climatic conditions, and the prevalence of plant pests. Scattered trees and clumps of bushes with open spaces between them are far more attractive, particularly to nesting birds, than the same area would be if completely overgrown. You need, then, to consider where you are, what plants you can grow, and what wildlife species you may expect to attract. Follow a plan, even if no more than a pencil sketch. Compile a list of the plants which will grow locally, which provide beauty in season, and which meet the needs of wildlife.

Obviously, the plants already growing naturally are suited to the habitat. Those which fit in with your plan should be retained and the others eliminated. Some homeowners may desire, with only the necessary amount of interference and control, to let nature have her way. (It's fun to watch what happens.) Others, who wish to expend a greater amount of time and effort, will follow a plan involving a greater measure of direction and control.

Soil conditions can, within limits, be altered and improved. To do this properly,

Snowberry.

and to avoid the probability of disappointment and the waste of money and materials, a soil analysis is necessary. Call or consult your county agricultural agent for directions and procedure.

Lists and information on appropriate plants for wildlife plantings are readily available. Recommended sources are State and Federal wildlife conservation and agricultural agencies, State and local bird clubs, National Audubon Society, garden clubs, garden centers, and libraries.

A list of trees, shrubs, vines, and annuals, together with many of the birds which utilize them, has been prepared by the U.S. Fish and Wildlife Service, Bureau of Sport Fisheries and Wildlife, Atlanta, Ga. The list concludes with these helpful suggestions:

"Local nurseries may be consulted for suggestions of most suitable plants for soils and landscape plans. When space permits, a corner of the yard should be allowed to grow wild with weeds and bushes which offer protection and nesting places for many kinds of birds. A brush pile will afford additional cover. A dead or dying tree, or hollow tree, will attract

Cottontail rabbit emerges from hedgerow to nibble clover on the lawn.

woodpecker, nuthatch, titmouse, chickadee, crested flycatcher, and starling. A feeding shelf on a window ledge or pole can be supplied with various seeds and grains, suet, peanut butter, cornbread, cracked nuts, raisins, cut apples, and similar foods. A birdbath will be used for drinking and bathing. Hummingbirds are attracted to red, orange, and purple flowers and even to small vials of sugar water or thinned honey."

The Book of Bird Life by the late Arthur A. Allen, professor of ornithology at Cornell University (published by D. Van Nostrand Co., Inc., New York, in 1930), gives on pages 351–353 a list of fruit-bearing trees, shrubs, and vines to attract birds and the months during which the fruit is available. Suggestions for the arrangement of the shrubbery so as to give the maximum number of nesting places are included. Your library may have a copy of this book.

Wildlife Habitat Improvement, published in 1966 by the National Audubon Society, includes recommendations for upgrading habitat for birds and mammals on homesites and special areas.

The following lists of trees, shrubs, vines, and annuals are suggested for yards and gardens to furnish food and shelter for many kinds of birds. Figures given after the names of some trees and shrubs indicate the number of species of birds which have been found to feed upon the plants. This is adapted from the list prepared by the Bureau of Sport Fisheries and Wildlife in Atlanta and cited earlier.

TREES—Flowering dogwood (98), wild black cherry (84), mulberry (59), hackberry (48), beech, sour gum (40), redcedar (juniper) (54), pines (63), oaks (62), and holly (49).

Alder, ash, birch, and elm have seeds that attract many birds.

SHRUBS—Elderberry (120), blackberry (149), bayberry (86), blueberry (93), pokeberry (53), pyracantha, viburnum, privet (ligustrum), snowberry (36), and althea (rose of sharon).

VINES—Virginia creeper, greenbrier (smilax), honeysuckle, trumpet vine, and wild grape attract 30 to 50 bird species.

ANNUALS—A number of commonly cultivated annuals belonging to the same groups as those upon which birds feed extensively in nature produce good crops of seeds and, being dependent upon cultivation, can be used without fear they will become pests. These are suggested: Abelia, aster, blessed thistle, buddleia, California poppy, centaurus, cosmos, forget-me-not, and love-lies-bleeding.

Easily identified by a brownish-red cap and a white stripe over his eye, this chipping sparrow (left) is raising a family in a small evergreen. At right is a robin nest.

Hidden Treasure in the Woods

GEORGE VITAS

OUR FAMILY lives in Alexandria, Va. Nancy, our 6-year-old daughter, had been after us for some time to visit Mr. and Mrs. Clint Davis in Silver Spring, Md., so she and her brother could see the chipmunks in the Davis backyard.

When we arrived, we found Clint in the backyard firing up several bucket type charcoal grills. While the children roamed around the yard, I watched with interest as Clint laid the porterhouse steaks on the grills. Then, I looked with astonishment as Clint reached into a bucket of water for a handful of wet wood chips.

"I'm going to give those steaks a real hickory smoked flavor," he said while he spread the wet hickory chips on the coals.

A combination of steam and smoke enveloped the steaks. In 10 minutes he added more wet chips and turned the meat. Fifteen minutes later we were eating the most deliciously smoke-flavored steaks we had ever eaten.

After the meal, I asked Clint, "Where did you get the chips?"

"I bought them in a grocery store." He showed me a small cloth bag that held about 3 pounds of hickory wood chips.

Ever since that day our family has used the Davis system of barbecuing meat, and we've enjoyed the product immensely.

My experience at the Davis home made me curious about meat smoking. Looking into the subject, I found out that USDA's meat inspection regulations permit the use of genuine smoke as well as approved artificial smoke preparations. When the latter are used, the labels upon the meat products must clearly indicate that artificial smoke flavorings have been added.

Green hickory wood and sawdust are the standard fuels used for smoking meat, but almost any heavy hardwood such as oak, apple, maple, or ash is permitted. However, resinous woods such as pines are prohibited, because they blacken the meat and also give it an undesirable flavor.

This means that the bacon, ham, and smoked sausage you eat is linked with the forest as certainly as the maple sirup that may sit on your breakfast table.

Yes, there is more in a forest than timber. Many other products are grown and harvested there. They include floral supplies, Christmas decorations, ornamental plants, flowering shrubs, transplant stock, seeds and cones, edible products, medicinal materials, aromatic materials, naval stores, and soil conditioners.

Forest-grown plants used by florists and decorators provide further proof that our forests grow more than timber. For example, the Southern Appalachian forests produce many perennial plants which are used for decorative purposes. Among these, the galax leaf is one of the best-sellers. It is a small heart-shaped leathery deep green leaf which is very attractive in a floral arrangement.

ꙮ ꙮ ꙮ

George Vitas is a *Staff Assistant* in the Division of Information and Education, Forest Service. He is the author of *Forest and Flame in the Bible, Every Forester a Timber Owner,* and other publications.

Old and new in maple sirup production. In the old method, shown above near Ashfield, Mass., sap is collected in buckets hung on the trees, then poured into a gathering tank and taken by horse-drawn sled to the sugarhouse. Below, plastic tubes bring the sap from tree taps to a roadside collection tank, in Bainbridge, N.Y. A suction line then carries the sap to a tank truck, in this new technique.

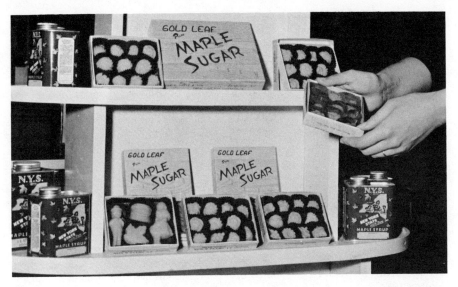

Some maple sirup products.

Galax grows best in partial shade. It is usually found in patches along the forest edges and in openings in dense forests.

Most Appalachian galax harvesters are women, older men, and—on weekends—children. It is a family affair. Each member is equipped with a burlap bag tied around the shoulder so that it will drag behind the harvester while being convenient for storing the leaves.

The picked leaves are packed tightly into the bags.

At the end of each day, the sacks are emptied on the floor at home and the family sorts and grades the leaves.

A woman in her fifties, living in the Mount Mitchell area of North Carolina, is a fairly typical example of a galax harvester. She works to supplement her family's farm income—her husband concentrates on farming. Working an average of 3 days a week for about 9 months of the year, she averages around $1,100 annually. Although this income is not large, it can be an important contribution to the life of a low income family. Frequently, especially with the older people, it is a matter of pride of being self-supporting and staying off the welfare rolls.

The deliciously different black walnuts we eat in ice cream, cake, and candy come from forest trees.

Black walnut has become the most prized and the most expensive furniture veneer, gunstock material, and paneling wood in America.

However, while its wood value is high so is the value of its nuts.

About 40 million pounds of hulled nuts are gathered and sold to processors annually, bringing from $2 to $4 per hundred pounds to the seller.

It is interesting to note that this special forest product was first mass produced for its shell and not its kernel. The dense hard walnut shells made a fine activated carbon that was used in gas mask filters. Today, the ground shells have numerous other uses, such as drilling mud in the oilfields, abrasives to polish castings and automatic transmissions, jet engine cleaning, and for plastics. There is a tranquilizer in the hulls which someday may be used in the drug business.

Black walnut gathering can be the occasion of a family outing or a festive affair, and it could pay its way.

A full grown walnut tree can produce 200 to 400 pounds of unshelled nuts per year. Processing plants in Missouri, Arkansas, Tennessee, Virginia, and Kentucky are the principal destinations of one of America's important forest crops—black walnuts.

Billy the Kid Becomes a New Drawing Card

WALTER C. BUNCH

BILLY THE KID . . . New Mexico's most famous outlaw . . . remains today as during his lifetime the source of controversy.

Some believe that Henry McCarty, alias Billy Antrim, alias William H. Bonney, alias Billy the Kid, was a mad-dog killer.

Others insist he was a kind of Robin Hood of the old Southwest, fiercely loyal to friends, implacable foe of enemies.

But all agree Billy the Kid wrote large on the pages of New Mexico history. And all agree that in death Billy is a bigger drawing card than he was in real life.

The folks at Fort Sumner, N. Mex., are about to cash in on Billy's notoriety in a big way. He is expected to become their No. 1 tourist attraction.

Under the Greenspan provision of the Cropland Adjustment Program of the U.S. Department of Agriculture, the village of Fort Sumner received a grant to help purchase cropland containing the original Bosque Redondo Indian Reservation and Fort Sumner. This land, and the cemetery adjoining it, will become—Fort Sumner residents hope—a mecca for historians of the Southwest and a top tourist attraction for visitors traveling U.S. 60 or U.S. 84 in eastern New Mexico.

Fort Sumner was established in 1862 by Brig. Gen. James H. Carleton to protect area settlers from Indian attackers. It was a six-company army post in the "Bosque Redondo"—Spanish for "grove of trees."

General Carleton, determined to corral marauding Indians at the fort, assigned the task of bringing them in to Col. Kit Carson. By the end of 1864, several thousand Indians had been brought to the fort and an effort to teach them to farm the white man's way was commenced. Due to drought and insects, the venture failed. However, in the meantime the town had become established and served as a trading center for early-day settlers. It was an important supply post on the Goodnight-Loving cattle trail, which ran from west Texas to Colorado and Wyoming.

The Fort Sumner Military Post was abandoned in 1868. Shortly afterwards it was sold to the Fort Sumner Land and Cattle Co., whose chief stockholder was Lucien B. Maxwell, pioneer stockman and former owner of the vast Maxwell Land Grant in northeastern New Mexico. After Lucien's death, the property passed to his son, Pete.

It was in Pete Maxwell's home on the east bank of the Pecos that Billy the Kid was shot to death by Sheriff Pat Garrett on July 18, 1881.

Billy was born in New York City November 3, 1859, as Henry McCarty. The McCartys moved to a rural area near Coffeyville, Kans., in 1861. Billy's father died and his mother married William H. Antrim. They moved to Silver City, N. Mex. Here Billy attended school under the name of Billy Antrim.

ψ ψ ψ

Walter C. Bunch is an *Information Specialist* with the Agricultural Stabilization and Conservation Service.

Billy the Kid.

⚘

FINAL IRONY

Billy and two outlaw friends are buried in the Fort Sumner military cemetery. Their graves are far better marked than the nearby grave of Lucien B. Maxwell, famous pioneer of the Southwest.

⚘

Legend has it that Billy killed his first man when he was between 12 and 15 years of age. The incident has several versions: One has Billy stabbing a man to death for allegedly insulting his mother. Another version has Billy shooting the man to death with a stolen gun.

Billy fled to Arizona where he worked briefly as a cowboy. With a Mexican partner, Billy spent the next few years ambushing and robbing Indian trappers.

More killing and scrapes with the law caused him to flee once more—this time across the border into Mexico. Here his career broadened into operation of a gambling hall. He had to leave once again because of a quarrel which ended with Billy's gun blazing faster than that of his opponent.

Next he moved to Chihuahua, where reportedly he courted the local senoritas. But in 1877 Billy grew homesick for his homeland and friends in New Mexico.

This next period is generally known as the cattle and horse rustling period of Billy's life.

Many times he and his friends crossed and recrossed the Rio Grande with cattle and horses stolen on one side of the river and sold on the other.

However, by mid-1877 the famous Lincoln County feud was ready to erupt, and Billy was in the middle of it. John H. Chisum, the noted New Mexico cattle king, accused small ranchers of rustling his cattle. The small ranchers, in turn, made similar charges against Chisum and his associates, a lawyer named McSween, and an Englishman by the name of John H. Tunstall.

Billy had decided to settle down and was working as a cowboy on the Tunstall Ranch. Oldtimers recalled that his good nature made him a great favorite with all the other hands. Billy was also a good friend of John Chisum.

The smaller ranchers were led by the firm of Murphy and Dolan, a supply store in Lincoln County.

Most historians agree that about this time the feud took on political overtones. Murphy managed to get a cowboy named Brady elected sheriff of Lincoln County. Brady's posse downed several rounds of whisky in Murphy's saloon and headed

In the Bosque Redondo (grove of trees) area of the Pecos River country in New Mexico, soldiers and Indians built the original Fort Sumner and Indian Reservation. Here, new company quarters are being erected by Indians. The cottonwood limbs set out along the irrigation ditches later became large trees. Construction materials are adobe bricks. The Pecos River is in the background.

This photograph of company quarters was made after construction was completed. The view is from the sutler's store, straight down the street and into the wooded area west of the compound. Note the open ditch and plank crossing. Pioneer citizens and Indians mingled freely within the historic fort, named for General Edwin Vose Sumner, who died March 21, 1863, as the new fort was being built.

for the Tunstall Ranch. They met Tunstall on the road and killed him. The story also relates that Billy swore a solemn oath he would track down and kill every man who had helped to murder his friend and benefactor.

Sheriff Brady posted a reward for Billy the Kid "Dead or Alive." Shortly afterward Sheriff Brady was killed, and Billy was charged with his murder.

This was the crime for which Billy was later sentenced to hang.

President Rutherford B. Hayes had removed Territorial Governor Samuel B. Axtell in 1878 and replaced him with Gen. Lew Wallace. Wallace issued a pardon to all participants in the Lincoln County war except Billy the Kid. He sent word he would like a meeting with Billy to discuss his surrender and trial for the killing of Sheriff Brady.

New Mexico historians agree Governor Wallace told the Kid that if he would surrender and stand trial for the killing of Sheriff Brady he would be pardoned if he was convicted.

He also was to be pardoned for all of his other crimes.

In April of 1881 Billy was captured and put on trial. He was convicted of Brady's murder, and the court ordered him to be hanged on May 13, 1881.

On April 28, Billy escaped, killing two deputies.

He was trailed to the Maxwell House in De Baca County. Here he was shot and killed by Sheriff Pat Garrett.

Billy the Kid was buried in the old military cemetery.

Rogue, desperado, western badman? As the Spanish Americans would say, "¿Quien sabe?" which translates "Who knows?"

Certain it is that some will curse the day that such a fiend was spawned, while others will recount with reverent awe the 21 notches he carved on his pistol butt.

Meanwhile, let the controversy rage. It should bring more and more people to the site to look and talk and conjecture.

That's what will make the folks happy in Fort Sumner.

Looking back the other way from company quarters toward the sutler's store you can see soldiers standing at ease and dogs sleeping in the street. Captain John C. Cremony in his book, "Life Among the Apaches," described in detail the careful selection of the site on which Fort Sumner and the Indian Reservation were erected. He called it "the most beautiful Indian fort in the United States."

The Law and Your Recreation Enterprise

W. JOSEPH BRAY

IF BEFORE getting up each morning you worried about all the requirements the law would make upon you that day, you might well hesitate to put even a first foot on the floor. However, knowing in general and accepting those requirements, you set forth into each new day. So it is with an outdoor recreation enterprise. Satisfy yourself beforehand as to the legal requirements in the particular enterprise that you choose and, with the law as your friend, go on your way.

ZONING LAWS—The first question is, Are there city, county, or State zoning laws which affect or prohibit the enterprise? Many counties have zoning laws which may affect the use of land. Certain recreation enterprises may involve a need to change from "farm" to "commercial" or "business" classification.

In addition to the zoning laws, safety regulations may be involved, such as a ban against discharging firearms in certain areas, safety regulations in the use and occupancy of buildings, and regulations concerning location, fencing, and the operation of swimming pools. If new buildings are to be constructed for any recreation enterprise, there may be building codes that apply, and fire, sanitary, and safety regulations.

A nearby city may have authority to regulate some phases of the enterprise. Many cities are given authority to regulate the use of land adjacent to streams that furnish their water supply. In some fast growing areas, cities have been given authority to control development of areas considerably beyond their limits which in time are expected to be incorporated in the cities.

TAXES—New or different taxes may apply to a recreation enterprise. In many areas there is a difference in the tax base for commercial or business property and farm property. Thought should be given and inquiry made as to whether a contemplated enterprise will result in such a change, which would substantially increase taxes.

LABOR—The landowner changing over from a farming operation to a recreation enterprise may be faced with minimum wage and maximum hour laws that did not apply to his farming operation. Are you going to have any children working? Watch out for this change. In the farm operation, your small children or teenagers no doubt took their share of the chores and work. But when it comes to a recreation enterprise, you may be concerned with State child labor laws. Your small children may no longer work.

In some types of occupations the employment of teenagers is forbidden, such as hazardous work, jobs involving the handling of certain beverages, or in some instances serving food. And the number of hours of work per day, as well as the number of hours per week that minors may work, is often limited, even where

W. Joseph Bray is an *Attorney,* Forestry and Soil Conservation Division, Office of the General Counsel, USDA.

the working hours of adult employees may not be.

HEALTH AND SAFETY LAWS—A recreation enterprise that involves the sale or serving of food will probably be subject to the State or county health laws and regulations. These regulations quite often require periodic physical examinations and chest X-rays of employees handling food. Quite often the regulations provide standards for food preparation and dispensing that must be followed.

If lodging is provided for vacationists, many States have "innkeeper" laws that apply. These laws protect both patron and innkeeper, regulating things like bedding, the sanitary and building facilities, water purity, and fire and safety equipment.

Will there be a swimming pool? Some local ordinances regulate the number of qualified lifeguards who must be on hand at all times and the number of hours they can work at a given time. This may also be a condition in any insurance policy protecting the landowner against liability.

Sanitary and garbage facilities of campsites and picnic areas are also regulated in some jurisdictions.

SPECIAL LAWS—If a recreation enterprise is based upon the taking of game, fencing and posting may be required to protect your enterprise.

The game and fish laws of the 50 States vary so much that it is not possible in this short chapter to discuss their effect on the recreational enterprises involving game and fish. Any landowner planning such an enterprise will wisely assume that in many respects—such as open seasons, the catch or bag limits, individual size or species which may be taken—the game laws will not only apply to the sportsman patron, but will have some application to the recreation enterprise. Any landowner establishing a recreation enterprise that involves game or fish should become thoroughly familiar with the State laws.

LIABILITY—Any recreation enterprise carries with it responsibilities and duties for the well-being of its patrons.

Generally speaking, intelligent management and supervision will minimize problems of liability. Zealous insistence upon use of good safety practices is of the first order of importance to a recreation enterprise to avoid injuries to patrons, whether or not the operator is liable. Adequate insurance coverage could make the difference between a successful enterprise and a losing one. So talk to a reputable insurance agent.

Despite all safeguards, accidents still will happen. Therefore, in managing and supervising a recreation enterprise, you need to know areas where liability could occur. Reading this chapter or any other article is a poor substitute for talking to a local lawyer about a particular enterprise.

The general rule is that a person is liable in damages for his acts of negligence which result in injury to the person or the property of another. What constitutes negligence depends on the amount of care toward others which the law, in any given case, imposes upon the owner of the recreation enterprise. Normally, liability is not imposed upon the landowner as such, but upon the one having control of the land or who is operating the enterprise. In this chapter, for convenience's sake we will speak of the person having the liability as the "landowner." The amount of care imposed on landowners and thus the measure of their liability will depend upon whether other persons come on the land as (1) trespassers, (2) licensees, or (3) invitees.

In the case of a recreation enterprise the patrons will be the invitees here discussed. A number of States have passed trespasser or landowner liability laws that seek to protect the landowners, especially those engaging in recreation enterprises, from liability to trespassers. Few of these laws have been fully tested in court.

A trespasser is a person who comes on the land without the consent and against the will of the landowner. To a trespasser the landowner owes only the duty not to willfully, or wantonly, injure him. There are some exceptions to this rule.

A licensee is a person who comes on property of a landowner with the landowner's permission, but not primarily for the landowner's benefit. This permission may be active, passive, or implied by law. One example of a licensee is the game warden coming on the land to see that the hunters, fishermen, and the premises comply with the law.

393

A landowner is required to refrain from willfully or wantonly injuring a licensee.

Although the duty owed to trespassers and licensees is generally expressed in the same terms, the difference applied by the courts is that the landowner is required to anticipate the licensee coming on the land and to warn him of any known dangers which are not open and obvious. Such dangers could be vicious animals, quicksand bogs, pits, holes and old wells covered over with brambles. The rule as to licensees also has its exceptions.

An invitee is a person who comes on the land at the express invitation and for the benefit of the landowner. The express invitation may be implied. All persons coming on the land to enjoy the recreation facilities and paying the fee to be charged would be invitees. These, of course, are not necessarily the only persons who can become invitees. To the invitee, the landowner owes the duty of ordinary and reasonable care. The term "ordinary and reasonable" care is deceptively simple. It is subject to wide latitude of interpretation by the courts.

With the foregoing principles of liability in mind, the areas or situations of liability include:

• Injury or death resulting from the landowner's own negligent acts or his omissions. This primarily relates to licensees and invitees on the land, but the landowner may not willfully or wantonly cause injury to trespassers.

• Injury or death resulting from some natural dangers on the land like old open wells, holes, and other earth variations, hidden harmful obstacles, and known dangerous natural conditions. This liability would be primarily to the invitees although it may extend to licensees. As to invitees in this category of liability, the duty of care is greater, in that it is required not only as to known dangers, but also as to those which should have been known. In regard to licensees, the landowner need only warn of those dangers within his knowledge.

The degree of care required in these cases, as pointed out above, will vary depending upon many factors—whether there are any children "of tender years" involved, the number of people gathered

at one time, and the like. In certain types of recreational areas where amusement facilities are provided (or certain facilities are used for amusement by children) and the children are known and permitted to come and play, the "playground rule" applies. Under this rule, the landowner may experience liability for things he should have foreseen were dangerous and would cause injury to children. The playground rule applies both to invitees and to licensees.

• Injury or death resulting from an attractive nuisance or a dangerous instrumentality. Pools, ponds and lakes, and reservoirs are of themselves not attractive nuisances or dangerous instrumentalities, and the landowners generally will incur no liability from them. However, the addition of certain recreational facilities, such as an inadequate or improper diving platform, or some natural changes of conditions, such as a silted over shelf of ice which appears to be a part of the bank, might subject the landowners to liability. The attractive nuisance doctrine applies only to children. The dangerous instrumentality rule applies to persons of all ages, although the degree of care required of the landowner increases or decreases depending on the ability of the person to comprehend or know the danger.

• Injury or death of licensee or invitee from known vicious domestic animals owned by the landowner. This includes biting and kicking horses; butting cows, bulls, and goats; vicious dogs, hogs, and boars, etc. For the landowner to be liable, he must know of the animal's vicious propensities. There is an old saying that every dog is entitled to one bite. But, despite the rule of law in these cases that viciousness must be known, we would hesitate to advise that there would be no liability in any vacation farm situation where a city child picked up a piglet and was attacked by the mother sow.

• Injury or death of invitee by another invitee. Ordinarily the landowner would not be liable for injury or death caused by one invitee to another. As pointed out above, the degree of care required varies with the number of persons brought or gathered together. Certain hunting, swimming, and boating accidents could occur because too great a number of persons were brought together in situations requiring a considerably increased degree of care for their safety. The landowner could under these circumstances become liable for injuries caused by one invitee to another. To some degree this liability could be assumed by the patrons by way of contract, as a part of their admission. Signs and other notices and consents might lessen the degree of risk, but of themselves might not completely obviate liability.

• Trespass by invitees on the lands of another. In certain instances, there could be liability where the landowner may have misled invitees as to property lines, and injury is done to property of adjacent neighbors. While normally the landowner is not liable for trespass by others, the degree of care the landowner owes toward

his neighbors will increase with their proximity, the sparseness of community development, etc. A golf driving range so situated that driven golf balls would likely cause injury to nearby houses or people would illustrate this. Picnic areas may lead to the liability of the landowner for littering and other health menaces. When invitees break the landowner's fences, permitting his stock to escape and do damage, the landowner may be liable.

• Injury by invitees to employees of the landowner. Employees normally assume the risks attendant to their employment. Where the normal risks of employment are increased, such as a farmhand working in the field being shot by a hunter or a farmhand being injured by animals unreasonably excited by guests of a dude ranch, the landowner may become liable for the damages.

Our Heritage—
The Countryside

LLOYD E. PARTAIN

A FUNDAMENTAL HERITAGE of the American people has been the opportunity to know the outdoors—its character, its challenges, and its wonders. Traditionally, experience and activity in the open country have been an important part of the lives of most of our people— first as a wilderness to be conquered, and then as a source of livelihood, inspiration, and enjoyment.

As our Nation has progressed from primarily agrarian to a vast industrial complex, an increasing percentage of our total population began, of necessity, to reside in the cities and towns. A vast number of those living in urban places even today, however, were either born in rural areas

or are only one generation removed from the farm. Most parents of today's youth remember experiences in the country with grandfather and grandmother, an uncle or aunt, or a family friend. But few of our children have that chance. This situation need not prevail, however.

Rural America has adequate space for more people to live, work, and play; to perpetuate our heritage; and to assure a strong community and family life with gainful employment and wholesome leisure. The enduring strength of our society

ψ   ψ   ψ

Lloyd E. Partain is *Assistant to the Administrator* on Recreation, Soil Conservation Service.

may well depend on the future development and use of America's countryside.

Only five out of a hundred Americans are primarily employed in producing the food, fiber, and a substantial portion of the shelter which we all need today—and even more than that, substantial farm commodities available for export.

There is every indication that production efficiency can be much greater in the future. In fact, the ingenuity of the American people under our competitive, capitalistic system permits us to produce more of just about everything than we can now use. In the case of agricultural production, we can do it on fewer and fewer acres.

As production per acre and per animal goes up, the amount of land required goes down. Land areas most suited to modern farming become more intensively used. Other land areas are released for non-farm uses. This is true in most States. Nearly 60 percent of the land area of the highly industrialized State of Pennsylvania now grows trees and brush with the smallest percentage in cultivation since before 1890. And the percentage is even higher in such States as Connecticut, North Carolina, and Missouri. Only about 50 percent of the land area of New York State is required for farming, industries, cities and suburban dwelling, roads, highways, airports, and other intensive uses.

In the countryside across the Nation, lands are available for recreation and open space, natural beauty, new home expansion, industrial and commercial sites, nature centers, travelways and transportation services. All these potential uses of rural space require well-planned resource conservation and development programs in which multiple purposes can be incorporated to meet local, State, and national needs. The U.S. Department of Agriculture, in cooperation with other Federal, State, and local agencies, organizations, groups, and individuals, supports a Rural Areas Development program in the national interest. This program has many integrated facets.

Small watershed projects authorized by Public Law 83–566, as amended, offer excellent opportunity for development of multiple uses. Even though flood control and agricultural water management are the prime purposes, these projects often can provide rural, municipal, and industrial water supplies, water-based outdoor recreation, and fish and wildlife development. Once floodwaters are harnessed, many rural communities can develop safe and attractive places for industry, homes, and wholesome recreation.

Add to this some 2 million farm ponds, most of which are stocked for fishing, and the managed waters of rural America become a great attraction to people of town and country alike.

Since the strong surge of emphasis and interest in outdoor recreation began about 5 or 6 years ago, USDA has constantly accelerated its efforts toward helping meet national needs for recreation.

The almost universal recognition of the dependence on private land development as a means of supplying a major portion of the outdoor recreation demands led to new functions of the Federal, State, and local agencies and organizations. Important among these functions has been expansion of the Nation's soil and water conservation programs to include outdoor recreation as an alternative land use to be considered by the private landowners and operators requesting technical assistance from the Soil Conservation Service. The goal has been a three-point one: To appropriately use and conserve natural resources, to provide an income-producing operation for farmers, and to help meet the needs of rural and urban people alike.

Since 1962, Soil Conservation Service technicians have helped 34,700 rural landowners and operators to establish one or more income-producing recreation enterprises. More than 3,200 of them derive their major income from recreation.

Through March of 1967, the Farmers Home Administration has made recreation loans to 345 nonprofit rural associations totaling $44 million, and to 550 farmers amounting to $4 million.

Between 1961 and 1966, Rural Electrification Administration borrowers helped to establish over 250 recreation projects.

The Cooperative Extension Service now has about 35 recreation specialists and 26 wildlife specialists working on recreation and related activities.

USDA's Agricultural Stabilization and

Conservation Service—through its Agricultural Conservation Program and Cropland Adjustment Program—performs an important role in cost-sharing on conservation practices necessary for recreational use of land. Under the Cropland Adjustment Program alone, about 800,000 acres of farmland have been made available for public recreation uses. Grants are also being made to the State and local governments to help buy cropland for recreation, fish and wildlife purposes under the Greenspan program.

Many landowners today, with large homes on farms or ranches that are fully modernized for comforts comparable to city living, convert a part of their acres to income-producing outdoor recreation uses. Some make vacation farming or dude ranching a major source of income. The majority prefer to continue their operations as working farms or ranches with recreation and vacation services as a supplementary source of income.

Most of these rural recreation enterprises feature moderate rates, quality food served family style, comfortable lodging, and a wide variety of facilities for enjoying a rest away from the masses.

A vacation on a farm or ranch is only one of many opportunities to enjoy rural recreation activities. Landowners and operators in many parts of the country, especially in areas near large centers of population, have installed facilities and services for those who have only a few hours, a day, a weekend, or a month to spend enjoying the open country.

On private rural lands across the country you will find picnicking, camping, trailer parks, fishing, hunting, swimming, boating, and water skiing; tobogganing, sledding, skating, skiing, and other winter sports; guided trail rides, canoeing, river float trips, horseback and pony riding stables, hayrides and wagon trains, group camping, nature trails, cave and cavern exploration, playing fields and courts, and golfing.

In our countryside's vastness lies the greatest portion of the Nation's developed and undeveloped natural resources. Nearly three-fourths of this land space is privately owned, comprising a continuing source of our new wealth. From it come our food and fiber, most of our fresh water, wood, and minerals, and our outdoor recreation opportunities.

Competition for that rural space grows with population increase, greater affluence among our people with increased mobility, higher standards of living, improved access, and more and more leisuretime.

———————— ✿ ————————

NATURE'S TEACHINGS

A child learns through all of his senses when roaming woods and fields. He feels soft, spongy pine needles under his feet and later in life he can better understand the water-holding capacities of forest soils. He also learns the sharp unyielding feel of natural stone. He smells the fresh tilled soil. He feels the cool breeze through the trees, and tastes the freshness of filtered spring water—no chemicals added. With his hands he learns the feel of rough tree bark, the resiliency of a sapling, the peace of solitude and quiet, interrupted only by an occasional bird call, buzzing insect, or rustle of a squirrel in late fall.

—Ivan R. Martin

———————— ✿ ————————

But fortunately, too, a vast amount of knowledge is available to cope with the problems of conservation and wise use of this Nation's renewable natural resources. Science and technology provide the basis for practical multiple use of our farm, ranch, and forest lands.

The U.S. Department of Agriculture and its cooperating State and local agencies are applying their scientific, technological, and resources management principles more and more to broad area resource planning and development. Urban as well as rural areas are involved. Enlightened local initiative and leadership, technical and financial assistance, continued research and effective education from sound public programs—all of these insure a more rewarding countryside environment for both rural and urban people and preserve a great heritage.

Photographers

Photographers represented in this Yearbook are credited unless the name of the person who took the picture is not known. Most of the photos are by U.S. Department of Agriculture photographers. In general, this is the case where only a photographer's name is given. USDA photos may be ordered from the Photography Division, Office of Information, U.S. Department of Agriculture, Washington, D.C. 20250. Please refer to the 1967 Yearbook of Agriculture, and give the page the photo appears on. USDA black and white photos are free to news media, and media may borrow color transparencies.

The Editor of the Yearbook is indebted to Albert W. Matthews, Chief of the Photography Division, and to the Division for help in obtaining photos. Russell T. Forte played a major role in photo selection, and William C. Allen and the Office of Information Photo Lab produced high quality prints. Also of great assistance were Robert B. Branstead of the Soil Conservation Service, Bluford W. Muir of the Forest Service, and the Forest Service Photo Lab.

NOTE: Roman numeral page numbering begins with the first page carrying a color photo.

H. E. ALEXANDER, Back end papers.
ARKANSAS PUBLICITY & PARKS COMMISSION, 132.
RAY ATKESON, XII, XIII, XVIII (bottom), XIX (bottom), 39, 51, 54.
O. F. BAILEY, 351 (top).
F. S. BAKER, 341.
TOM BEEMERS, 357 (upper right).
J. R. BELL, 348 (top).
JOHN BOWERS, 9.
R. O. BRANDENBERGER, 49.

ROBERT B. BRANSTEAD, X, XIV (bottom), XX (top), XXIV (top), XXV, XXXI, XXXII (top), XLI, 298 (top).
HUGO BRYAN, XV (bottom), 278, 312.
BUCYRUS-ERIE COMPANY, 360.
BUREAU OF INDIAN AFFAIRS, 342, 377.
BUREAU OF PUBLIC ROADS, 254 (top).
BUREAU OF RECLAMATION, XV (top), 53.
MELVIN H. BURKE, 319.
CECIL CHANEY, 170.
HOWARD V. CHENEY, 277.

Roy M. Clark, xxiii (upper right), 276, 310, 311, 374 (upper right).

Erwin W. Cole, xxiii (bottom), xxiv (bottom), 247, 258, 291, 292, 375.

Sam Cole, 313 (bottom), 329.

J. Cotterill, Bureau of Reclamation, 347.

A. R. Croft, 86.

J. M. Cross, 178, 374 (lower left).

C. D. Crowley, 376.

Allan D. Cruickshank, National Audubon Society, Inc., 346.

Clint Davis, 14, 26.

Clarence J. DeLand, 265, 336.

Mrs. Morrill Donnald, xxvi (top).

R. C. Erickson, Fish and Wildlife Service, 343 (lower left).

Ray M. Filloon, 103.

Fish and Wildlife Service, 344.

Florida Development Commission, VII (bottom).

Russell T. Forte, 307, 323 (upper left), 398 (photo of USDA photographer Murray D. Lemmon).

Fredericksburg Standard (Tex.), 303.

Luther Goldman, Fish and Wildlife Service, 117, 118.

W. Dean Gordon, 140.

George A. Grant, 243.

Roy A. Grizzell, 111.

Wayne R. Grube, 260.

E. P. Haddon, Fish and Wildlife Service, 339 (bottom).

J. Hansen, 238.

John W. Hart, xxi.

Jack Hayes, xxx, 357 (center left), 359.

P. Freeman Heim, 38, 306.

Everett Henson, 334.

Jay Higgins, 42.

Ted Hopkins, 366 (bottom).

John B. Hungerford, 351 (bottom).

Wayne Hypes, 335.

Frank H. Jeter, Jr., 189.

Marilyn H. Johnson, 232, 233.

Edward G. Konieczny, 386 (top).

C. E. Koontz, 137.

C. J. Lammers, 369.

Everett Leadbetter, Front end papers, 145.

Murray D. Lemmon, 214.

Library of Congress, 151.

G. A. Limstrom, 362.

Sull McCartney, 139.

John McConnell, 37.

W. Grant McFarland, Fish and Wildlife Service, 343 (lower right).

B. C. McLean, 298 (lower left).

H. Robert Mansfield, 8.

Phil Miller, 61.

H. P. Moore, 123.

Bluford W. Muir, 5, 109, 313 (top), 368.

Pete Murdick, 283.

W. W. Nace, 324.

National Arboretum, 194.

National Cotton Council, 339 (center left).

Nebraska Game Commission, 287, 288.

Robert Nelson, xxii (bottom).

A. E. Newby, 348 (lower right).

Robert E. Nipp, 373.

L. J. Northern, 173.

Robert W. Oertel, 138.

D. F. Olson, Jr., 400 (with Dan O. Todd).

George Pace, 322.

Hermann Postlethwaite, 354.

Leland J. Prater, xi (top), xiv (top), xviii (top), 2, 13, 17, 64, 80, 94, 156, 250, 255, 285, 323 (lower right), 348 (lower left), 380.

Larry Rana, 252.

W. R. Ratledge, vii (top).

C. M. Rector, 72.

Frank M. Roadman, xxxii (bottom), 107.

Bernhard A. Roth, 263.

Arnold Rothstein, 340 (top).

Douglass F. Roy, 242.

Salt River Project, 125, 126, 128.

Roy Dale Sanders, xvi, xvii, 18.

Jack S. Schneider, 3, 206.

Donald C. Schuhart, xi (bottom), 325 (lower left).

Kevin Shields, 19.

Signal Corps, National Archives, 390, 391.

Leon Sisk, 323 (upper right).

Ed Slusher, 63.

Gordon S. Smith, 267, 298 (lower right).

M. G. Smithers, 304.

D. A. Spencer, 339 (upper right).

Paul Steucke, 105, 244.

W. E. Steuerwald, 68.

Margaret Stoval, 66.

Dale L. Swartz, 248.

E. A. Swenson, 305.

Selden Lee Tinsley, 315.

Dan O. Todd, 15, 76, 325, 349, 371, 372, 400 (with D. F. Olson, Jr.).

William W. Vetter, 75, 155, 353, 356.

George Vitas, 29.

Keith Walters, 366 (top).

David F. Warren, 191, 210, 241.

M. Woodbridge Williams, National Park Service, 355.

James M. Wise, 271 (top and bottom).

R. D. Wylie, 357 (bottom).

Index

400

404

405

U. S. GOVERNMENT PRINTING OFFICE : 1967 O - 235-917